Trivia Quiz

Trivia Quiz

ARCTURUS

Published by Arcturus Publishing Limited

This edition published 1998

Printed and bound in Great Britain

© Central Press Features Ltd/ Arcturus Publishing Ltd

ISBN1 900032 40 6

Entertainment

1. What is the name of the giant American actor who played 'Jaws' in two Bond movies?
2. Who plays Pauline Fowler in *EastEnders*?
3. Which American comedian starred in the film *Boomerang*?
4. Who duetted with Paul McCartney on the 1982 UK and US No. 1 single *Ebony and Ivory*?
5. Who played Ben Cartwright in the cowboy series *Bonanza*?
6. Which British group had a Top 10 hit with *A Million Love Songs*?
7. Who presents the long-running astronomy series *The Sky at Night*?
8. Who was the lead singer of the US group Talking Heads?
9. Who played Capt. Mainwaring in *Dad's Army*?
10. Which American singer starred in the 1988 film *Moonstruck*?
11. Which Swedish band had a Top 5 greatest hits album called *Gold*?
12. Who played detective Virgil Tibbs in the classic 1967 film *In the Heat of the Night*?
13. Which actress played the role of Alex Wilton in the drama series *Boon*?
14. Which Clint Eastwood film is about legendary gunslinger William Munny?
15. Which group had a UK & US No.1 in 1985 with *I Want to Know what Love is*?
16. What station is home to the firefighters of Blue Watch in the series *London's Burning*?
17. Which American actress appeared as a Mermaid in *Splash*?
18. Which former World Champion instructed young hopefuls how to *Play Snooker* on TV?
19. Who was the female vocalist of Yazoo who later began a successful solo career?
20. Who directed the *Star Wars* spoof entitled *Spaceballs*?

ANSWERS: 1 Richard Kiel, 2 Wendy Richard, 3 Eddie Murphy, 4 Stevie Wonder, 5 Lorne Greene, 6 Take That, 7 Patrick Moore, 8 David Byrne, 9 Arthur Lowe, 10 Cher, 11 Abba, 12 Sidney Poitier, 13 Saskia Wickham, 14 Unforgiven, 15 Foreigner, 16 Blackwall Fire Station, 17 Daryl Hannah, 18 Dennis Taylor, 19 Alison Moyet, 20 Mel Brooks.

General Knowledge

1. In Shakespeare's play, who killed Macbeth?

2. What type of animal is a macaque?

3. In which county is RAF aerodrome Manston?

4. Which actress was born Vera Jayne Palmer?

5. Which annual 24-hour motor race was founded in 1923?

6. Who wrote the *Just So Stories* in 1902?

7. Of which island group is Luzon the largest?

8. In which Dutch city was Rembrandt born?

9. On which river is Keighley?

10. With which country did England wage the War of Jenkins's Ear?

11. Which disease is popularly called 'the itch'?

12. To which animal family does the kinkajou belong?

13. Which career did Keats abandon for poetry?

14. What is the governing body of English horse racing?

15. Which country's name, in its native language, means land of the long white cloud?

16. Which French King Louis was called the Sun King?

17. Which bird lays the largest egg in relation to its own size?

18. Who wrote and directed the film *High Hopes* in 1989?

19. What was the nationality of the artist Paul Klee?

20. What relation of Queen Victoria was Belgium's Leopold I?

ANSWERS: 1 Macduff, 2 Monkey, 3 Kent, 4 Jayne Mansfield, 5 Le Mans, 6 Rudyard Kipling, 7 Philippines, 8 Leiden, 9 Aire, 10 Spain, 11 Scabies, 12 Raccoon, 13 Medicine, 14 Jockey Club, 15 New Zealand, 16 XIV, 17 Kiwi, 18 Mike Leigh, 19 Swiss, 20 Uncle.

General Knowledge

1.   What type of animal is an orange-tip?

2.   With what country would you associate Blue Mountain coffee?

3.   In which English county is Greenham Common?

4.   What is the German name for the Black Forest?

5.   Which Chinese river is also known as the Hwang Ho?

6.   Which international organization was promoted by Jean Henri Dunant?

7.   In what year was the battle of Magenta?

8.   Who wrote the song *White Christmas*?

9.   Who created the character Violet Elizabeth Bott?

10. What award is given for a wound incurred in action in the US Forces?

11. Who founded the first US detective agency in 1850?

12. What plant is also called 'shepherd's weatherglass'?

13. Who ruled England for nine days in 1553?

14. Which poet wrote *Sonnets from the Portuguese*?

15. Which metal is symbolised by the letters Co?

16. What was the original surname of film producer Sam Goldwyn?

17. What was the most famous TV role of actor Jay Silverheels?

18. Which jazz player wrote the song *Mood Indigo*?

19. What is the name of the professor in the game 'Cluedo'?

20. Which fruit has varieties such as Merton Glory and Napoleon Bigarreau?

ANSWERS: 1 *Butterfly*, 2 *Jamaica*, 3 *Berkshire*, 4 *Schwarzwald*, 5 *Yellow River*, 6 *The Red Cross*, 7 *1859*, 8 *Irving Berlin*, 9 *Richmal Crompton*, 10 *Purple Heart*, 11 *Allan Pinkerton*, 12 *Scarlet pimpernel*, 13 *Lady Jane Grey*, 14 *Elizabeth Barret Browning*, 15 *Cobalt*, 16 *Goldfish*, 17 *Tonto*, 18 *Duke Ellington*, 19 *Professor Plum*, 20 *Cherry*.

General Knowledge

1. Who wrote the opera *Hary Janos*?

2. Where was the first permanent British settlement in the US?

3. Between which countries is the Kattegat sea passage?

4. Who coined the term Iron Curtain?

5. What does an invertebrate lack?

6. Where is the Interpol HQ?

7. How is the *Book of Changes* better known?

8. Who is the author of the *Dune* series?

9. In which country was Graeme Hick born?

10. Which organ produces insulin?

11. Which planet features the Great Red Spot?

12. How are the Nicaraguan right-wing guerrillas known?

13. Which element is named after the Greek for violet?

14. Which former PM secured the release of three hostages in Iraq?

15. How many countries did Gulliver visit on his Travels?

16. Of which Dickens novel is Pip the central character?

17. What is the Italian word for 'scratched drawings'?

18. In which city is Holyrood House?

19. How many yards are there in a furlong?

20. In Greek legend, who cut the Gordian knot?

ANSWERS: *1 Zoltan Kodaly, 2 Jamestown, 3 Sweden and Denmark, 4 Winston Churchill, 5 Backbone, 6 Paris, 7 I Ching, 8 Frank Herbert, 9 Rhodesia, 10 Pancreas, 11 Jupiter, 12 Contras, 13 Iodine, 14 Sir Edward Heath, 15 Four, 16 Great Expectations, 17 Graffiti, 18 Edinburgh, 19 220, 20 Alexander.*

Entertainment

1. Who is the star of *Patriot Games*?

2. Which *Monty Python* star went *Around the World in 80 Days*?

3. Who sang with Elton John on the 1976 UK and US No. 1 hit *Don't Go Breaking My Heart*?

4. Who plays Diana in *Waiting for God*?

5. Which British actor played Robert McCall in *The Equalizer*?

6. Who had a No. 1 hit with *Sleeping Satellite*?

7. Who plays Mel Gibson's partner in the *Lethal Weapon* films?

8. Which former Commodores singer released an album called *Back To Front*?

9. Who is the usual presenter of *Points of View*?

10. Which star of *Cheers* played baby Mikey's mother in *Look Who's Talking*?

11. Who played Steve McGarrett in the crime series *Hawaii Five-O*?

12. Which 70s glam rock group had hits with *Blockbuster* and *Ballroom Blitz*?

13. Which British group had a 1979 hit album entitled *London Calling*?

14. Who won an Oscar for her starring role with James Caan in the film *Misery*?

15. Who stars as 'Bill' in the TV comedy series *2 point 4 Children*?

16. Who played the insane murderer Norman Bates in the classic thriller *Psycho*?

17. Which group had a No. 1 album in the UK called *Automatic for the People*?

18. Which *Soldier, Soldier* character is played by Sophie Heathcote?

19. Which actress starred with Bob Hope and Bing Crosby in numerous *Road To* ... films?

20. Which British group had an instrumental UK No. 1 hit with *Wonderful Land* in 1962?

General Knowledge

1. In which year was the US Declaration of Independence issued?

2. Which former Spurs star died in December 1993?

3. In which ocean are the Wake Islands?

4. Of what is Eddie George governor?

5. During whose reign was the name Saxe-Coburg-Gotha changed to Windsor?

6. How many players are there in a Gaelic football team?

7. How do we know the colourful bird erithacus rubecula?

8. In which country was gin first produced?

9. On which island is the resort of Cowes?

10. Which musical form is named after the Latin for 'flight'?

11. To which family of birds does the bittern belong?

12. In which religion is Brahma the creator god?

13. Which architect laid out Covent Garden?

14. What was the first major sound film?

15. What do Americans call eggplant?

16. Who played the sleuthing wife in the *Thin Man* films?

17. Which ideal state is named from the Greek for 'no place'?

18. Which river has Lake Tana as its source?

19. Which French king was married to Marie Antoinette?

20. Which organ is stimulated by the drug digitalis?

ANSWERS: 1 1776, 2 Danny Blanchflower, 3 Pacific, 4 Bank of England, 5 George V, 6 15, 7 Robin, 8 Holland, 9 Isle of Wight, 10 Fugue, 11 Heron, 12 Hinduism, 13 Inigo Jones, 14 The Jazz Singer, 15 Aubergine, 16 Myrna Loy, 17 Utopia, 18 Blue Nile, 19 Louis XVI, 20 Heart.

General Knowledge

1. Which breed of dog has border and bearded varieties?

2. Who wrote the four *Claudine* novels?

3. What was the nationality of Captain Kidd?

4. Which bird is also known as Mother Carey's chicken?

5. To which group of islands does Skye belong?

6. Which film star was born Harold Leek?

7. What is the capital city of Bavaria?

8. After which king is US state Georgia named?

9. Which Premiership football captain received an MBE in the 1994 New Year's Honours List?

10. On which US tycoon's life was *Citizen Kane* based?

11. Who played Fanny Brice in the 1968 film *Funny Girl*?

12. In which city was Christopher Columbus born?

13. Of which element is diamond a form?

14. What was the name of Donald Campbell's record-breaking boats and cars?

15. Of which ocean does the Kara Sea form a part?

16. What was the first nuclear-powered submarine?

17. Who, in 1956, was the first European Footballer of the Year?

18. Which musical instrument evolved from the sackbut?

19. To which family of birds do canaries and siskins belong?

20. Who was the first English actor to be knighted?

ANSWERS: 1. Collie, 2. Colette, 3. Scottish, 4. Storm petrel, 5. Inner Hebrides, 6. Howard Keel, 7. Munich, 8. George II, 9. Gary Mabbutt, 10. William Randolph Hearst, 11. Barbra Streisand, 12. Genoa, 13. Carbon, 14. Bluebird, 15. Arctic, 16. Nautilus, 17. Stanley Matthews, 18. Trombone, 19. Finches, 20. Henry Irving.

General Knowledge

1. What is the orbital period of Halley's Comet?

2. What do the letter PS stand for?

3. Which football team plays at Goodison Park?

4. Who wrote *The Naked Lunch*?

5. Which sitcom actress has been appointed to the Human Fertilisation and Embryology Authority?

6. Who wrote the play *The Doll's House* in 1879?

7. In which country is Montego Bay?

8. Which former Chancellor of the Exchequer's middle name is Winston?

9. King Juan Carlos's wife is the daughter of which country's former king?

10. Of which county is Rutland now a part?

11. Which German Nazi was known as the Butcher of Lyon?

12. By which name do we know the aquatic rodent Castor fiber?

13. Which fictional hero was created by Baroness Orczy?

14. Whose convalescent visit gave Bognor its Regis?

15. Which fabric causes the lung disease byssinosis?

16. Which popular cricket commentator died in January 1994?

17. Who, in Greek mythology, was the father of Jupiter, Neptune and Pluto?

18. Which author wrote *J'Accuse*, which concerned the Dreyfus affair?

19. What relationship is Oliver Reed to director Carol Reed?

20. Which city contains the residential district Beverly Hills?

ANSWERS: *1. 76 years, 2. Post scriptum, 3. Everton, 4. William Burroughs, 5. Penelope Keith, 6. Henrik Ibsen, 7. Jamaica, 8. Jonathon Porritt, 9. Greece, 10. Leicestershire, 11. Klaus Barbie, 12. Beaver, 13. The Scarlet Pimpernel, 14. George V, 15. Cotton, 16. Brian Johnston, 17. Saturn, 18. Emile Zola, 19. Nephew, 20. Los Angeles.*

Sports

1. Who achieved successive Grand Slams winning the Five Nations Championship in 1992?
2. Who won the men's singles at the 1995 French Open?
3. Who won the 1995 Test series between West Indies and England?
4. Which ex-Spurs player scored the winning goal in the 1995 European Cup-Winners' Cup Final?
5. At what sport does Max Sciandri compete?
6. Who was the 1992 Olympic welterweight boxing gold winner?
7. What nationality is golfer Frank Nobilo?
8. Which rugby player got into trouble after calling his bosses "57 old farts"?
9. Who won snooker's 1994 Thailand Open tournament?
10. Who won the 1995 US Open golf championship?
11. Which horse won the 1992 English Grand National?
12. In 1995, Pakistan lost their first home Test series in 15 years to which team?
13. Who did Chris Eubank lose to twice?
14. Who won the 1995 Walker Cup?
15. Which rider won the 1992 Tour de France?
16. Who was banned for 14 days after his ride on 'Raggerty'?
17. Who won the 1994 men's 1,000m speed skating gold?
18. El Loco is the nickname of which Colombian goalkeeper?
19. Which football team is nick-named 'The Canaries'?
20. At what sport does Paul Broadhurst compete?

ANSWERS: 1 England, **2** Thomas Muster, **3** Nobody (it was a draw), **4** Nayim, **5** Cycling, **6** Michael Carruth, **7** New Zealander, **8** Will Carling, **9** James Wattana, **10** Corey Pavin, **11** Party Politics, **12** Sri Lanka, **13** Steve Collins, **14** Great Britain and Ireland, **15** Miguel Indurain, **16** Richard Dunwoody, **17** Dan Jansen, **18** Rene Higuita, **19** Norwich City, **20** Golf.

General Knowledge

1.   By what name do we know the bird *sturnus vulgaris*?

2.   Which president's desk bore the legend 'the buck stops here'?

3.   Who wrote *The Caretaker* in 1960?

4.   Which city became France's capital for four days in WW2?

5.   In whose honour is the US state of Virginia named?

6.   Which bird has mistle and hermit varieties?

7.   What name did photographer Emmanuel Rudnitsky assume?

8.   What do we call the study of the surface shape of the land?

9.   Who is chairman of the charity Mencap?

10. Which Manchester soccer legend died in January 1994?

11. Which member of Mrs Thatcher's cabinet was a former airline pilot?

12. Which tree's Latin name is *Juglans regia*?

13. Who plays Woody Allen's wife in *Manhattan Murder Mystery*?

14. How do we know the rich vitamin B source *Saccharomyces cerevisiae*?

15. Which organisation was founded by Chad Varah in 1953?

16. By what name is the Fairs Cup now known?

17. What are studied by palaeontologists?

18. Which martial art uses bamboo replicas of samurai swords?

19. Which Scotland Yard detective led the hunt for Ronnie Biggs?

20. Which US state's capital is Springfield?

General Knowledge

1. Which form of political corruption is named after US politician Elbridge Gerry?

2. Who received an Oscar for his performance in *Going My Way*?

3. In which country was Vivien Leigh born?

4. What type of creature is the firefly?

5. What did Hippolyte Mege-Mouries invent in 1889?

6. In which ocean are the Mariana Islands?

7. Which sci-fi author wrote the screenplay for *2001: A Space Odyssey*?

8. What is the kernel of the tree *Myristica fragrans* called?

9. Which actor/dancer was born Frederick Austerlitz?

10. Which vehicle is named from the Hindi for 'Lord of the World'?

11. Who is TV's *Question Time*'s front-man?

12. By what name is a kangaroo's young commonly known?

13. What is the largest city in Switzerland?

14. Who wrote *Cat's Cradle* in 1963?

15. What is the world's best-selling magazine?

16. Which fish's young include alevins and smolts?

17. By which first name do we know Francis Morgan Thompson?

18. Of which building does the White Tower of c.1079 form a part?

19. Whose first novel is *A Parliamentary Affair*?

20. Which record company was founded in Detroit by Berry Gordy Jnr?

General Knowledge

1. In which constellation is Regulus the brightest star?

2. In the bay of which city is the prison Robben Island?

3. Which ice skater was attacked by associates of one of her rivals?

4. Which king was Regent during the Regency?

5. Which institution's motto is 'serve to lead'?

6. Who was the subject of the original 'warts and all' portrait?

7. Which satanic name comes from the Hebrew for 'Lord of the Flies'?

8. Who made the only attempt to steal the Crown Jewels?

9. Which sailing ship was named after a witch in a Robert Burns poem?

10. Which late US comedian was born Benjamin Kubelsky?

11. Which drink is named after the German for 'to store'?

12. To which family of fishes does the dab belong?

13. What was the capital of the Ottoman Empire?

14. Who is the patron saint of travellers?

15. Who played Gerard Conlon in *In The Name Of The Father*?

16. Who wrote the *Minute Waltz*?

17. What is the common name of the flower *Bellis perennis*?

18. Which member of the Royal Family has converted to Roman Catholicism?

19. In which constellation is the Crab Nebula?

20. Of which island does Haiti form the western part?

ANSWERS: *1. Leo, 2. Cape Town, 3. Nancy Kerrigan, 4. George VI, 5. Sandhurst Royal Military Academy, 6. Oliver Cromwell, 7. Beelzebub, 8. Colonel Blood, 9. Cutty Sark, 10. Jack Benny, 11. Lager, 12. Plaice, 13. Constantinople, 14. St Christopher, 15. Daniel Day-Lewis, 16. Chopin, 17. Daisy, 18. Duchess Of Kent, 19. Taurus, 20. Hispaniola*

Entertainment

1. Who played Baldrick in the *Blackadder* comedy series?

2. Which American actress played Major 'Hotlips' Houlihan in *M*A*S*H*?

3. Who played the title role in Mel Brooks's 1974 comedy film *Young Frankenstein?*

4. Which British band had a UK and US No. 1 hit in 1983 with *Every Breath You Take?*

5. Which British actress starred with Tom Conti in the film *Shirley Valentine?*

6. Who had a Top 10 hit with *It's My Life?*

7. Who is the writer of the TV comedy series *Bread?*

8. What is the surname of Clint Eastwood's character in the *Dirty Harry* films?

9. Who had a No.1 hit in 1980 with *Woman in Love*?

10. What is the name of the actress who played Tom Cruise's trainer in *Top Gun*?

11. Who played Adam Dalgleish in the P D James TV thriller series?

12. Who had a UK No.1 hit, with UB40, in 1985 with a cover version of *I Got You Babe*?

13. Who plays man-mad Dorien in the TV comedy *Birds of a Feather*?

14. Who played the title role in the Steven Spielberg film *Hook*?

15. Who had a Top 20 hit with *Sentinel?*

16. Which star of *Waiting For God* was a regular in *A Very Peculiar Practice*?

17. Who played the criminal mastermind leading the terrorist gang in the original *Die Hard* film?

18. Which American singer starred in the 1979 film *The Rose*?

19. Who played the title role in the 50's TV series *Ivanhoe*?

20. Which Irish band performed all the music in the TV series *Robin of Sherwood*?

General Knowledge

1. Which old British construction can be seen in Arizona's Lake Havasu City?

2. In which city is the Kelvingrove Art Gallery?

3. What type of creature is the frogmouth?

4. What was the Giotto space probe built to study?

5. Who won a directing Oscar for *Cabaret*?

6. Which country's parliament is the Althing?

7. Which Radio 4 presenter died in January 1994?

8. What is the day after Hallowe'en called?

9. Who was the first boxer to win world titles at five officially recognised weights?

10. Who was JFK's campaign manager in 1961?

11. Which film star was born Margarita Carmen Cansino?

12. Of which autonomous Spanish region is Pamplona capital?

13. Of what nationality was Errol Flynn?

14. At which racecourse is the Prix de l'Arc de Triomphe run?

15. Who, in the Old Testament, fashioned the Golden Calf?

16. Pennsylvania was originally established as a refuge for which religious sect?

17. Which Gospel author is patron saint of artists?

18. Which pipe-making material is also called sepiolite?

19. In which US state is Fort Knox?

20. How are artists Proesch and Passmore better known?

ANSWERS: 1 *The old London Bridge,* **2** *Glasgow,* **3** *A bird,* **4** *Halley's Comet,* **5** *Bob Fosse,* **6** *Iceland,* **7** *Brian Redhead,* **8** *All Saints' Day,* **9** *Sugar Ray Leonard,* **10** *Robert Kennedy,* **11** *Rita Hayworth,* **12** *Navarre,* **13** *Australian,* **14** *Longchamp,* **15** *Aaron,* **16** *Quakers,* **17** *St Luke,* **18** *Meerschaum,* **19** *Kentucky,* **20** *Gilbert and George.*

General Knowledge

1. Who chaired the arms-to-Iraq inquiry?

2. What is recorded using a sphygmomanometer?

3. Who painted the *Rokeby Venus*?

4. Into which river do the Great Lakes drain?

5. In which county was the churchyard of Thomas Gray's famous *Elegy*?

6. In which country is the Great Bear Lake?

7. For which element is Ba the symbol?

8. Who was the commander of Apollo 11?

9. Which Israeli prime minister was assassinated in November 1995?

10. Who wrote *Les Fleurs du mal*?

11. Which German school of design was closed by the Nazis in 1933?

12. Who was Hero's lover?

13. Which ore is the chief source of Uranium?

14. Who wrote the novel *Daniel Deronda*?

15. Which country's bobsleigh team inspired the film *Cool Runnings*?

16. Which painter immortalised his native village of Cookham in Berkshire?

17. How is the house plant *Chlorophytum elatum* better known?

18. On which metallic element does verdigris form?

19. By what name are the Trucial States now known?

20. Who played young attorney Andy Beckett in *Philadelphia*?

ANSWERS: 1 *Lord Justice Scott,* **2** *Blood pressure,* **3** *Velazquez,* **4** *St Lawrence,* **5** *Buckinghamshire,* **6** *Canada,* **7** *Barium,* **8** *Neil Armstrong,* **9** *Yitzhak Rabin,* **10** *Charles Baudelaire,* **11** *Bauhaus,* **12** *Leander,* **13** *Pitchblende,* **14** *George Eliot,* **15** *Jamaica,* **16** *Sir Stanley Spencer,* **17** *Spider plant,* **18** *Copper,* **19** *United Arab Emirates,* **20** *Tom Hanks.*

General Knowledge

1. Who killed Cock Robin?

2. Which British football team was the first to win a European trophy?

3. What was Wagner's last opera?

4. In which card game does a player get one for his nob?

5. Which former zcabinet minister and General Synod member has joined the Roman Catholic church?

6. Which literary critic wrote *The Great Tradition*?

7. In which discipline did Nicky Gooch win a Winter Olympic bronze medal in 1994?

8. How is deoxyribonucleic acid better known?

9. In what type of dance are zapateados performed?

10. By what name is the constellation Crux also known?

11. What is kerosene called in the UK?

12. Who ranks immediately below Lord Chief Justice?

13. In which city was Prince Charles rushed by David Kang?

14. How is paralysis agitans otherwise known?

15. Which US secret society was formed in 1866?

16. How is the rose bay shrub otherwise known?

17. In which religion is nirvana the attainment of perfect serenity?

18. Which two countries share the Pindus Mountains?

19. Which English writer's first novel was *Crome Yellow*?

20. Of which great orchestra was James Galway a member from 1969-75?

ANSWERS: 1 The fly, 2 Tottenham Hotspur, 3 Parsifal, 4 Cribbage, 5 John Gummer, 6 F R Leavis, 7 Speed skating, 8 DNA, 9 Flamenco, 10 Southern Cross, 11 Paraffin, 12 Master of the Rolls, 13 Sydney, 14 Parkinson's disease, 15 Ku Klux Klan, 16 Oleander, 17 Buddhism, 18 Greece and Albania, 19 Aldous Huxley, 20 Berlin Philharmonic.

Entertainment

1. Who replaced Sue Cook as presenter of *Crimewatch*?
2. Who played the title role in *Magnum*?
3. Who starred as agent 007 in the Bond Film *On Her Majesty's Secret Service*?
4. Which is the only Simon and Garfunkel single to make it to No. 1 in the UK charts?
5. Who directed the classic thriller *Psycho*?
6. Which female vocalist released an album called *Diva*?
7. Who played spook fighter Egon Spengler in *Ghostbusters*?
8. Which former 'Goon' presented *Highway* on TV?
9. Which British group had a hit with *The Theme from M*A*S*H**?
10. Who asks the questions in the satirical quiz show, *Have I Got News For You*?
11. Which American actress starred with Anthony Hopkins in *Silence of the Lambs*?
12. Which Lionel Richie song was a UK No 1 for six weeks in 1984?
13. Which film stars Sandra Bullock as a computer nerd?
14. What name was shared by a member of Duran Duran and a member of Queen?
15. Who had a top ten hit with a cover version of Gerry Rafferty's *Baker Street*?
16. Which Oscar-winning British actor starred in the remake of the *Last of the Mohicans*?
17. Which group had a UK No. 1 in 1966 with *Sunny Afternoon*?
18. Les Patterson is a comic creation of which Australian entertainer?
19. Who played Rigsby's long-suffering woman lodger in *Rising Damp*?
20. Which LP was selected by Richard Branson to launch his Virgin record label?

General Knowledge

1. Who wrote *Catch 22*?

2. With which county did the Isle of Ely merge in 1965?

3. Whose secretary was the original *éminence grise*?

4. Which horror actor was born William Henry Pratt?

5. Which is the USA's Sunflower State?

6. What is Edwin Landseer's most famous painting?

7. Which heiress included Cary Grant among her 7 husbands?

8. Which French playwright was born Jean Baptiste Poquelin?

9. Which legendary rock guitarist's middle name was Marshall?

10. Who was the last Holy Roman Emperor?

11. Which country surrounds The Gambia on three sides?

12. Which container is named after the Russian for 'self-boiling'?

13. Who lasted only one match as manager of Wales's football team?

14. What type of animal is a bongo?

15. Which rock group was fronted by Jim Morrison?

16. What name did Malcolm Little assume?

17. How is iron pyrites popularly known?

18. How are outlaws Parker and Barrow better known?

19. Of which creature is Queen Alexandra's birdwing the largest?

20. Who wrote the opera *Boris Godunov*?

ANSWERS: *1 Joseph Heller, 2 Cambridgeshire, 3 Cardinal Richelieu, 4 Boris Karloff, 5 Kansas, 6 Monarch of the Glen, 7 Barbara Hutton, 8 Molière, 9 Jimi Hendrix, 10 Francis II, 11 Senegal, 12 Samovar, 13 John Toshack, 14 Antelope, 15 The Doors, 16 Malcolm X, 17 Fool's gold, 18 Bonnie and Clyde, 19 Butterfly, 20 Modest Mussorgsky.*

General Knowledge

1. Who added the King's to King's Lynn?

2. Which popular author was born James Alfred Wight?

3. In which county is Stansted Airport?

4. Which philosopher asserted "I think, therefore I am"?

5. What relation are Clement and Lucian to Sigmund Freud?

6. For which flower is heartsease another name?

7. How is diamorphine better known?

8. Which programme's presenters defected from Radio 4 to Classic FM?

9. For which fictional hero did Alexander Selkirk provide the model?

10. Which football club sacked Justin Fashanu for 'unbecoming conduct'?

11. Who is credited with discovering penicillin in 1928?

12. In which country are the Queen's bodyguards the Royal Company of Archers?

13. What was IRA man Dominic McGlinchey's nickname?

14. Who wrote *Strangers on a Train*?

15. Which bird has honey and rough-legged varieties?

16. Which country was formerly known as the Gold Coast?

17. Which skier is known as *La Bomba*?

18. Who wrote *Our Man in Havana*?

19. Which river divides Kentish Men from Men of Kent?

20. Which composer's *Adagietto* from his 5th Symphony was used in the film *Death In Venice*?

General Knowledge

1. What is celebrated in Australia on April 25?

2. In Norse mythology, who was Balder's father?

3. Who wrote the opera *Prince Igor*?

4. In what year was the Boston Tea Party?

5. For what is myocardial infarct a technical term?

6. Which language dominates in the north of the Netherlands?

7. Of which US state is Topeka the capital?

8. How many lines are there in a limerick?

9. Who designed Marble Arch?

10. Which annual literary award was established in 1969?

11. Of which terrorist organisation was Black September a splinter group?

12. Who was the last British PM before John Major to sleep at the White House?

13. What is the name of the US President's private aircraft?

14. What is the capital of Jersey?

15. Which actress was born Harlean Carpenter?

16. In which occupation were the Molly Maguires a secret union?

17. In which US state is White Sands Missile Range?

18. Which British college did Herbert Beerbohm Tree found in 1904?

19. Which top jockey missed the 1994 Cheltenham Festival due to a ban?

20. Which cabinet minister is nicknamed Tarzan?

ANSWERS: *1 Anzac Day, 2 Odin, 3 Alexander Borodin, 4 1773, 5 Heart attack, 6 Frisian, 7 Kansas, 8 Five, 9 John Nash, 10 Booker Prize, 11 PLO, 12 Winston Churchill, 13 Air Force One, 14 St Helier, 15 Jean Harlow, 16 Coal mining, 17 New Mexico, 18 RADA, 19 Richard Dunwoody, 20 Michael Heseltine.*

Entertainment

1. Who presented the original *Take Your Pick* series?
2. Which Steve Martin film was based on *Cyrano de Bergerac*?
3. Which American pop megastar had a backing group called the *New Power Generation?*
4. Which former *Avengers* star appeared in *The Upper Hand?*
5. Who had a US No.1 hit with Lionel Richie in 1982 with *Endless Love?*
6. Who played Francisco Scaramanga in the 1974 Bond movie *The Man with the Golden Gun?*
7. Which TV presenter is married to Mike Smith?
8. Which French actor played Columbus in the film *1492 Conquest of Paradise?*
9. Who is the lead singer of *Simply Red?*
10. Who plays 'Compo' in *Last of the Summer Wine?*
11. Which band had a UK No.1 hit in 1967 with *A Whiter Shade of Pale?*
12. Who won an Oscar for his title role in the 1983 Richard Attenborough film *Gandhi?*
13. What was the name of the guitar-playing rabbit in *Magic Roundabout?*
14. *Nessun Dorma*, adopted as the 1990 World Cup theme, was written by which opera composer?
15. Which heart-throb from *EastEnders* turned up in *Heartbeat* as a village policeman?
16. Who played Michael Douglas's psychotic lover in *Fatal Attraction?*
17. Which Scottish band had a Top 10 hit with *Love Songs/Alive and Kicking?*
18. Who starred as Terry Scott's wife in ten series of their hit domestic comedy?
19. Which Walt Disney cartoon was nominated for Best Picture at the 1991 Oscars?
20. Which US vocalist had a UK No.1 in 1983 with *Uptown Girl?*

General Knowledge

1.   Which branch of learning is named from the Greek for 'love of wisdom'?

2.   On which river is the Texan capital Austin?

3.   The Egyptian god Anubis had which animal's head?

4.   Who wrote *Black Beauty* in 1877?

5.   What is Germany's major airline?

6.   In which country did the Romans build the Antonine Wall?

7.   Who succeeded Oliver Cromwell as Lord Protector of the Commonwealth?

8.   Of which metal is malachite an ore?

9.   What is the capital of Rhode Island?

10. Which philosopher wrote *On Liberty*?

11. Who wrote *Moby Dick* in 1851?

12. Which star of the film *Uncle Buck* died in March 1994?

13. Of what is the Victoria Cross now made?

14. Who was the mother of Richard I and John?

15. In which London park is the Serpentine?

16. What does the Russian word 'soviet' mean?

17. What is the first day of Lent called?

18. What land did the US buy from Russia in 1867?

19. What is the capital of Paraguay?

20. Which charity was founded by Canon Milford in 1942?

ANSWERS: *1 Philosophy, 2 Colorado, 3 Jackal, 4 Anna Sewell, 5 Lufthansa, 6 Scotland, 7 Richard Cromwell, 8 Copper, 9 Providence, 10 John Stuart Mill, 11 Herman Melville, 12 John Candy, 13 Gunmetal, 14 Eleanor of Aquitaine, 15 Hyde Park, 16 Council, 17 Ash Wednesday, 18 Alaska, 19 Asuncion, 20 Oxfam.*

General Knowledge

1. Which Athenian philosopher died by drinking Hemlock?

2. What nationality was Christopher Columbus?

3. What is the capital of Tanzania?

4. Which Tudor warship is in a dry dock in Portsmouth?

5. What was the main river of Hades in Greek mythology?

6. Who created Maigret?

7. What sort of creature is an axolotl?

8. Who was the first woman MP to sit in the House of Commons?

9. Where did Davy Crockett die?

10. Who wrote *The Murders in the Rue Morgue*?

11. Which spirit is made from the juice of an agave?

12. Which battle took place on June 18, 1815?

13. Which metal has the chemical symbol Au?

14. Who claimed to have won "peace in our time"?

15. Which historical conflict was between the Houses of Lancaster and York?

16. Who is the patron saint of Russia?

17. Of which South African city is Soweto a suburb?

18. What was the pen name of novelist Mary Ann Evans?

19. What is the capital of Venezuela?

20. Which Sioux chief led the massacre of General Custer and his men?

ANSWERS: 1 Socrates, **2** Italian, **3** Dar es Salaam, **4** Mary Rose, **5** The Styx, **6** Georges Simenon, **7** A salamander, **8** Nancy Astor, **9** At the Alamo, **10** Edgar Allen Poe, **11** Tequila, **12** Waterloo, **13** Gold, **14** Neville Chamberlain, **15** Wars of the Roses, **16** St Nicholas, **17** Johannesburg, **18** George Eliot, **19** Caracas, **20** Sitting Bull.

General Knowledge

1. By what name, meaning 'our thing', is the mafia known in the US?

2. Which poet is buried in a country churchyard in Stoke Poges?

3. Whose operas are performed annually at Bayreuth?

4. Which US state has Dover as its capital?

5. Which prime minister became Earl of Stockton?

6. Who was the first Roman emperor?

7. In which century did the Peasants' Revolt take place?

8. During which Crimean War Battle did the Charge of the Light Brigade take place?

9. In which novel did Sherlock Holmes first appear?

10. What is the lowest-pitched member of the violin family?

11. Who is the patron saint of doctors and artists?

12. Which Agatha Christie play opened in London in 1952?

13. In which English city is the headquarters of the Open University?

14. How was writer Samuel Langhorne Clemens better known?

15. Who was known as the Butcher of Lyon?

16. How many Muses are there in Greek mythology?

17. Which substance gives blood its colour?

18. Which gangster was imprisoned for tax evasion in 1931?

19. Which jazz trumpeter died in 1991 at the age of 65?

20. Which Scottish mathematician invented logarithms?

ANSWERS: *1 Cosa Nostra, 2 Thomas Gray, 3 Richard Wagner, 4 Delaware, 5 Harold Macmillan, 6 Augustus, 7 14th, 8 Balaclava, 9 A Study in Scarlet, 10 Double bass, 11 St Luke, 12 The Mousetrap, 13 Milton Keynes, 14 Mark Twain, 15 Klaus Barbie, 16 Nine, 17 Haemoglobin, 18 Al Capone, 19 Miles Davis, 20 John Napier.*

Entertainment

1. Which Scotsman presented *Blue Peter* and *Scavengers*?

2. Who directed and starred in *Dances with Wolves*?

3. Which US group had a No.1 in 1979 with *Heart of Glass*?

4. Who played Bradley Hardacre in *Brass*?

5. Who starred with Steve Martin in *Housesitter*?

6. What is the name of the village in which *Noel's House Party* takes place?

7. Which Australian comedian played the title role in *Crocodile Dundee*?

8. Which American band had a Top Ten hit with *Keep the Faith*?

9. Who is Caron Keating's famous mother?

10. Which American singer released an album entitled *Timeless (The Classics)*?

11. Which war hero was the subject of the classic 1957 film *Reach For The Sky*?

12. Who played Dr. Leonard 'Bones' McCoy in the *Star Trek* series?

13. What is the name of Tom Petty's backing band?

14. Who played the role of the fire chief in *Towering Inferno*?

15. Who duetted with Phil Collins on the 1985 No.1 hit *Easy Lover*?

16. Who played Dorothy in *The Golden Girls*?

17. Which actress appeared in Two Bond movies, *The Man With The Golden Gun* and *Octopussy*?

18. Which US group had a No.1 hit with *End of the Road*?

19. Which famous British comedienne starred in *Just Like A Woman*?

20. Who plays Cindy in *EastEnders*?

General Knowledge

1. In Greek mythology who was the sister and wife of Zeus?

2. When did Queen Victoria succeed to the throne?

3. Jomo Kenyatta was prime minister of which country?

4. Who wrote the *Emperor Concerto*?

5. How many gills are in one pint?

6. In which American state is Fort Knox?

7. Which element has the symbol Ar?

8. Who wrote the *Palliser* novels?

9. What was the first James Bond film?

10. Which Shakespeare play features the character Polonius?

11. What is the ninth sign of the zodiac?

12. What is a turkey brown?

13. In which country is Casablanca?

14. In which ship did Drake circumnavigate the world in 1577-80?

15. Who wrote the play *Hay Fever*?

16. In which war was the Battle of Borodino?

17. Who painted *The Laughing Cavalier*?

18. In which country was Albert Einstein born?

19. What is the capital of Sicily?

20. What was the pen-name of the Irish writer Brian O'Nolan?

ANSWERS: *1 Hera, 2 1837, 3 Kenya, 4 Beethoven, 5 Four, 6 Kentucky, 7 Argon, 8 Anthony Trollope, 9 Dr No, 10 Hamlet, 11 Sagittarius, 12 An angler's name for a species of mayfly, 13 Morocco, 14 Golden Hind, 15 Noel Coward, 16 The Napoleonic War, 17 Frans Hals, 18 Germany, 19 Palermo, 20 Flann O'Brien.*

General Knowledge

1. How many years does a sapphire wedding anniversary celebrate?

2. Which country's vehicle registration letters are RCH?

3. Which vegetable has the varieties Nevada and Canberra?

4. Which line is coloured grey on a London underground map?

5. Which shipping forecast area lies between Fastnet and Irish Sea?

6. In which forest is *As You Like It* set?

7. On which river does Florence stand?

8. Which singer was born Robert Allan Zimmerman?

9. What was the name of the dog in the film *The Wizard of Oz*?

10. Phobos and Deimos are satellites of which planet?

11. What is acrophobia?

12. What was the last film to take all four major Oscars?

13. Who was the Roman god of wine?

14. Which composer's last words were reputedly "I shall hear in heaven"?

15. Who was the arch rival of Dan Dare?

16. What is the symbol of the element sodium?

17. What is the capital of the Canadian province of British Columbia?

18. In what year was the QEII launched?

19. Which Old Testament book comes between Joshua and Ruth?

20. In which US city is Logan airport?

ANSWERS: *1 45, 2 Chile, 3 Cauliflower, 4 Jubilee, 5 Lundy, 6 Forest of Arden, 7 Arno, 8 Bob Dylan, 9 Toto, 10 Mars, 11 The fear of heights, 12 The Silence of the Lambs, 13 Bacchus, 14 Beethoven, 15 The Mekon, 16 Na, 17 Victoria, 18 1967, 19 Judges, 20 Boston.*

General Knowledge

Your rating: ● 0-5   Join a library   ● 6-10   Keep at it
● 11-15   Join a quiz team   ● 16-20   Enter Mastermind

1. What does the abbreviation ASLEF stand for?

2. Which war lasted from 1854-56?

3. In which year did Louis Bleriot cross the English Channel?

4. Which vegetable's scientific name is *Brassica napobrassica*?

5. TAP is the airline of which country?

6. What is the more common name of Schubert's Symphony No 8 in B Minor?

7. What is the middle name of Ronald Reagan?

8. What was the name of the dog that went into space in 1957?

9. In architecture, what is a campanile?

10. On which river does Berlin stand?

11. Which comedian's real name is Joseph Levitch?

12. Who was shot by Nathuran Godse on September 17th, 1948?

13. Which poet wrote *The Lake Isle of Innisfree*?

14. What, according to the Beaufort Scale, is a wind of 64-72 m.p.h.?

15. What is dendrophobia the fear of?

16. In which year was the Mary Celeste found unmanned near the Azores?

17. Who won the 1990 Nobel Peace Prize?

18. In which musical is the song *76 Trombones* featured?

19. Which instrument did Glenn Miller play?

20. What is the capital of Chile?

ANSWERS: 1 Associated Society of Locomotive Engineers and Firemen, 2 The Crimean, 3 1909, 4 Swede, 5 Portugal, 6 The Unfinished Symphony, 7 Wilson, 8 Laika, 9 A belltower, 10 Spree, 11 Jerry Lewis, 12 Mahatma Gandhi, 13 W.B Yeats, 14 A storm, 15 Trees, 16 1872, 17 Mikhail Gorbachev, 18 The Music Man, 19 Trombone, 20 Santiago.

- 28 -

Entertainment

1. Who is the host of the hi-tech gameshow *Catchphrase*?
2. Who played Rose, the parlour maid, in the series *Upstairs, Downstairs*?
3. Which American actress received her second Oscar for her role in *Sophie's Choice*?
4. Who had a No. 1 hit with the single *Ebeneezer Goode*?
5. What animal appeared in the title role of the Walt Disney cartoon *Robin Hood*?
6. Which famous comedienne performed *Murder Most Horrid* on TV?
7. Who was the lead singer of the Four Seasons?
8. Which sinister terror organisation did James Bond battle against in several films?
9. Which British band had a No.1 hit in the US and UK, in 1984, with *The Reflex*?
10. Who starred opposite Humphrey Bogart as the female lead in *Casablanca*?
11. Which member of Queen had a hit with *Too Much Love Will Kill You*?
12. Which star of *The Singing Detective* played *Maigret*?
13. Which US actor starred with wife Nicole Kidman in *Far and Away*?
14. Who is the host of the *Antiques Roadshow*?
15. Which founder member of Genesis had a hit with *Digging in the Dirt*?
16. In what town is the Australian soap *Home and Away* set?
17. Which former Miami Sound Machine front-person released an album entitled *Abriendo Puertas*?
18. Which former busker had a No.1 hit with *When I Need You*?
19. Who starred as *The Swimmer* in 1968?
20. Who played Motel owner Meg Richardson in *Crossroads*?

ANSWERS: *1 Roy Walker, 2 Jean Marsh, 3 Meryl Streep, 4 The Shamen, 5 A Fox, 6 Dawn French, 7 Frankie Valli, 8 Spectre, 9 Duran Duran, 10 Ingrid Bergman, 11 Brian May, 12 Michael Gambon, 13 Tom Cruise, 14 Hugh Scully, 15 Peter Gabriel, 16 Summer Bay, 17 Gloria Estefan, 18 Leo Sayer, 19 Burt Lancaster, 20 Noele Gordon.*

General Knowledge

1. In the novel *Gulliver's Travels* what was Gulliver's christian name?

2. In which year did Castro seize power in Cuba?

3. With which art form do you associate Louis Daguerre?

4. Of which country was King Zog monarch?

5. Which Oscar-winning actor was born Reginald Truscott-Jones?

6. What is the 49th state of the United States of America?

7. Which year saw the birth of Isaac Newton and the death of Galileo?

8. When did the League of Nations come into being?

9. In which country is the mountain Aconcagua?

10. What does the musical term andante mean?

11. Who won the 1964 Nobel peace prize?

12. Which 'pop' artist do you associate with Campbell's soup cans?

13. On which river does Washington DC stand?

14. Which zodiac sign straddles December and January?

15. What were the christian names of HG Wells?

16. Who was the Roman god of war?

17. Which country's flag is a yellow cross on a blue background?

18. In which country is the schilling a monetary unit?

19. What is the collective noun used to describe a group of crows?

20. In which year did the Japanese attack a US fleet in Pearl Harbor?

ANSWERS: 1 Lemuel, 2 1959, 3 Photography, 4 Albania, 5 Ray Milland, 6 Alaska, 7 1642, 8 1920, 9 Argentina, 10 Walking pace, 11 Martin Luther King, 12 Andy Warhol, 13 Potomac, 14 Capricorn, 15 Herbert George, 16 Mars, 17 Sweden, 18 Austria, 19 Murder, 20 1941.

General Knowledge

1. Which poet wrote *Paradise Lost*?

2. Who was the eldest son of Queen Victoria?

3. Which Welsh actor was born Richard Jenkins in 1925?

4. How did bank robber Ned Kelly die?

5. When was the first London to Brighton veteran car rally?

6. With which item of clothing would you associate Mary Phelps Jacob?

7. Which Apollo 12 astronauts made the second moon landing?

8. On what date was the Anglo-Irish Agreement signed?

9. What is the Sooner state of the U.S.A.?

10. Where is the Sea of Rains?

11. Who was the British commander at the Battle of Jutland?

12. In which year did King Juan Carlos become head of state in Spain?

13. What is the more familiar name of William H Bonney?

14. Which island was once called Van Diemen's Land?

15. What nationality was former UN Secretary-General U Thant?

16. Which cartoonist created the strip 'Peanuts'?

17. In which Irish county was actress Pat Phoenix born?

18. Whom did William Shakespeare marry?

19. In which country was thriller writer Ngaio Marsh born?

20. Who was born first, Laurel or Hardy?

ANSWERS: *1 John Milton, 2 Edward VII, 3 Richard Burton, 4 He was hanged, 5 1927, 6 The bra (she patented it), 7 Conrad and Bean, 8 15th November 1985, 9 Oklahoma, 10 The moon, 11 Admiral Jellicoe, 12 1975, 13 Billy the Kid, 14 Tasmania, 15 Burmese, 16 Charles Schulz, 17 County Galway, 18 Anne Hathaway, 19 New Zealand, 20 Laurel.*

General Knowledge

1. With which instrument is Jascha Heifetz associated?

2. How old was Buddy Holly when he died?

3. Which American president was present at the 1945 Yalta conference?

4. Who invented the first fully automatic machine gun?

5. Of which country is 'Waitangi Day' the national day?

6. What was the nickname of landscape gardener Lancelot Brown?

7. Which imaginary country features in *The Prisoner of Zenda*?

8. In which year was Shergar stolen?

9. What opened in London's Fleet St and Bedford St in 1852?

10. Which French chef was known as 'The King of Cooks'?

11. What nationality was detective writer Georges Simenon?

12. In what year was the St Valentine's Day massacre?

13. What is the profession of entertainers Edgar Bergen and Ray Alan?

14. Who was born first, Yoko Ono or John Lennon?

15. With which branch of science do you associate Copernicus?

16. Which agricultural pioneer invented the seed drill?

17. Which city stands on the river Wensum?

18. From which country did the US buy Florida?

19. Of which country was Juan Peron the president?

20. What does RADAR stand for?

ANSWERS: 1 Violin, 2 22, 3 Franklin D Roosevelt, 4 Hiram Maxim, 5 New Zealand, 6 Capability, 7 Ruritania, 8 1983, 9 The first men's and women's public flushing lavatories, 10 Escoffier, 11 Belgian, 12 1929, 13 Ventriloquists, 14 Yoko Ono, 15 Astronomy, 16 Jethro Tull, 17 Norwich, 18 Spain, 19 Argentina, 20 Radio detection and ranging.

Sports

1. Who captained Europe's victorious Ryder Cup team in 1995?

2. From which country does tennis player Ronald Agenor come?

3. Who described Damon Hill's crash at Silverstone as "really stupid - a crazy move"?

4. At what age did Judit Polgar become chess grandmaster?

5. For which county does Robin Smith play?

6. Which Wimbledon defender made a £4m move to Newcastle United in 1995?

7. Which rugby union position is in the middle of the front row?

8. At which sport do the Oldham Celtics compete?

9. What nationality is golfer Nick Price?

10. In which ski resort is the Cresta Run?

11. Who won the 1994 US Masters golf championship?

12. Which football team plays at Filbert Street?

13. In which year did Steffi Graf win her first Grand Slam title?

14. Which snooker player was known as *The Grinder*?

15. Of which French football team was Bernard Tapie president?

16. In which city did the 1994 Tour of Britain start?

17. Whose drop goal gave England victory over Australia in the 1995 World Cup quarter final?

18. For which Italian football team did Des Walker play in 1992/3?

19. What sport do Norma Shaw and Diana Hunt compete at?

20. Which German World Cup star joined Spurs for the 1994-95 season?

General Knowledge

Your rating: ● 0-5   Join a library   ● 6-10   Keep at it
               ● 11-15 Join a quiz team   ● 16-20   Enter Mastermind

1. In which Australian state is Ayers Rock?

2. What is killer Albert De Salvo better known as?

3. What are Limburger and Camembert?

4. Who was the wife of Othello?

5. Who created Winnie-the-Pooh?

6. What Roman goddess is equivalent to the Greek Aphrodite?

7. In which city is the Uffizi art gallery?

8. What in France is the TGV?

9. On what island was Napoleon first exiled?

10. Which country produces Saab cars and missiles?

11. What was the nickname of Baron von Richthofen?

12. With which city do you associate the Raffles hotel?

13. Which monarch is found on a Penny Black stamp?

14. Who was the Indian boy in Kipling's *Jungle Books*?

15. Who wrote *The Ginger Man?*

16. In what year was Harrods founded?

17. What is the US equivalent of the British postcode?

18. In what US state is Yale University?

19. In what year was the Jarrow hunger march?

20. Which country is the 'Land of the Midnight Sun'?

ANSWERS: *1 Northern Territory, 2 The Boston Strangler, 3 Cheeses, 4 Desdemona, 5 A.A Milne, 6 Venus, 7 Florence, 8 High speed train, 9 Elba, 10 Sweden, 11 The Red Baron, 12 Singapore, 13 Queen Victoria, 14 Mowgli, 15 J.P Donleavy, 16 1849, 17 The Zip Code, 18 Connecticut, 19 1936, 20 Norway.*

General Knowledge

Your rating: ● 0-5   Join a library   ● 6-10   Keep at it
               ● 11-15 Join a quiz team   ● 16-20   Enter Mastermind

1. Who is James Bond's service chief?

2. What is the name of the hunchback of Notre-Dame?

3. What is the Latin name for Switzerland?

4. What is the name of the main canal in Venice?

5. Which British airship crashed on a flight to India in 1930?

6. How long, approximately, is Route 66?

7. Who was the eldest son of Adam and Eve?

8. What is the 4th constellation of the Zodiac?

9. What was the name of King Arthur's magic sword?

10. Which king was 'Farmer George'?

11. What was the nickname of jazz pianist Ferdinand Morton?

12. What was the imaginary flying island in *Gulliver's Travels?*

13. Who are the feuding families in *Romeo and Juliet?*

14. What is a Sam Browne?

15. What was the nickname of Louis Armstrong?

16. What does the Sikh name 'Singh' mean?

17. In which Bavarian village is a famous passion play performed?

18. Which German battleship sunk HMS Hood?

19. In what year was the Reuter news agency founded?

20. What is the professional organisation of British magicians called?

ANSWERS: 1 M, 2 *Quasimodo*, 3 *Helvetia*, 4 *Grand Canal*, 5 R-101, 6 2,200 *miles*, 7 *Cain*, 8 *Cancer*, 9 *Excalibur*, 10 *King George III*, 11 *Jelly Roll*, 12 *Laputa*, 13 *The Montagues and Capulets*, 14 *A military officer's wide belt*, 15 *Satchmo*, 16 *Lion*, 17 *Oberammergau*, 18 *Bismarck*, 19 1851, 20 *The Magic Circle*.

General Knowledge

1. In which year did Anthony Eden become prime minister?

2. Which famous Australian soprano died in 1931?

3. Who was the TUC General Secretary from 1960-70?

4. What does the musical term rallentando mean?

5. How many chains are in a furlong?

6. In classical mythology, who turned Odysseus's men into swine?

7. How are the Islas Malvinas better known?

8. In which city is the Quai d'Orsay?

9. Which engineer built the Suez canal?

10. Who wrote *Treasure Island*?

11. Whom did Pilate set free in preference to Jesus?

12. In which Dickens book would you find the character Job Trotter?

13. In which year did the Jodrell Bank telescope become operational?

14. Which was the first country to grant women the vote?

15. In which year did Oliver Cromwell die?

16. What nationality was the composer Bedrich Smetana?

17. What is gynophobia?

18. Which car manufacturer made the Healey and Interceptor models?

19. Which London Underground line is coloured black on the network map?

20. What does the heraldic term mullet denote?

ANSWERS: *1 1955, 2 Dame Nellie Melba, 3 George Woodcock, 4 Slowing down, 5 Ten, 6 Circe, 7 The Falkland Islands, 8 Paris, 9 Ferdinand de Lesseps, 10 R.L Stevenson, 11 Barabbas, 12 Pickwick Papers, 13 1957, 14 New Zealand, 15 1658, 16 Czech, 17 Fear of women, 18 Jensen, 19 Northern line, 20 A Star.*

Entertainment

1. Who was the lead singer with Soft Cell?
2. From which musical does the song *Send In The Clowns* come?
3. Who played the tough hero of *Mad Max*?
4. What is the name of *Tintin*'s dog?
5. Which actress was a New York husband's *Seven Year Itch*?
6. Which Beatle married Linda Eastman?
7. Which group with a beastly name made *House of the Rising Sun*?
8. Who produced, co-wrote, directed and starred in *Reds*?
9. Which '90s teen-group had a hit with their *Babe*?
10. Who played Harry in *When Harry Met Sally*?
11. Which actor played Dave in *Minder*?
12. Which ex-*EastEnder* played Mick Raynor in *99-1*?
13. Which football manager co-wrote *Hazell*, who was played on screen by Nicholas Ball?
14. For which American pop idol was *G I Blues* a movie vehicle?
15. *Mork and Mindy* was a spin-off from which comedy series?
16. Who sang *Nights in White Satin*?
17. In which former British colony was *The Piano* set?
18. With which sex symbol did Peter Sellers record the 1960 Top Ten hit *Goodness Gracious Me*?
19. Who intended to make 1994 *The Perfect Year*?
20. Which film starring John Hurt, was based on the Profumo affair?

ANSWERS: *1 Marc Almond, 2 A Little Night Music, 3 Mel Gibson, 4 Snowy, 5 Marilyn Monroe, 6 Paul McCartney, 7 The Animals, 8 Warren Beatty, 9 Take That, 10 Billy Crystal, 11 Glynn Edwards, 12 Leslie Grantham, 13 Terry Venables, 14 Elvis Presley, 15 Happy Days, 16 The Moody Blues, 17 New Zealand, 18 Sophia Loren, 19 Dina Carroll, 20 Scandal.*

General Knowledge

1. Whose only opera was *Fidelio*?

2. Who was the queen consort of Edward VII?

3. Which US state is known as the Heart of Dixie?

4. Of what nationality was Django Reinhardt?

5. Of which country is Port Moresby the capital?

6. Which boxer was known as The Manassa Mauler?

7. In which craft did Yuri Gagarin become the first man in space?

8. In which Texan city is the Alamo?

9. Of which ballet company was Nureyev a member when he defected?

10. Whom did George I succeed as monarch?

11. Which party is named from the Gaelic for Soldiers of Destiny?

12. Of which city were the Medici a noble family?

13. Who wrote *Breakfast at Tiffany's*?

14. How is Holy Innocent's Day also known?

15. Which world leaders met at the 1943 Casablanca Conference?

16. Which film tells the story of Sally Bowles?

17. Who wrote the operetta *The Merry Widow*?

18. Which officer is served by an aide-de-camp?

19. What was the profession of Sir George Gilbert Scott?

20. By how many does the prefix giga- multiply a number?

ANSWERS: 1 *Beethoven*, 2 *Alexandra*, 3 *Alabama*, 4 *Belgian*, 5 *Papua New Guinea*, 6 *Jack Dempsey*, 7 *Vostok 1*, 8 *San Antonio*, 9 *Kirov*, 10 *Queen Anne*, 11 *Fianna Fáil*, 12 *Florence*, 13 *Truman Capote*, 14 *Childermas*, 15 *Churchill and Roosevelt*, 16 *Cabaret*, 17 *Franz Lehár*, 18 *General*, 19 *Architect*, 20 *Thousand million*.

General Knowledge

1.   When was Count von Zeppelin's first airship built?

2.   Which famous king was son of Findlaech?

3.   What sort of fruit is a morello?

4.   In which year did Sitting Bull die?

5.   What is a pixel?

6.   What is the capital of Corsica?

7.   What is the SI unit of electrical charge?

8.   Which artist painted *Nude Descending a Staircase*?

9.   In which country is Casablanca?

10. What are the international vehicle registration letters for Bahrain?

11. Who was the second president of the US?

12. On which river does Baghdad stand?

13. Which Soviet president died in 1985?

14. Which composer wrote *The Sorcerer's Apprentice*?

15. What was a farthingale?

16. What were WS Gilbert's forenames?

17. In which year did Marilyn Monroe marry Arthur Miller?

18. What is the busiest airport in France?

19. What is the oldest university in Scotland?

20. What is a lazy Susan?

ANSWERS: *1 1900, 2 Cherry, 3 Macbeth, 4 1890, 5 A single dot on a computer screen, 6 Ajaccio, 7 Coulomb, 8 Marcel Duchamp, 9 Morocco, 10 BRN, 11 John Adams, 12 Tigris, 13 Konstantin Chernenko, 14 Paul Dukas, 15 A hooped petticoat, 16 William Schwenk, 17 1956, 18 Orly, 19 St Andrews, 20 A revolving tray for holding condiments.*

General Knowledge

1. In what year was Bob Geldof given an honorary knighthood?

2. Who was Australian PM from 1949-66?

3. Who was Foreign Secretary in the 1974-6 Wilson government?

4. Which composer wrote the ballet *Billy The Kid*?

5. Which planet is only 3,500 km in diameter?

6. Who was the Roman goddess of the dawn?

7. Between which two islands is the Denmark Strait?

8. What is the Arabian camel also known as?

9. Which Italian modern art movement was initiated by Marinetti?

10. Who wrote the novel *Washington Square*?

11. In the Bible, who owned the vineyard adjoining King Ahab's palace?

12. What sort of bird is a yaffle?

13. Who were the handmaidens of Odin who served at the Valhalla banquets?

14. In which city is Yeshiva University?

15. In which country was the first British atomic missile exploded in 1953?

16. On which instrument was the 'Harry Lime Theme' played?

17. What art gallery is situated at Millbank, London?

18. Where is 'The Street Which is Called Straight'?

19. What does the cooking term nivernaise mean?

20. What, in American slang, is a 'Holy Joe'?

ANSWERS: 1 1986, **2** Sir Robert Menzies, **3** Jim Callaghan, **4** Aaron Copland, **5** Pluto, **6** Aurora, **7** Greenland and Iceland, **8** Dromedary, **9** Futurism, **10** Henry James, **11** Naboth, **12** Woodpecker, **13** The valkyries, **14** New York City, **15** Australia, **16** Zither, **17** The Tate Gallery, **18** Damascus, **19** With carrots, **20** Forces' chaplain.

Entertainment

1. Who played Alf Garnett in *Till Death Us Do Part*?
2. Who won an Oscar for the role of Sally Bowles in the film *Cabaret*?
3. Which group had a US No.1, in 1985, with *Everybody Wants To Rule The World*?
4. Who had a Top Ten Hit in 1974 with *Seven Seas of Rhye*?
5. Which UK vocalist had a No.1 hit with *You Wear It Well* in 1972?
6. Which former athlete co-presents *Record Breakers*?
7. Which American actor/singer played 'Hutch' in *Starsky and Hutch*?
8. What sport is the subject of the film *White Men Can't Jump*?
9. Which British group's only No.1 hit was *Glad All Over*, in 1963?
10. Which famous historical character was the subject of the most recent *Carry On* film?
11. What off-beat science-fiction series about time-travel stars Scott Bakula?
12. Which Australian rock band had a hit with *Taste It*?
13. Which TV drama series was based on Mary Norton's books about a miniature family?
14. Who played rock legend Jerry Lee Lewis in the 1989 film *Great Balls of Fire*?
15. Which female French singer and model had a hit with *Be My Baby*?
16. Which actor played a publican in *EastEnders* and a nightclub owner in *The Paradise Club*?
17. Who directed *Husbands and Wives*?
18. Which female American singer had a hit with *I Will Always Love You*?
19. Which *Big* US comedy actor starred with Geena Davis and Madonna in *A League of Their Own*?
20. Which comedienne stars as Edie in *Last of the Summer Wine*?

ANSWERS: 1 *Warren Mitchell,* 2 *Liza Minnelli,* 3 *Tears for Fears,* 4 *Queen,* 5 *Rod Stewart,* 6 *Kriss Akabusi,* 7 *David Soul,* 8 *Basketball,* 9 *The Dave Clark Five,* 10 *Columbus,* 11 *Quantum Leap,* 12 *INXS,* 13 *The Borrowers,* 14 *Dennis Quaid,* 15 *Vanessa Paradis,* 16 *Leslie Grantham,* 17 *Woody Allen,* 18 *Whitney Houston,* 19 *Tom Hanks,* 20 *Thora Hird.*

General Knowledge

1. What does the Latin term *sub judice* mean?

2. What is the currency of Venezuela?

3. Who was the first president of the US to die in office?

4. In the Bible, what was the home town of Abraham?

5. What name is applied to the poets Wordsworth, Southey and Coleridge?

6. In what year was the Battle of Trafalgar?

7. What is the star Sirius better known as?

8. What is a narghile?

9. In which Australian state is Wagga Wagga?

10. Who was the mythical son of Laius and Jocasta?

11. What are the international vehicle registration letters for Finland?

12. Which vegetable's scientific name is *Nasturtium officinale?*

13. What is the nickname of Tchaikovsky's Symphony No 3 in D?

14. In which year was the first walk in space?

15. On which river does Strasbourg stand?

16. What is androphobia?

17. What instrument do you associate with Jack Teagarden?

18. On which river is the Kariba dam?

19. What is the alter ego of cartoon character Wonder Woman?

20. In what year was Dr Crippen executed?

ANSWERS: *1 Under consideration, 2 Bolivar, 3 William H Harrison, 4 Ur, 5 The Lake Poets, 6 1805, 7 The dog-star, 8 An oriental tobacco pipe, 9 New South Wales, 10 Oedipus, 11 SF, 12 Watercress, 13 Polish Symphony, 14 1965, 15 Rhine, 16 Fear of men, 17 Trombone, 18 Zambezi, 19 Diana Prince, 20 1910.*

General Knowledge

1. Who succeeded Cecil Parkinson in 1983 as Conservative party chairman?

2. What are Formentera, Ibiza, Minorca and Majorca collectively known as?

3. What cargo was HMS Bounty carrying when the mutiny occurred?

4. In what year was NATO established?

5. In which village did Jesus reputedly turn water into wine?

6. In which year did Mao Tse-tung die?

7. Which Italian PM was kidnapped by the Red Brigade in 1978?

8. Who wrote *The Life of Dr Johnson*?

9. In which country is the Jutland peninsula?

10. In which country, other than Malawi, is the kwacha a unit of currency?

11. How many US presidents have been called Adams?

12. Who wrote *Love and Mr Lewisham*?

13. In what year was the Turner wing in the London Tate Gallery opened?

14. Between what years was the Spanish Civil War fought?

15. What was the seventh month of the Old Roman calendar?

16. What is a John Dory?

17. What is ambergris?

18. What is the atomic number of carbon?

19. Who do you associate with the phrase 'Cogito, ergo sum'?

20. What were Sir Winston Churchill's middle names?

ANSWERS: *1 John Selwyn Gummer, 2 The Balearic Islands, 3 Breadfruit, 4 1949, 5 Cana, 6 1976, 7 Aldo Moro, 8 James Boswell, 9 Denmark, 10 Zambia, 11 Two, 12 H.G Wells, 13 1910, 14 1936-9, 15 September, 16 A fish, 17 A waxy substance produced in the intestines of the sperm whale, 18 6, 19 Rene Descartes, 20 Leonard Spencer.*

General Knowledge

1. In which magazine were *The Adventures of Sherlock Holmes* serialised?

2. Which two dams were destroyed by the 'bouncing bombs' of Barnes Wallis?

3. Who wrote the hymn 'Hark, the Herald Angels sing'?

4. Which dynastic family ruled in Brandenberg-Prussia from 1415-1918?

5. What is the largest British prison for women?

6. In which city are The Gorbals?

7. From which country does the cheese Port Salut come?

8. In which year was Popeye created?

9. Who is the Greek equivalent of the Roman sun-god Sol?

10. In what century was the Taj Mahal built?

11. What is finocchio?

12. What is the capital of Bermuda?

13. In financial terms, what do the initials IBRD stand for?

14. What did Elias Howe reputedly invent in 1846?

15. What is the German name for Gdansk?

16. From which language is the world coleslaw derived?

17. What is a fumarole?

18. Who founded the Bauhaus in Germany in 1919?

19. In which year did Chiang Kai-shek die?

20. In which North American city is Bay Street the financial centre?

Entertainment

1. Which former member of *The Young Ones* became *The New Statesman*?
2. Who was the lead singer for Liverpool band Frankie Goes To Hollywood?
3. What famous character was played by Daniel Day Lewis in the 1992 film *Last of the Mohicans*?
4. Which British group's only UK No.1 was *Jealous Guy* in 1981?
5. Which star of *The New Avengers* was in *Absolutely Fabulous* form on TV?
6. Which US actress played the naturalist Diane Fosse in *Gorillas in the Mist*?
7. Which actress played the role of John Steed's assistant Tara King in *The Avengers*?
8. Which star of *Dirty Dancing* and *Ghost* played a drop-out doctor in the film *City of Joy*?
9. Who had a No.1 hit with *Would I Lie To You*?
10. What is the name of the super-snooper who peered *Through the Keyhole* for David Frost?
11. Which American Heavy Metal band had a hit with *Yesterdays*?
12. What is the name of the Canadian actress who played Miss Moneypenny in 14 Bond films?
13. Which star of *Till Death Us Do Part* played Aunt Sally in *Wurzel Gummidge*?
14. Which US vocal group had its only UK No.1 hit in 1966 with *Reach Out I'll Be There*?
15. Which US comic actor was the star of the classic 1921 film *The Paleface*?
16. Who played Arkwright's long-suffering assistant, Granville, in *Open All Hours*?
17. Which actor turned in a devilish performance in the film *The Witches of Eastwick*?
18. Which UK group had a hit with *Who Needs Love (Like That)*?
19. Which 1981 British soap had as it's unlikely setting a North Sea ferry?
20. Which band had a No.1 hit with *Don't You Want Me* in 1983?

ANSWERS: *1 Rik Mayall, 2 Holly Johnson, 3 Hawkeye, 4 Roxy Music, 5 Joanna Lumley, 6 Sigourney Weaver, 7 Linda Thorson, 8 Patrick Swayze, 9 Charles and Eddie, 10 Loyd Grossman, 11 Guns n' Roses, 12 Lois Maxwell, 13 Una Stubbs, 14 The Four Tops, 15 Buster Keaton, 16 David Jason, 17 Jack Nicholson, 18 Erasure, 19 Triangle, 20 Human League.*

General Knowledge

1. The flag of which American state bears the legend 'December 7, 1787'?

2. In which year did Jamaica become independent?

3. What was the middle name of inventor Thomas Edison?

4. What does the French expression 'hors de combat' mean?

5. Which country did Margaret, Maid of Norway, rule between 1286 and 1290?

6. Who was the first Democrat American president?

7. In the Bible, who was the wife of Ahab?

8. What nationality is author Ngugi Wa Thiong'o?

9. Which bird's Latin name is *Passer domesticus?*

10. In which year of the 1970s was the Suez Canal reopened?

11. Which ceremony takes place during the 3rd week of July on the Thames?

12. In which Dickens novel does the quotation "Barkis is willin'" appear?

13. In which country was the Rosetta stone found?

14. In what sort of building would you find a rood screen?

15. In which London park is Rotten Row?

16. What sort of animal is a drongo?

17. What is the former residence of the Moorish kings at Seville called?

18. What is the Italian name of the city of Turin?

19. Who was the youngest of the four Beatles?

20. In which country was Israeli politician Menachem Begin born?

General Knowledge

1. Which Biblical book mentions 'A land flowing with milk and honey"?

2. In which Shakespeare play does Caliban appear?

3. In which year did Canada adopt a maple leaf emblem for its flag?

4. What is the administrative centre of Mid Glamorgan?

5. How old was outlaw Clyde Barrow when he died?

6. The phalanges are the bones of which parts of your body?

7. Who wrote *Northanger Abbey*?

8. To which country did Alexander Graham Bell emigrate in 1870?

9. What nationality was composer Dvorak?

10. With which of the arts would you associate Sir Alfred Munnings?

11. Who was the Leader of the House of Commons from 1976-9?

12. In which country is the Athos peninsula?

13. Who was the companion of Don Quixote?

14. In which two months are the Dog-days?

15. To which crop is the Colorado Beetle a serious pest?

16. What is the gnu also known as?

17. Of what family is the guinea-pig a member?

18. How many gallons did a kilderkin once represent?

19. Which is the brightest of the planets?

20. In which country is Innsbruck?

ANSWERS: 1 Exodus, 2 The Tempest, 3 1965, 4 Cardiff, 5 25, 6 Fingers and toes, 7 Jane Austen, 8 Canada, 9 Czech, 10 Painting, 11 Michael Foot, 12 Greece, 13 Sancho Panza, 14 July and August, 15 Potato, 16 Wildebeest, 17 Cavy, 18 16 or 18, 19 Venus, 20 Austria.

General Knowledge

1. In which European country is the region of Aragon?

2. What were the forenames of WH Auden?

3. On which island is the Bay of Pigs?

4. Which Indian city has a Victoria station?

5. Who constructed the labyrinth in Greek mythology?

6. What is a lava-lava?

7. What is the fifth sign of the zodiac?

8. In what year did rock singer Jim Morrison die?

9. What sort of flower is a naked lady?

10. Who wrote the play *Separate Tables*?

11. Of which planet is Rhea is satellite?

12. In which ocean is the Sargasso Sea?

13. In which American state is the city of Yonkers?

14. What sort of a bird is a wryneck?

15. How did British soldier Orde Wingate die?

16. What is the fifth note of the sol-fah scale?

17. What is scrimshaw?

18. Which architect designed the 1851 Crystal Palace?

19. In Australian slang, what does 'the good oil' mean?

20. What is a gibus?

ANSWERS: *1 Spain, 2 Wystan Hugh, 3 Cuba, 4 Bombay, 5 Daedalus, 6 A Polynesian skirt-like garment, 7 Leo, 8 1971, 9 Orchid, 10 Terence Rattigan, 11 Saturn, 12 North Atlantic, 13 New York State, 14 Woodpecker, 15 In an air crash, 16 Soh, 17 Decorating or carving shells and ivory, 18 Sir Joseph Paxton, 19 True or reliable information, 20 A collapsible opera hat.*

Entertainment

1. Who played the title role in *Bergerac*?

2. Which Hollywood actress provided the speaking voice for 'Jessica' in *Who Framed Roger Rabbit*?

3. Which American band had a US No.1 hit in 1975 with *Best of My Love*?

4. Who was the female member of *Three of a Kind*?

5. Which Sheffield band made the Top 10 twice with *Temptation*?

6. Which British actor/director stars in *Peter's Friends*?

7. Which former weather girl co-presents *Gladiators*?

8. Which US actress played a singer who takes refuge in a convent in *Sister Act*?

9. Which US guitarist had his only UK No.1 hit with *Voodoo Chile*?

10. Which English actor, famous for villainous roles, played 'Blofeld' in *You Only Live Twice*?

11. Who presents the darts quiz game *Bullseye*?

12. Who played Sgt. Harriet Makepeace in *Dempsey and Makepeace*?

13. Which female duo had a hit with *Hello (Turn Your Radio On)*?

14. Who played rock legend Jim Morrison in the 1991 film *The Doors*?

15. Which former *Generation Game* hostess also presented *Come Dancing*?

16. Which star of *The Great Gatsby* lead a team of computer hackers in the film *Sneakers*?

17. Who co-starred with Meryl Streep in *Kramer vs Kramer*?

18. *All You Can Eat* is the latest album by which alternative country star?

19. Which female US vocalist had a US No.1 hit with *Typical Male* in 1986?

20. Who released an LP entitled *God's Great Banana Skin*?

General Knowledge

1. Who was the Roman goddess of peace?

2. In which book by Dickens does Nathaniel Winkle appear?

3. When is the first day of the grouse-shooting season?

4. Who wrote the light opera *Tales of Hoffmann*?

5. What, in communications, does the abbreviation STD stand for?

6. Who directed the film *Orphee*?

7. What is a Buff Orpington?

8. Which composer wrote the symphonic poem *Finlandia*?

9. From which country do the Ainu people come?

10. In which ocean is the Banda Sea?

11. What, in film-making, is a blimp?

12. Between which two countries is the Brenner Pass?

13. In which century did printer William Caxton live?

14. Who was the Muse of history in Greek mythology?

15. What is the international car registration for Denmark?

16. In which year was the Eiffel tower erected?

17. What is the term for a person who makes arrows?

18. In which country are one hundred grosz worth one zloty?

19. What was the real name of Al Jolson?

20. What sort of animal is a kob?

General Knowledge

1. What does derv stand for?

2. What was the former name of Ho Chi Minh City?

3. Which actor returned to England to play a dustman called Nev?

4. Which golfer played the wrong ball during the 1994 Open Championship?

5. Who wrote the popular one-act opera *Cavalleria Rusticana*?

6. Who wrote the tragedy *Andromache*?

7. Which president declared Ellis Island a National Historic Site in 1964?

8. How is the ground squirrel also known?

9. In which sport is the Stanley Cup contested?

10. Who designed Lady Sarah Armstrong-Jones's wedding dress?

11. Which US poet and artist had the first names Edward Estlin?

12. Who is the president of the European Commission?

13. Which composer wrote the piano pieces *Gymnopedies*?

14. Who conducted the music for Disney's *Fantasia*?

15. What is Britain's only poisonous snake?

16. Who secretly married Lisa Marie Presley?

17. In which ocean are the Wake Islands?

18. The launch of whose 600th book coincided with her 93rd birthday?

19. Of what is rayon made?

20. Of which animal is the ichneumon the Egyptian variety?

General Knowledge

1. What is a cicatrice?

2. In which year did Enid Blyton die?

3. What is the northernmost of the four main islands of Japan?

4. Which pop album was the world's number one best seller in 1967?

5. What nationality was the composer Georges Auric?

6. What sort of bridge is the Forth rail bridge?

7. What was the soldier Rodrigo Diaz de Vivar more commonly known as?

8. How many lbs in a cwt?

9. In which year did Edward VIII die?

10. Approximately how many million Model T Ford cars were manufactured?

11. Where is the seat of the UN International Court of Justice?

12. What branch of the arts do you associate with Jean Ingres?

13. How many popes have been called Leo?

14. Which body of water separates Italy from Sicily?

15. Of which country was Milton Obote president?

16. What is pinchbeck?

17. Who founded Singapore in 1819?

18. What does the Russian word samovar mean?

19. Of which country was Mario Soares made president in 1986?

20. Where was the liner Queen Elizabeth destroyed by fire in 1972?

ANSWERS: 1 The scar left by a healed wound, 2 1968, 3 Hokkaido, 4 Sergeant Pepper's Lonely Hearts Club Band, 5 French, 6 Cantilever, 7 El Cid, 8 112, 9 1972, 10 15 million, 11 The Hague, 12 Painting, 13 13, 14 Strait of Messina, 15 Uganda, 16 A goldlike alloy of copper and zinc, 17 Thomas Stamford Raffles, 18 Self-boiling, 19 Portugal, 20 Hong Kong.

Entertainment

1. Which former tennis star kept herself fit by running around the country on *Treasure Hunt*?

2. Which US singer/songwriter wrote the hit song *Knocking on Heaven's Door* ?

3. Which part man, part machine law enforcer was played by Peter Weller?

4. Which Australian vocalist joined ELO to record *Xanadu*?

5. Which American actress played Pam Ewing in *Dallas*?

6. Who starred as the Ringo Kid in the classic 1939 John Ford western *Stagecoach*?

7. Who had a No.1 hit in the UK with *Rhythm is a Dancer*?

8. Who starred with Meryl Streep and Goldie Hawn in the black comedy *Death Becomes Her*?

9. Who played the title role in *Dixon of Dock Green*?

10. What was the name of the Anglo-Roman TV comedy starring Rory McGrath and Jimmy Mulville?

11. Which female vocalist had a No.1 hit in 1966 with *You Don't Have To Say You Love Me*?

12. In which US city, in the year 2019, is the classic sci-fi film *Bladerunner* set?

13. Who played mother-dominated Tim in the comedy series *Sorry!*?

14. *The Celts* was a Top 10 album for which female vocalist?

15. The son of which legendary martial arts actor starred in the film *Rapid Fire*?

16. Which imported adult drama series is set in Wentworth Detention Centre?

17. Who had a No 1 Hit in 1965 with *Crying in the Chapel*?

18. Which actress co-starred as Hester in *Fresh Fields* and *French Fields*?

19. Who had a No.1 hit with *My Sweet Lord* in 1970?

20. Which actress, from a famous acting family, starred in the thriller *Single White Female*?

General Knowledge

1. Which author was married from 1965-83 to writer Elizabeth Jane Howard?

2. Who directed the film *Babette's Feast*?

3. Which explorer led the youth project Operation Drake?

4. When is the feast day of St Bridget?

5. What nationality was the clown Charlie Cairoli?

6. Who won a Best Actress Oscar for *It Happened One Night*?

7. Which murderer was murdered in Walpole Prison, Massachusetts, in 1973?

8. Who wrote the songs *Camptown Races* and *Beautiful Dreamer*?

9. In which state was evangelist Billy Graham born?

10. Who patented the first sewing machine?

11. At which Oxford College did politician Roy Jenkins study?

12. Who became chairman of CND in 1987?

13. What nationality was painter El Lissitzky?

14. What was playwright Jean Baptiste Poquelin better known as?

15. Which British Labour politician was in the merchant navy from 1955-63?

16. Which composer's first film score was for 1937's *Knight Without Armour*?

17. What was the comic strip *Peanuts* originally called?

18. Who was Liberal MP for North Devon from 1959-79?

19. Whose first novel was *Player Piano*?

20. Which politician managed Gerald Ford's 1976 presidential campaign?

General Knowledge

1. On which date is St George's Day?

2. Of which island group is Jura a member?

3. Who painted *A Bigger Splash* in 1967?

4. Which disease is also called varicella?

5. Who founded the Grey Friars in 1209?

6. Which part of the body is affected by impetigo?

7. With which instrument is Fritz Kreisler associated?

8. Which TV vet was trampled by a herd of sheep?

9. In which US state is Las Vegas?

10. In geometry, what do 60 minutes make?

11. Which company designed the Merlin engine of the Spitfire and Hurricane?

12. What is the name of the lowest region on the Earth's surface?

13. Which nut is obtained from the areca palm?

14. In the Old Testament, who was Jacob's older twin brother?

15. Of which sea creature is the argonaut a type?

16. Which number Ivan was 'the Terrible'?

17. Which sea touches the shores of Denmark, Norway and Holland?

18. In Greek mythology, what hung on an oak tree at Colchis?

19. Which actor wrote *Snakes and Ladders* in 1978?

20. Of which creature is *Psittacus erithacus* the talkative variety?

ANSWERS: 1 April 23, 2 Inner Hebrides, 3 David Hockney, 4 Chicken pox, 5 St Francis of Assisi, 6 Skin, 7 Violin, 8 James Herriot, 9 Nevada, 10 A degree, 11 Rolls-Royce, 12 Marianas Trench, 13 Betel nut, 14 Esau, 15 Octopus, 16 IV, 17 North Sea, 18 Golden Fleece, 19 Dirk Bogarde, 20 Parrot.

General Knowledge

Your rating: ● 0-5   Join a library   ● 6-10   Keep at it
            ● 11-15 Join a quiz team   ● 16-20 Enter Mastermind

1. At the end of which war was the Treaty of Sevres?

2. Of which two countries, other than England, was Canute king?

3. In which Scottish region is Edinburgh?

4. What is the most recent Disney film called?

5. What does HIV stand for?

6. Whom did Josephine de Beauharnais marry in 1796?

7. Which unit of time may be synodic, sidereal or calendar?

8. Of which nationality was the composer Carl Nielsen?

9. Which Labour MP is an ex-Cunard waiter?

10. Which of its four official languages is exclusive to Switzerland?

11. Which merchant bank collapsed in February 1995?

12. Which part of the brain controls balance and coordination?

13. Which animal has red, grey and Arctic varieties?

14. Where in your body would you find bronchioles and alveoli?

15. In which river are the Thousand Islands?

16. Who was the father-in-law of Moses?

17. Which poet's middle name was Bysshe?

18. Which Dutch queen's husband was Prince Bernhard?

19. Which French philosopher coined the term 'property is theft'?

20. To which family does the okapi belong?

ANSWERS: 1 WWI, 2 Denmark and Norway, 3 Lothian, 4 Pocahontas, 5 Human Immunodeficiency Virus, 6 Napoleon Bonaparte, 7 Month, 8 Danish, 9 John Prescott, 10 Romansch, 11 Barings (Baring Brothers), 12 Cerebellum, 13 Fox, 14 In the lungs, 15 St Lawrence, 16 Jethro, 17 Shelley, 18 Juliana, 19 Pierre Proudhon, 20 Giraffe.

Entertainment

Your rating:
- 0-5   Buy a TV
- 11-15   Join a quiz team
- 6-10   Keep at it
- 16-20   Enter Telly Addicts

1. Which highly successful film sequel was sub-titled *Lost in New York*?
2. Which star of *Yes, Minister* played the role of Jerry Leadbetter in *The Good Life*?
3. Which controversial female vocalist had a Top 10 hit with *Deeper and Deeper*?
4. Who played Bob in the classic comedy series *The Likely Lads*?
5. Which *Sea of Love* actress starred with her husband, Gabriel Byrne, in *Into the West*?
6. Which long-enduring UK vocalist had a top 10 hit with *I Still Believe in You*?
7. Which prototype rock star and teen idol starred in the 1967 musical *Half a Sixpence*?
8. Which actress, who died in 1983, played the irascible Ena Sharples in *Coronation Street*?
9. Which US band had US and UK No.1 hits in 1980 with both *Call Me* and *The Tide Is High*?
10. Which writer/broadcaster presents the *It'll Be Alright On The Night* compilation shows?
11. In 1933, *Flying Down to Rio* marked the start of Fred Astaire's long partnership with whom?
12. Which female US vocalist had a UK Top 20 hit with *If We Hold on Together*?
13. Who played Indiana Jones's father, Henry, in *Indiana Jones and the Last Crusade*?
14. Which actress played Ma Larkin in *The Darling Buds of May*?
15. Which British band had a UK No.1 hit with *Blackberry Way* in 1968?
16. Which ska group had a No 1 in 1981 with *Ghost Town*?
17. Which British actor starred as Scrooge in *The Muppet Christmas Carol*?
18. Which group had a US No.1 in 1971 with *How Can You Mend A Broken Heart*?
19. Which American early-learning series uses a host of 'Muppets' to help present the show?
20. Which female US vocalist/composer had a US No. 1 hit with *It's Too Late*, in 1971?

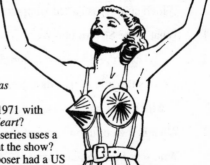

General Knowledge

1. Into which planet did fragments of comet SL9 crash?

2. How is the aurora borealis also known?

3. Who is the actress mother of Tory politician Jeremy Hanley?

4. The Schick test is used to determine immunity to which disease?

5. Which metal forms rust?

6. To which department was the Department of Employment added?

7. What came between the Stone and Iron Ages?

8. Which golfer was disqualified from the Senior British Open after signing for the wrong score?

9. Which creature did Edgar Allan Poe have say 'Nevermore'?

10. In which city is the hill Arthur's Seat?

11. Who is the captain of the South African cricket team?

12. What do the letters HRT stand for?

13. Which country is called Hanguk in its native language?

14. What is the Severn bore?

15. For what is the Spanish city Jerez de la Frontera famous?

16. What is the title of the Marquess of Blandford's father?

17. In which year was the Thames barrier completed?

18. What is the common name of the fruit *Citrus reticulata*?

19. Who was Poet laureate from 1972 to 1984?

20. Which king had to deal with the Peasants' Revolt of 1381?

ANSWERS: *1 Jupiter, 2 Northern Lights, 3 Dinah Sheridan, 4 Diphtheria, 5 Iron, 6 Education, 7 Bronze Age, 8 Tony Jacklin, 9 The Raven, 10 Edinburgh, 11 Kepler Wessels, 12 Hormone Replacement Therapy, 13 South Korea, 14 A tidal wave, 15 Sherry, 16 Duke of Marlborough, 17 1982, 18 Tangerine, 19 Sir John Betjeman, 20 Richard II.*

General Knowledge

1. What do we call the city Den Haag?

2. To whom are the Old Testament Psalms traditionally ascribed?

3. Which US state is nicknamed the Centennial State?

4. Which former *Blue Peter* presenter was the first civilian in Britain to free-fall from five miles up?

5. Which race did legendary ruler Hengist command?

6. Which part of the body is affected by glaucoma?

7. Who wrote the opera *Carmen*?

8. Through which mountain range do the St Bernard Passes pass?

9. In which constellation is Rigel?

10. Which fruit comes from the tree *Prunus persica*?

11. On which island is the port Launceston?

12. What type of animal is a duiker?

13. Which driver was engulfed in flames after refuelling in the 1994 German Grand Prix?

14. Of what is the angstrom a unit?

15. Against whom did Afghanistan wage the Afghan Wars?

16. Which conductor established the Royal Philharmonic Orchestra in 1946?

17. What is the middle period of the Mesozoic era called?

18. Who is the leader of the RMT?

19. Which term for a group of hostile infiltrators originated in the Spanish Civil War?

20. What is the full name for the medical condition ME?

ANSWERS: *1 The Hague, 2 David, 2nd king of Israel, 3 Colorado, 4 John Noakes, 5 Jutes, 6 Eye, 7 Georges Bizet, 8 Alps, 9 Orion, 10 Peach, 11 Tasmania, 12 Antelope, 13 Jos Verstappen, 14 Length, 15 Britain, 16 Thomas Beecham, 17 Jurassic, 18 Jimmy Knapp, 19 Fifth column, 20 Myalgic encephalitis.*

General Knowledge

1. Which actress was the BBC's *Girl Friday*?

2. In which US state is the Grand Canyon?

3. From which word are 'tsar' and 'kaiser' derived?

4. Which herb is also called milfoil?

5. Which unit is defined as one nautical mile per hour?

6. Which Russian writer declined the 1958 Nobel prize for literature?

7. In which country are the Southern Alps, highest point Mount Cook?

8. Who was World Snooker Champion six times in the 70s?

9. What is the world's southernmost active volcano?

10. From which fruit is the drink Tokay made?

11. Who was Spandau's last prisoner?

12. What is the largest of the Society Islands?

13. Which illness is also known as pertussis?

14. Which sport holds the Super Bowl contest?

15. Which superhero made his debut in Action Comics in 1938?

16. Which organ is affected by otitis?

17. Who was Ptolemy XIV's mother?

18. Of which bird is *Meleagris gallopavo* the domestic variety?

19. What was the first British film to break the £20m box office barrier?

20. Which game was devised by William G Morgan in 1895?

ANSWERS: 1 Joanna Lumley, 2 Arizona, 3 Caesar, 4 Yarrow, 5 Knot, 6 Boris Pasternak, 7 New Zealand, 8 Ray Reardon, 9 Mount Erebus, 10 Grape, 11 Rudolf Hess, 12 Tahiti, 13 Whooping Cough, 14 American football, 15 Superman, 16 Ear, 17 Cleopatra, 18 Turkey, 19 Four Weddings and a Funeral, 20 Volleyball.

Sports

1. Which rugby league team used to play at the Watersheddings ground?
2. In 1995, which manager moved from Luton Town to Sheffield Wednesday?
3. Who won his 70th snooker title at the 1995 Regal Welsh Open?
4. Which cricket umpire runs a Post Office in North Devon?
5. Who rode Shergar to Derby victory in 1981?
6. Which Manchester United player appeared in a French TV commercial for ladies' razors?
7. In which country were the 1994 Commonwealth Games held?
8. Which two British riders wore the yellow jersey in the 1994 Tour de France?
9. Which tennis-player won the 1995 Australian Open women's singles title?
10. In 1980, who became the first player to score a century and take 10 wickets in a Test?
11. Who won the 1995 Charity Shield?
12. In 1995, who scored half centuries in successive innings against the West Indies at Lord's?
13. Which football team play at Maine Road?
14. Which country ended Britain's 14-year domination of the European Hang Gliding Championships?
15. For whom did Manchester United pay £7 million in 1995?
16. What nationality was tennis player Fred Stolle?
17. Which well-known jockey won the 1992 Irish Two Thousand Guineas?
18. How many teams are in the Scottish Premier football league?
19. Who won the 1994 world indoor singles bowls title?
20. Which football team plays at the Riverside Stadium?

General Knowledge

1.   Which royal gave birth to Columbus in 1994?

2.   Within which present-day country is the ancient Sumerian city of Ur?

3.   Of what nationality was former UN secretary-general U Thant?

4.   Which Chinese philosophical terms mean 'dark' and 'bright'?

5.   Which river forms 1,500 miles of the US-Mexican border?

6.   What was the pen name of the novelist Marie Henri Beyle?

7.   Which Labour MP called for the selling-off of Buckingham Palace and Windsor Castle?

8.   Who wrote *The Railway Children* in 1906?

9.   Which Church's doctrine is set out in the Thirty-Nine Articles?

10. Which Greek herald lost a shouting contest with Hermes?

11. Of which country is Lusaka the capital?

12. Who wrote the opera *Sir John In Love* in 1929?

13. What is the highest mountain in the Cairngorms?

14. What type of creature is the mudskipper?

15. By what name was Robert MacGregor better known?

16. Which sport's principal forms are strokeplay and matchplay?

17. Who is the patron saint of Scotland?

18. Which disease is also called Hansen's disease?

19. What is a saluki?

20. Which country's all-woman team won the three-day event at the 1994 World Equestrian Games?

ANSWERS: 1 Lady Helen Taylor, 2 Iraq, 3 Burmese, 4 Yin and Yang, 5 Rio Grande, 6 Stendhal, 7 Mo Mowlam, 8 E Nesbit, 9 Anglican, 10 Stentor, 11 Zambia, 12 Ralph Vaughan Williams, 13 Ben Macdhui, 14 A fish, 15 Rob Roy, 16 Golf, 17 St Andrew, 18 Leprosy, 19 A dog, 20 Great Britain.

General Knowledge

1. Of what is ikebana the Japanese art?

2. Who won his third European 100m title in Helsinki in 1994?

3. To whom did Hampton Court Palace belong before Henry VIII moved in?

4. On which Greek island is St John said to have written the NT Book of Revelation?

5. Who wrote *Jane Eyre* in 1847?

6. From which country did Algeria declare independence in 1962?

7. Of which metal is magnetite an ore?

8. Of what is there a special (1905) and a general (1915) theory?

9. What type of animal is a chinchilla?

10. Of what nationality was the philosopher Spinoza?

11. Who wrote a trilogy of books featuring the spy Bernard Samson?

12. Of which fruit is the plantain a subspecies?

13. From which football club did Billy Bonds claim he was forced out after 27 years?

14. Between which two countries was the former kingdom of Navarre divided?

15. Of which county is Parts of Holland a former separate administrative county?

16. Who wrote the cantata *Carmina Burana*?

17. From which tree is gum arabic obtained?

18. In which country is the province Friesland?

19. Who was the first Irish athlete ever to win a gold medal at the European Championships?

20. By what name was Rodrigo Diaz de Vivar better known?

ANSWERS: *1 Flower arrangement, 2 Linford Christie, 3 Cardinal Wolsey, 4 Patmos, 5 Charlotte Brontë, 6 France, 7 Iron, 8 Relativity, 9 A rodent, 10 Dutch, 11 Len Deighton, 12 Banana, 13 West Ham United, 14 France and Spain, 15 Lincolnshire, 16 Carl Orff, 17 Acacia, 18 Netherlands, 19 Sonia O'Sullivan, 20 El Cid.*

General Knowledge

Your rating: ● 0-5   Join a library   ● 6-10   Keep at it
              ● 11-15 Join a quiz team   ● 16-20   Enter Mastermind

1. According to the Old Testament, on which mountain did Moses receive the Ten Commandments?

2. Which great horror actor died in August 1994?

3. In which country was Princess Margaret born?

4. Wiltshire's White Horse celebrates whose victory over the Danes?

5. Who was European Footballer of the Year in 1968?

6. To what did Burma change its name in 1989?

7. With which instrument is Miles Davis primarily associated?

8. What is a loquat?

9. What is the wife of a marquess called?

10. Of which religion was Joseph Smith the founder?

11. Of which words is pixel a contraction?

12. In which county is Scafell Pike?

13. Who played the love interest in *Batman Forever*?

14. How is the N American caribou also known?

15. In Greek mythology, of what was Irene the goddess?

16. By what name is the marsupial *Sarcophilus harrisi* better known?

17. In which castle was Edward II murdered?

18. What is the name of the twice-weekly publication of official UK government announcements?

19. At which game is actor Omar Sharif an expert?

20. Which subatomic particle is named after the Greek for 'first'?

ANSWERS: *1 Mount Sinai, 2 Peter Cushing, 3 Scotland, 4 Alfred the Great, 5 George Best, 6 Myanmar, 7 Trumpet, 8 A tree or its fruit, 9 Marchioness, 10 Mormonism, 11 Pictures element, 12 Cumbria, 13 Nicole Kidman, 14 Reindeer, 15 Peace, 16 Tasmanian devil, 17 Berkeley Castle, 18 London Gazette, 19 Bridge, 20 Proton.*

Entertainment

Your rating:
- 0-5 Buy a TV
- 11-15 Join a quiz team
- 6-10 Keep at it
- 16-20 Enter Telly Addicts

1. Which UK vocalist had a No. 1 hit in 1973 with *Can The Can*?
2. Who played the title role in the 1982 film *Tootsie*?
3. Which American actor plays the title role in *Columbo*?
4. Which famous duo provided soundtrack music for the 1967 film *The Graduate*?
5. In which department store was the comedy series *Are You Being Served* located?
6. Which UK vocalist's only solo No. 1 hit single was *Wuthering Heights*?
7. Which American actor provides a link between the films *Lethal Weapon 3* and *Home Alone 2*?
8. Which female wine expert has introduced the series *Vintners' Tales*?
9. Which US superstar had a UK No. 2 hit with *Heal the World*?
10. Which John Steinbeck novel has been released as a film starring John Malkovich?
11. Which American actress played long-suffering Sue Ellen in *Dallas*?
12. Which US group had a UK and US No. 1 hit in 1965 with *Mr. Tambourine Man*?
13. Which actor plays 'Clegg' in *Last of the Summer Wine*?
14. Which American singer made her acting debut in the film *Bodyguard* with Kevin Costner?
15. Which blind US vocalist had a UK and US No. 1 hit in 1962 with *I Can't Stop Loving You*?
16. Which veteran US actor starred with Al Pacino in *Glengarry Glen Ross*?
17. Which British band released an album entitled *Live - The Way We Walk*?
18. Which Australian soap opera featured the Blakeney twins as Caroline and Christina?
19. Which female American singer starred with Richard Dreyfuss in the 1988 film *Nuts*?
20. Which British vocalist sung about *Tom Traubert's Blues*?

ANSWERS: 1 *Suzi Quatro*, 2 *Dustin Hoffman*, 3 *Peter Falk*, 4 *Simon and Garfunkel*, 5 *Grace Brothers*, 6 *Kate Bush*, 7 *Joe Pesci*, 8 *Jancis Robinson*, 9 *Michael Jackson*, 10 *Of Mice and Men*, 11 *Linda Gray*, 12 *The Byrds*, 13 *Peter Sallis*, 14 *Whitney Houston*, 15 *Ray Charles*, 16 *Jack Lemmon*, 17 *Genesis*, 18 *Neighbours*, 19 *Barbra Streisand*, 20 *Rod Stewart*.

General Knowledge

1. Which tycoon pledged £1m to keep Canova's *The Three Graces* in Britain?

2. By what name do we know the fish *Hippoglossus hippoglossus*?

3. In which country does the heir apparent bear the title of Prince of Asturias?

4. Who plays the title role in the film *The Madness of King George*?

5. Which city is known in its own language as Baile Atha Cliath?

6. By which nickname is Venezuelan-born Ilich Ramirez Sanchez better known?

7. Which acid is the active chemical constituent of aspirin?

8. What is the second highest mountain in the world?

9. Who wrote the book *Absolute Beginners* in 1959?

10. Which colourful European allegedly gave Greenland its name?

11. Which group of minerals form the chief constituents of igneous rock?

12. Which *Heartbeat* heartthrob became British TV's highest paid actor?

13. Of what name has Britain had two kings and France ten?

14. In which country were the first Commonwealth Games held in 1930?

15. In which country was the Cultural Revolution of 1966-69?

16. In which game may a player use the words 'j'adoube'?

17. Which footballer joined Liverpool from Coventry City as the country's most expensive defender?

18. With what is philology concerned?

19. Who wrote the opera *Castor and Pollux* in 1737?

20. In which sport are Doggett's Coat and Badge awarded?

General Knowledge

1. Which Gestapo chief has the Jackal's lawyer Jacques Verges also defended?

2. Which Far East capital was known as Batavia until 1949?

3. What do the initials QED stand for?

4. Which perennial plant is also called Lady's Smock?

5. Which satellite relayed the first live TV transmission between the USA and Europe?

6. Of what nationality is the novelist and politician Mario Vargas Llosa?

7. To which king did Parliament present the Nineteen Propositions?

8. Of which metal is galena the chief ore?

9. What is the capital of West Bengal state?

10. Which inflammation is also called muscular rheumatism?

11. Which once widespread group of languages is divided into Brythonic and Goidelic groups?

12. Which comic and quiz show presenter had planned a career in judo?

13. Which king abdicated to marry Wallis Simpson?

14. Who wrote *King Solomon's Mines* in 1885?

15. Which gas was identified in the same year by both Priestley and Scheele?

16. Which country has its former premier Nawaz Sharif confirmed as having the atom bomb?

17. What is a leucocyte?

18. Which footballer received a fifteen-month worldwide ban after failing a drugs test at the World Cup?

19. Which bay separates Miami Beach from Miami?

20. Who won the 1995 US Masters at Augusta?

ANSWERS: 1 *Klaus Barbie*, 2 *Jakarta/Djakarta*, 3 *Quod erat demonstrandum*, 4 *Cuckooflower*, 5 *Telstar*, 6 *Peruvian*, 7 *Charles I*, 8 *Lead*, 9 *Calcutta*, 10 *Fibrositis*, 11 *Celtic*, 12 *Tony Slattery*, 13 *Edward VIII*, 14 *H Rider Haggard*, 15 *Oxygen*, 16 *Pakistan*, 17 *White blood cell or corpuscle*, 18 *Diego Maradona*, 19 *Biscayne Bay*, 20 *Ben Crenshaw*.

General Knowledge

1. Of which Christian group is a Latter-day Saint a member?

2. Whom did Brian Hitchen replace as editor of the *Sunday Express*?

3. To which family of birds does the roadrunner belong?

4. What did weightlifter John McEwan break while competing in the Commonwealth Games?

5. What is the technical name for nettle rash?

6. What is the capital of the Ukraine?

7. What type of flower is a michaelmas daisy?

8. During which revolution was the Reign of Terror?

9. Which animal was once called a foul marten?

10. What flavour does the liqueur curacao have?

11. Which American Indian woman saved the life of Captain John Smith?

12. What type of animal is an ibex?

13. Which are the only two planets in our solar system not to have moons?

14. Which British film director died in France in 1994?

15. Which element has the symbol P?

16. Within which group of islands is Scapa Flow?

17. Whose sidekick was Violet Elizabeth Bott?

18. To whom is the Greek epic poem *The Odyssey* attributed?

19. In which country is the Seikan Tunnel, the world's largest underwater tunnel?

20. For which party was Emmeline Pankhurst a prospective parliamentary candidate?

ANSWERS: *1 Mormons, 2 Eve Pollard, 3 Cuckoo, 4 His right arm, 5 Urticaria, 6 Kiev, 7 Aster, 8 French, 9 Polecat, 10 Orange, 11 Pocahontas, 12 A goat, 13 Mercury and Venus, 14 Lindsay Anderson, 15 Phosphorus, 16 Orkneys, 17 Just William, 18 Homer, 19 Japan, 20 Conservative.*

Entertainment

1. What was the name of the ranch in *Bonanza*?
2. Which character was played by Anthony Hopkins in *The Silence of the Lambs*?
3. Which British group's only UK No. 1 hit was *House of Fun* in 1982?
4. Who played Julie Diadoni in *Jake's Progress*?
5. Who played the Vicomte de Valmont in the 1988 film *Dangerous Liasons*?
6. Which British female vocalist's first big hit was *All Around The World*?
7. Which actress played Tessa in *Love Hurts*?
8. Which film by Richard Attenborough was a biopic of a famous comedy actor?
9. Which female singer had a hit with *Time After Time*?
10. Which string-vested Scottish street philosopher is played by Gregor Fisher?
11. Which band were *In Bloom* at No. 1 in the Heavy Metal Charts?
12. Which American actor played the title role in *American Gigolo*?
13. Which UK group had a US No. 1 hit in 1983 with *Owner of a Lonely Heart*?
14. Which British actor played Simon Templar in *The Return of The Saint*?
15. What was the name of Han Solo's spaceship in *Star Wars*?
16. Which famous singer had a posthumous Top 10 hit with *In My Defence*?
17. Which lawyer *Talks Back* on Channel 4?
18. Which American actor starred with Lorraine Bracco in the 1992 film *Traces of Red*?
19. Which group of muscle-bound sportsmen had a Top 5 hit with *Slam Jam*?
20. Which heavyweight comedienne is often found creating comic mayhem with Russ Abbot?

ANSWERS: 1 Ponderosa, 2 Hannibal Lecter, 3 Madness, 4 Julie Walters, 5 John Malkovich, 6 Lisa Stansfield, 7 Zoe Wanamaker, 8 Chaplin, 9 Cyndi Lauper, 10 Rab C Nesbitt, 11 Nirvana, 12 Richard Gere, 13 Yes, 14 Ian Ogilvy, 15 Millenium Falcon, 16 Freddie Mercury, 17 Clive Anderson, 18 James Belushi, 19 WWF Superstars, 20 Bella Emberg.

General Knowledge

1. Who won Oscars for *Klute* and *Coming Home*?

2. In which mountains are St Bernards employed?

3. Which plant's leaves are the common antidote to nettle stings?

4. Which TV programme did Roy Castle present for 22 years?

5. The 38th parallel became a boundary within which country in 1945?

6. Of which organisation did Ros Hepplewhite resign as head in 1994?

7. Which brothers based an opera on a novel by DuBose Heyward?

8. What type of fish is a torpedo fish?

9. Which *Carry On* star has joined *EastEnders*?

10. Which temperature scale starts at absolute zero?

11. Which sinister oriental villain was the creation of Sax Rohmer?

12. On which island is the active volcano Pico de Teide?

13. In which novel did Squire Trelawney sail the Hispaniola?

14. What did America develop in the Manhattan Project?

15. Which car registration letter was launched in 1994?

16. Which clergyman is 'Primate of England'?

17. Which actor was born Richard Jenkins?

18. What is the collective name for birds of the genus *Corvus*?

19. Which sport adopted the Queensberry rules in 1867?

20. Which comedian co-wrote the book *Life and How to Survive It*?

General Knowledge

1. Which bird has golden and argus varieties?

2. Which group recorded Britain's highest-selling pop song of the decade?

3. In which constellation is Deneb the brightest star?

4. After which French city is denim named?

5. Which supermodel has 'written' the novel *Swan*?

6. Of which place is Baron Hailsham baron?

7. Of what is a magneto a simple example?

8. In which US city is the Grand Old Opry?

9. Of what is John Monks general secretary?

10. What sort of creature is a loon?

11. Which prefix denotes one thousand millionth part?

12. In which country is the town of Hamelin, famous for the Pied Piper legend?

13. What can a corundum gem of any colour but red be called?

14. How is the viral disease rubeola better known?

15. Of which mountains is Crete de la Neige the highest?

16. Which tree is also called cob?

17. Which *Emmerdale* star is Brian Rix's sister?

18. Which novelist was secretary to the Maharajah of Dewas in 1921?

19. Which tree has English, white and slippery varieties?

20. What is sorghum?

General Knowledge

1. Of which country have there been four King Waldemars?

2. Which Hollywood film studio was founded in 1915 by Carl Laemmle?

3. Who painted *The Bathers* and *La Loge*?

4. Which plant is also known as hardhead?

5. With which metal is the Iron Cross edged?

6. From which birds do humans contract psittacosis?

7. Which beverage may be black or green?

8. What is the largest county in The Republic of Ireland?

9. On which river is Leicester?

10. Which two countries have a Brabant province?

11. What was the name of MGM's lion?

12. Who resigned as Protector a year after succeeding Oliver Cromwell?

13. Which fruit is obtained from the tree *Ficus carica*?

14. With which art form is Frederick Ashton associated?

15. Where are the Sussex Stakes run?

16. With whom did Karl Marx collaborate on *The Communist Manifesto*?

17. In which year was the Jarrow Crusade?

18. Of what is pinchbeck an imitation?

19. In which country was Salman Rushdie born?

20. What was poet Gerard Manley Hopkins's other calling?

ANSWERS: *1 Denmark, 2 Universal, 3 Pierre-Auguste Renoir, 4 Knapweed, 5 Silver, 6 Parrots, 7 Tea, 8 Cork (Corcaigh), 9 Soar, 10 Belgium and the Netherlands, 11 Leo, 12 Richard Cromwell, 13 Fig, 14 Ballet, 15 Goodwood, 16 Friedrich Engels, 17 1936, 18 Gold, 19 India, 20 Jesuit priest.*

Entertainment

1. Who played navigation officer Mr Sulu, in *Star Trek*?
2. Which star of *The Shining* crossed swords with Tom Cruise in *A Few Good Men*?
3. Which famous Australian folk song has been covered by The Pogues and Rod Stewart?
4. Which actress plays Kathy Beale in *EastEnders*?
5. Which 1953 film of a classic H. G. Wells book won an Oscar for Special Effects?
6. Which Take That hit single was a cover version of a Barry Manilow song?
7. Which former presenter of *Children's BBC* co-hosted *What's Up Doc?* on ITV?
8. What is the name of the 'Beauty' in Disney's *Beauty and the Beast*?
9. Which group had a No. 1 hit with *Do You Really Want To Hurt Me*, in 1982?
10. What is the name of magician Paul Daniels's wife and assistant?
11. Who is the central character of *A Nightmare on Elm Street* and its sequels?
12. Which UK group had a US No.1 hit in 1966 with *Wild Thing*?
13. Who played Arnold Schwarzenegger's twin brother in *Twins*?
14. Who wrote and directed *What's Up, Tiger Lily?*
15. Which Ken Loach film is set during the Spanish Civil War?
16. Which award-winning comedy series is set in a TV news station called 'Globelink'?
17. Which Country and Western singer starred in the 1980 film *Nine to Five*?
18. Which US brother/sister duo had a US No.1 hit in 1973 with *Top of the World*?
19. Who played Charlie Hungerford, in *Bergerac*?
20. Who played the title role in the 1990 film *Pretty Woman*?

General Knowledge

1. Which hills range from Bristol to Chipping Camden?

2. Which biological divisions include Animalia, Plantae and Fungi?

3. Which athlete set six world records in less than an hour in 1935?

4. How many kings called James has Scotland had?

5. For what is epistaxis the technical term?

6. Of which mountain range is Pico de Orizaba the highest point?

7. Which author is best known for *Shogun*?

8. Which legendary figure is said to have been born at Tintagel?

9. In which US state is Detroit?

10. Who was the last Norman king of England?

11. In which continent is the Drakensberg mountain range?

12. How do we now know Brighthelmstone?

13. From which flower is orrisroot obtained?

14. For which film did Jessica Tandy receive an Oscar at 80?

15. Which king handed Parliament the Crown Estate in exchange for the civil list?

16. Of which Irish province is Dublin the capital?

17. With which magician is Claudia Schiffer romantically linked?

18. Which is the only metal to burn in nitrogen?

19. To where did brothers Ross and Keith Smith make the first flight from England?

20. What do we call the mammal *Lutra lutra*?

ANSWERS: 1 Cotswolds, 2 Kingdoms, 3 Jesse Owens, 4 Seven, 5 Nosebleed, 6 Sierra Madre, 7 James Clavell, 8 King Arthur, 9 Michigan, 10 Stephen, 11 Africa, 12 Brighton, 13 Iris, 14 Driving Miss Daisy, 15 George III, 16 Leinster, 17 David Copperfield, 18 Titanium, 19 Australia, 20 Otter.

General Knowledge

1. Of which country is Gozo a part?

2. What was the 1944 Allied invasion of Normandy called?

3. Who are the father and son team at Barcelona Football Club?

4. Which type of pilot is named from the Japanese for 'wind of the gods'?

5. At which port were five people killed when a gangway collapsed in 1994?

6. Which English composer's middle name is Kemp?

7. Which actor/director was born Allen Stewart Konigsberg?

8. Of which country is the Irrawaddy the chief river?

9. Who was the chief author of the US Declaration of Independence?

10. Who was the father of Jacob and Esau?

11. In Roman mythology, of what was Janus god?

12. Who wrote *The History Man* in 1975?

13. What type of creature is a rorqual?

14. What is the brightest star in Ursa Minor?

15. Which novelist gave the Wars of the Roses their name?

16. In which novelist's works does the basketball player Rabbit Angstrom recur?

17. How many beats per bar are there in a waltz?

18. When is the feast day of St Patrick?

19. In which ocean are the Sea Islands?

20. Of which name has England had one king, France two and Poland three?

ANSWERS: *1 Malta, 2 Operation Overlord, 3 Johan and Jordi Cruyff, 4 Kamikaze, 5 Ramsgate, 6 Sir Michael Tippett, 7 Woody Allen, 8 Myanmar (Burma), 9 Thomas Jefferson, 10 Isaac, 11 Doorways and passages, 12 Malcolm Bradbury, 13 A whale, 14 Polaris, 15 Walter Scott, 16 John Updike, 17 Three, 18 March 17, 19 Atlantic, 20 John.*

General Knowledge

1. What is the international agreement which covers the rights of POWs called?

2. From which bean is chocolate obtained?

3. In which country did John Bull compose our national anthem?

4. Which Labour leader's middle names were Todd Naylor?

5. How many riders take part in a speedway heat?

6. In which city did the St Valentine's Day Massacre take place?

7. With what is the Wendell Sea usually covered?

8. What is the longest river in Scotland?

9. For which motor-racing team does Damon Hill drive?

10. What type of creature is a merganser?

11. What is Riccardo Muti's occupation?

12. What is the chief residence of the Archbishop of Canterbury?

13. Whom was the *Big Issue* magazine set up to help?

14. Of what nationality is author Laurens van der Post?

15. To which species of bird does the mynah belong?

16. Which composer wrote the music for *Gypsy* and *Funny Girl*?

17. In which Cornish resort is the Barbara Hepworth museum?

18. Which playwright wrote *The Browning Version* in 1948?

19. What are auctioned at Tattersall's in London?

20. Who composed the incidental music for *Peer Gynt*?

ANSWERS: 1 *The Geneva Convention,* 2 *Cocoa/cacao,* 3 *Belgium,* 4 *Hugh Gaitskell,* 5 *Four,* 6 *Chicago,* 7 *Ice,* 8 *Tay,* 9 *Williams,* 10 *A duck,* 11 *Conductor,* 12 *Lambeth Palace,* 13 *The homeless,* 14 *South African,* 15 *Starling,* 16 *Jule Styne,* 17 *St Ives,* 18 *Terence Rattigan,* 19 *Racehorses,* 20 *Edward Grieg.*

Entertainment

1. Who played small-time crook George in the 1986 film *Mona Lisa*?
2. What is the name of Arthur Daley's 'local' in *Minder*?
3. *Duophonic* was the debut album for which chart-topping duo?
4. Who co-starred with Billy Crystal in *When Harry Met Sally*?
5. Which star of *Duty Free* became one of *The Good Guys*?
6. Which US band had a Top 20 success with a cover version of *Mrs Robinson*?
7. Who played the title role in the cult 1968 film *Barbarella*?
8. Which UK vocalist had a No. 1 hit with *Ashes to Ashes*?
9. Which Manchester band released the album *(What's The Story) Morning Glory* ?
10. Which veteran US comic played the role of God in three films during the 1980's?
11. Which television station took over from TVS in the South of England?
12. Which Heavy Metal US band had a hit with a cover version of *Easy*?
13. Which child star played the central role in *Home Alone*?
14. Which Sean is the star of *Sean's Show*?
15. Who played time-travelling Marty McFly in the *Back to the Future* films?
16. *With A Little Help From My Friends* was a No. 1 hit for which UK vocalist, in 1968?
17. Who played the title role in the classic 60's TV series *Dr Finlay's Casebook*?
18. Which veteran comedienne played Mrs. Slocombe in *Are You Being Served*?
19. Who directed *Rumble Fish*?
20. Which band had a No. 1 hit with *Dancing Queen*, in

ANSWERS: *1 Bob Hoskins, 2 The Winchester Club, 3 Charles and Eddie, 4 Meg Ryan, 5 Keith Barron, 6 The Lemonheads, 7 Jane Fonda, 8 David Bowie, 9 Oasis, 10 George Burns, 11 Meridian, 12 Faith No More, 13 Macauley Culkin, 14 Sean Hughes, 15 Michael J. Fox, 16 Joe Cocker, 17 Bill Simpson, 18 Mollie Sugden, 19 Francis Coppola, 20 Abba.*

General Knowledge

1. To which PM was Baroness Falkender secretary?

2. Which pet's varieties include the black-bellied and golden?

3. What is the lowest point in North America?

4. Which English composer set Blake's *Jerusalem* to music?

5. For what is a casus belli justification?

6. In which ocean is the Oceania group of islands?

7. Which tycoon brothers' names are Mohamed, Ali and Salah?

8. What is the more common name of the bird *Alcedo atthis*?

9. Which King Henry was Henry of Bolingbroke?

10. Of which country is President Assad ruler?

11. Who was born Agnes Bojaxhiu in 1910?

12. How is soya bean curd also known?

13. What is the largest lake in Italy?

14. With which drink is Armagnac associated?

15. Which is the largest desert?

16. For what, in America, is the Grand Old Baby a popular name?

17. From what is the alcoholic drink perry made?

18. What is the common name of the annual plant *Lycopersicon esculentum*?

19. Which English explorer discovered the magnetic North Pole in 1831?

20. In which city did the Peterloo massacre take place?

ANSWERS: 1 Harold Wilson, 2 Hamster, 3 Death Valley, 4 Parry, 5 War, 6 Pacific, 7 Fayed brothers, 8 Kingfisher, 9 Henry IV, 10 Syria, 11 Mother Teresa, 12 Tofu, 13 Lake Garda, 14 Brandy, 15 Sahara, 16 Republican Party, 17 Pears, 18 Tomato, 19 James Clark Ross, 20 Manchester.

General Knowledge

1. The infectious disease dourine affects what sort of animals?

2. In which city did Mikhail Baryshnikov defect?

3. Who was *Monty Python*'s animator?

4. In which TV series did Elizabeth Montgomery star?

5. What is the female equivalent of the Oedipus complex called?

6. Of which county is Lifford the county town?

7. Which film star was born Joseph Levitch?

8. To what did Nyasaland change its name in 1964?

9. Who composed *In a Summer Garden* in 1908?

10. Which philanthropic society was founded by US lawyer Paul Harris in 1905?

11. Who became potter to George III in 1806?

12. By what name was potassium nitrate formerly known?

13. What was the name of the ferry that sank on the Baltic Sea in 1994?

14. Who was the last Grand Prix world champion to drive a Lotus?

15. Which talent show started Pam Ayres's career?

16. What did Sir Alexander Fleming discover in 1928?

17. To which note does an orchestra tune?

18. What do we call the biennial plant *Brassica rapa*?

19. Of which constellation is *Spica* the brightest star?

20. What type of creature is the boomslang?

ANSWERS: 1 Horses, 2 Toronto, 3 Terry Gilliam, 4 Bewitched, 5 Electra complex, 6 Donegal, 7 Jerry Lewis, 8 Malawi, 9 Frederick Delius, 10 Rotary Club, 11 Josiah Spode, 12 Saltpetre or nitre, 13 Estonia , 14 Mario Andretti, 15 Opportunity Knocks, 16 Penicillin, 17 A, 18 Turnip, 19 Virgo, 20 Snake.

General Knowledge

1. Who was born Elizabeth Angela Marguerite Bowes-Lyon?

2. On which island is the Foreign Legion's main base?

3. Which Bond producer died in September 1994?

4. What are divided into tropical, continental and rain-shadow?

5. What type of plant is traveller's joy?

6. Who is the Bishop of Durham?

7. Whose wrote *The Seagull*?

8. In which port is the National Girobank HQ?

9. What is an ondes Martenot?

10. To what did Rangoon change its name in 1989?

11. How were the six daughters of Lord Redesdale better known?

12. Which marine mammal's two N hemisphere varieties are the Steller's and the Californian?

13. Which country's mafia is called the Yakuza?

14. Who wrote the play *Chips with Everything* in 1962?

15. From which words does the Modem derive its name?

16. Who plays the female lead in the film *Pulp Fiction*?

17. Which philosopher was Socrates's pupil and Aristotle's teacher?

18. What is the only place in England still to use the title alderman?

19. What do the letters RIP stand for?

20. Who is the patron saint of Spain?

ANSWERS: 1 *The Queen Mother, 2 Corsica, 3 Harry Salzman, 4 Deserts, 5 Clematis, 6 Rt Rev Michael Turnbull, 7 Anton Chekhov, 8 Bootle, 9 Electronic musical instrument, 10 Yangon, 11 Mitford Sisters, 12 Sea lion, 13 Japan , 14 Arnold Wesker, 15 Modulator-demodulator, 16 Uma Thurman , 17 Plato, 18 City of London, 19 Requiescat in pace, 20 St James.*

Entertainment

1. Which British group had a hit with *Ordinary World*?
2. Which Shakespearian actor played a sadistic Nazi in the 1976 film *Marathon Man*?
3. Who played the title role in the *Miss Marple* TV series from 1984-1992?
4. Who starred in *Mermaids*, *Edward Scissorhands* and *Dracula*?
5. Which band had a Top 5 hit with *Phorever People*?
6. Which actress played Dot Cotton in *EastEnders*?
7. Who topped the charts with *Wandrin' Star*, sung in the 1969 film *Paint Your Wagon*?
8. Which famous naturalist narrated *Wildlife on One*?
9. Which American band had a US No 1 hit in 1984 with *Jump*?
10. Who starred as Marian in *Robin Hood: Prince of Thieves*?
11. Which comedy series about a country hotel was a spin-off from *Are You Being Served*?
12. Which band had a hit with *Step It Up*?
13. Which actor/singer played the role of Vince in *Just Good Friends*?
14. Who provided the voice of Lady Penelope in the puppet series *Thunderbirds*?
15. Who starred with husband Kenneth Branagh in *Peter's Friends*?
16. Which American vocal band had a No 1 hit with *My Girl* in 1965?
17. In which zoo was the fly-on-the-wall documentary *The Ark* filmed?
18. Which group had a Top 10 hit with *The Devil You Know*?
19. The 1992 film *Sarafina!* is a musical set in which South African township?
20. Who played Napoleon Solo in *The Man From UNCLE*?

General Knowledge

1. How many gallons are there in a bushel?

2. With which composer is the Malvern Festival associated?

3. From which post did Dr John Habgood retire in August 1995?

4. The Lourdes shrine is a shrine to which saint?

5. What is a mandrill?

6. Who won a Victoria Cross for leading the Dam Busters' raid?

7. Which journalist wrote *Princess In Love* with the assistance of James Hewitt?

8. Of which range do the Tatra Mountains form a part?

9. What was Holy Roman Emperor Frederick I's nickname?

10. In medicine, what does the acronym SIDS stand for?

11. Which religion's holy book is the Guru Granth Sahib?

12. Which sporting entertainers were founded in 1927 by Abraham Saperstein?

13. What, in the SI system, replaced the erg?

14. Which singer's autobiography is called *Take Me Home*?

15. What was Queen Victoria's residence on the Isle of Wight?

16. Which king of England was James VII of Scotland?

17. Who provides the voice for wicked Uncle Scar in *The Lion King*?

18. Whose band were the Crickets?

19. Which US state is nicknamed the Garden State?

20. Who conducted the *Three Tenors*?

ANSWERS: *1 Eight, 2 Elgar, 3 Archbishop of York, 4 St Bernadette, 5 A monkey, 6 Guy Gibson, 7 Anna Pasternak, 8 Carpathians, 9 Barbarossa, 10 Sudden Infant Death Syndrome, 11 Sikhism, 12 Harlem Globetrotters, 13 Joule, 14 John Denver, 15 Osborne House, 16 James II, 17 Jeremy Irons, 18 Buddy Holly, 19 New Jersey, 20 Zubin Mehta.*

General Knowledge

1. Of which animal is the babirusa a wild variety?

2. Which cult was involved in alleged mass suicides in Switzerland and Canada in 1994?

3. Which museum is now on the site of 'Bedlam' Hospital?

4. Which film comic was born William Claude Dukenfield?

5. Which ocean has the largest tidal range?

6. Which flower is named after the French for lion's tooth?

7. What has the same tune as the US's America (*My Country 'Tis Of Thee*)?

8. What is currently Britain's fastest-growing religion?

9. Which record producer was famous for his *Wall of Sound*?

10. What are used in the Rorschach test?

11. What does the M stand for in JMW Turner?

12. What do we call a quasi-autonomous non-governmental organisation?

13. Which actor's first names are John Uhler III?

14. Which plant has bird's-foot and hop varieties?

15. By which king was the inch defined in statute?

16. In which year was Greenpeace founded?

17. To which region did Cain go after he had killed Abel?

18. In which country are the Plains of Abraham?

19. Which city lies on the north side of the Firth of Tay?

20. To which flower family does vanilla belong?

ANSWERS: 1 Pig, 2 Order of the Solar Temple, 3 Imperial War Museum, 4 W C Fields, 5 North Atlantic, 6 Dandelion, 7 God Save the Queen, 8 Buddhism, 9 Phil Spector, 10 Ink blots, 11 Mallard, 12 Quango, 13 Jack Lennon, 14 Trefoil, 15 Edward II, 16 1971, 17 Land of Nod, 18 Canada, 19 Dundee, 20 Orchids.

General Knowledge

1. What nationality was the painter Paul Klee?

2. In which war were the Battles of Bull Run fought?

3. Who won the 1994 Booker Prize?

4. With which film did Marlene Dietrich win world fame?

5. Whose wife was Helen of Troy?

6. Of which Canadian province is Winnipeg the capital?

7. Which insurance salesman was Britain's highest earner in 1994?

8. Which element has the symbol Na?

9. What is a pond-skater?

10. Which calendar includes the months Messidor and Thermidor?

11. Who wrote the Aldwych farces of the 1920s?

12. Of which well-known effect is red shift an example?

13. In which market town did Judge Jeffreys hold the Bloody Assizes of 1685?

14. Which health resort lies between Lakes Brienz and Thun?

15. Which King Harold was killed at the Battle of Hastings?

16. In which art gallery is the *Mona Lisa*?

17. Which mathematical functions did John Napier discover in 1614?

18. Between which two fruits is the ugli a cross?

19. Which sugar forms five per cent of cow's milk?

20. Who wrote *And Quiet Flows The Don*?

ANSWERS: *1 Swiss, 2 US Civil War, 3 James Kelman, 4 The Blue Angel, 5 Menelaus, 6 Manitoba, 7 Peter Wood, 8 Sodium, 9 A water bug, 10 French revolutionary calendar, 11 Ben Travers, 12 Doppler effect, 13 Taunton, 14 Interlaken, 15 Harold II, 16 Louvre, 17 Logarithms, 18 Grapefruit and tangerine, 19 Lactose, 20 Mikhail Sholokhov.*

Entertainment

1. Which singer and guitarist had a No 1 hit in 1970 with *I Hear You Knocking*?
2. Which actress played down-trodden Else Garnett in *'Till Death Us Do Part*?
3. In which country was the 1992 film *Strictly Ballroom* made?
4. Which TV *Sherlock Holmes* died in 1995?
5. Which female US vocal group had a hit with *We Are Family*?
6. Which tragic singer played Dorothy in *The Wizard of Oz*?
7. Which famous American actor/singer starred as Clayton Farlow in *Dallas*?
8. Which UK group had a US No 1 hit in 1985 with *Holding Back The Years*?
9. Which Irish actor starred in *Suspect* and *The Dead Pool*?
10. Which American comedian played the title role in the 1989 film *Uncle Buck*?
11. Which actor played Luke Skywalker in the *Star Wars* films?
12. Which US vocal group had a No 1 hit with *Baby Love* in 1964?
13. The film *Midnight Sting* is set in the world of which sport?
14. Which actress enjoyed 20 years of comic TV playing Eric Sykes's sister?
15. Which film starred comedian Lee Evans as a mime artist?
16. Which TV station replaced Thames TV in the London/Southeast area?
17. Which star of *The Fly* played a crooked D.A. in *Deep Cover*?
18. Which ex-Beatle had a hit with *Hope of Deliverance*?
19. Who hosted the off-beat variety show *Saturday Zoo*?
20. Who played Robert de Niro's lover in the remake of the classic film *Night and the City*?

General Knowledge

1. With which country did Israel signed a peace treaty to end 46 years of conflict?

2. Whose poem *The Waste Land* was first published in 1922?

3. Which US state has the nickname the Hawkeye State?

4. What does the c in E=mc squared represent?

5. How has Labour Party HQ been renamed?

6. Which group of military leaders takes its name from the Spanish for 'council'?

7. Which member of the Monty Python team appears in Kenneth Branagh's *Mary Shelley's Frankenstein*?

8. What is the more common term for harijan, a member of India's lowest caste?

9. What is another name for the mountain ash?

10. Which area of open downland contains Stonehenge?

11. Who wrote *All Quiet on the Western Front*?

12. With Wimbledon, which championships form the tennis grand slam?

13. Who translated the *New Testament* into German in 1522?

14. What is the male hormone called?

15. How many arms does a starfish usually have?

16. In computing, what do the letters AI stand for?

17. Of what is malocclusion a defect?

18. Which TV programme has devoted two editions to the business affairs of Terry Venables?

19. What is the official language of the New Caledonia island group?

20. Which George Eliot novel is subtitled *A Study of Provincial Life*?

ANSWERS: 1 Jordan, 2 TS Eliot, 3 Iowa, 4 Speed of light, 5 John Smith House, 6 Junta, 7 John Cleese, 8 Untouchable, 9 Rowan, 10 Salisbury Plain, 11 Erich Maria Remarque, 12 US, French and Australian opens, 13 Martin Luther, 14 Testosterone, 15 Five, 16 Artificial intelligence, 17 Teeth, 18 Panorama, 19 French, 20 Middlemarch.

General Knowledge

1. What is a serval?

2. What is the name of the traditional Muslim women's headscarf?

3. For which film did choirmistress Iris Stevenson provide the inspiration?

4. In which city is Maracana football stadium, the world's largest?

5. Who is deputy prime minister?

6. Which substance takes its name from the Italian for 'baked earth'?

7. Of what type of animal in the yapok the only aquatic variety?

8. The USSR's invasion of which country in 1940 was known as the Winter War?

9. Which post does Lord Mackay hold?

10. By what name do we know the tree *Pyrus communis*?

11. Which people's word for a European means 'the big eyebrows'?

12. Who has turned down £8m to make a sequel to the *Silence of the Lambs*?

13. Which two countries originally contested the Ryder Cup?

14. Of which beetle is the wireworm the larva?

15. What is a mountain lion or cougar more correctly called?

16. Who regained the world heavyweight boxing championship after more than 20 years?

17. In which country was the first Women's Institute group founded in 1897?

18. Who is the only US president to have been elected for four consecutive terms?

19. Of which country have there been three king Victor Emmanuels?

20. Who succeeded Bobby Fischer as world chess champion in 1975?

ANSWERS: *1 African wildcat, 2 Yashmak, 3 Sister Act , 4 Rio de Janeiro, 5 Michael Heseltine , 6 Terracotta, 7 Marsupial, 8 Finland, 9 Lord Chancellor , 10 Pear tree , 11 Eskimos, 12 Sir Anthony Hopkins , 13 USA and Great Britain, 14 Click beetle, 15 Puma, 16 George Foreman , 17 Canada, 18 Franklin D Roosevelt, 19 Italy, 20 Anatoly Karpov.*

General Knowledge

1. From which post did John Profumo resign in 1963?

2. Who wrote the allegory *Pilgrim's Progress*?

3. In which country are the Pampas plains?

4. Which bird is called the chickadee in America?

5. Of what is agaric a type?

6. By what name do we know Michel de Notredame?

7. What is a quebracho?

8. Which sport contests the Pilkington Cup?

9. Which prominent politician was in the band Ugly Rumours in the 70s?

10. What type of bird is a condor?

11. What is old sparky, recently reinstated in New York state?

12. Which *Old Testament* character's supposed age of 969 made him a byword for longevity?

13. Which is the largest type of mackerel?

14. Which psychedelic drug is also called MDMA?

15. Who is Everton FC's manager?

16. Of which instrument was the shawm an early version?

17. What is the largest of the big cats?

18. Which sign of the zodiac is also known as the Water Carrier?

19. What is the name of the National Lottery organising group?

20. What type of flower is a jonquil?

ANSWERS: *1 Secretary of State for War, 2 John Bunyan, 3 Argentina, 4 Tit, 5 Fungus, 6 Nostradamus, 7 A South American tree, 8 Rugby Union, 9 Tony Blair, 10 A vulture, 11 The electric chair, 12 Methuselah, 13 Tuna, 14 Ecstasy, 15 Joe Royle, 16 Oboe, 17 Tiger, 18 Aquarius, 19 Camelot, 20 A daffodil.*

Sports

Your rating: ● 0-5   Wooden spoon   ● 6-10   Bronze medal
               ● 11-15 Silver medal   ● 16-20   Gold medal

1. What nationality is golfer Vijay Singh?
2. Who won the 1962 footballWorld Cup?
3. Which rider won individual world three-day event titles in 1974 & 1978?
4. In 1995, which British boxer beat Sergio Rafael Liendo in the second round?
5. Who were the top male and female seeds in the 1994 Wimbledon tournament?
6. In which city was golfer Fred Couples born?
7. Who missed the last penalty of the 1994 football World Cup?
8. Which sprinter said to the press in 1995, "I don't want to see blood shed on the airport carpet, but if you want some..."?
9. At what sport did Betty Snowball compete for England?
10. Which football team won the 1994 Makita International Tournament?
11. Which British driver came third in the Indy 500 in 1993?
12. Who replaced Graham Turner as Wolverhampton Wanderers manager?
13. In which year were there two false starts in the Grand National?
14. Which sport does New Zealander Simon Mannix play?
15. Calum Giles plays for Havant at which sport?
16. Who beat Brazil in the final of 1995's Copa America?
17. Who beat Steffi Graf in the Barcelona Olympic women's final?
18. At what sport do the New York Knicks and Houston Rockets compete?
19. Which ex-soccer manager accused Alan Sugar of walking "like a spiv"?
20. Which country entered 'Dolphin & Youth' in the Whitbread Round the World race?

ANSWERS: 1 *Fijian*, 2 *Brazil*, 3 *Bruce Davidson*, 4 *Prince Naseem Hamed*, 5 *Pete Sampras and Steffi Graf*, 6 *Seattle*, 7 *Roberto Baggio*, 8 *Linford Christie*, 9 *Cricket*, 10 *Arsenal*, 11 *Nigel Mansell*, 12 *Graham Taylor*, 13 *1993*, 14 *Rugby union*, 15 *Hockey*, 16 *Uruguay*, 17 *Jennifer Capriati*, 18 *Basketball*, 19 *Brian Clough*, 20 *Britain*.

General Knowledge

1. With which saxophone is Sidney Bechet associated?

2. Who resigned in November 1994 as head of the Number 10 policy unit?

3. In which year was the CBI established?

4. Whose epic silent film *The Birth of a Nation* is considered the first film masterpiece?

5. Who was the first member of the Royal Family to visit Argentina since the Falklands conflict?

6. From which language is Afrikaans directly descended?

7. Which French philosopher wrote *Being and Nothingness* in 1943?

8. With which two cities is Italian painter Canaletto chiefly associated?

9. Which lyricist who collaborated with Andrew Lloyd Webber received a Knighthood?

10. What are the dangerous group of islands off Land's End called?

11. Which millionaire zoo owner has seen three tiger keepers killed in fourteen years?

12. Who wrote *Whisky Galore*?

13. Which country was Britain's ally in the Seven Years' War?

14. To which family of fish does the minnow belong?

15. Which former England captain is now Spurs manager?

16. Which US city is named after a chairman of the United States Steel Corporation?

17. What is a kora?

18. Which dog is named after the German for 'badger-dog'?

19. What is the capital of Italy's Tuscany region?

20. What nationality was playwright and novelist August Strindberg?

ANSWERS: *1 Soprano, 2 Sarah Hogg, 3 1965, 4 DW Griffith, 5 Prince Andrew, 6 Dutch, 7 Jean-Paul Sartre, 8 London and Venice, 9 Tim Rice, 10 The Longships, 11 John Aspinall, 12 Compton Mackenzie, 13 Prussia, 14 Carp, 15 Gerry Francis, 16 Gary, 17 African stringed instrument, 18 Dachshund, 19 Florence, 20 Swedish.*

General Knowledge

1. From where did Amy Johnson take off on her 1930 solo flight to Australia?

2. Who assassinated Jacobin leader Jean Paul Marat?

3. How is the extinct *Raphus cucullatus* better known?

4. To which family of instruments does the cor anglais belong?

5. Which official's country residence is Dorneywood in Buckinghamshire?

6. What do the letters AD stand for?

7. Where does the London Boat Race start?

8. What is a quetzal?

9. In which gulf is Prince William Sound?

10. Who is the muse of dance and choral song?

11. Which South African PM was assassinated in 1966?

12. In which sport was Britain's Carl Furrer world champion in 1982?

13. What is the capital of Nevada?

14. What type of animal is a brocket?

15. Who was the Beatles' producer?

16. In which field did Wole Soyinka win the 1986 Nobel Prize?

17. Of which county was Parts of Lindsey a division?

18. Which inventor's middle name was Alva?

19. What was Colin McRae the first Briton to win for 18 years?

20. Which political figure wrote the play *Largo Desolato* in 1985?

ANSWERS: *1 Croydon, 2 Charlotte Corday, 3 Dodo, 4 Oboe, 5 Chancellor of the Exchequer, 6 Anno Domini, 7 Putney, 8 A Central American bird, 9 Gulf of Alaska, 10 Terpsichore, 11 Hendrik Verwoerd, 12 Trampolining, 13 Carson City, 14 A deer, 15 George Martin, 16 Literature, 17 Lincolnshire, 18 Thomas Edison, 19 The RAC Rally, 20 Vaclav Havel.*

General Knowledge

1. What was captured from Spain by admiral George Rooke in 1704?

2. In which sport is the annual Stanley Cup contested?

3. With which instrument is Keith Jarrett associated?

4. Which Bond film features a Louis Armstrong hit song?

5. What do the letters UHT stand for?

6. Of which country is Karachi the largest city?

7. In Greek mythology, who tried to bring Eurydice back from the dead?

8. Niacin belongs to which group of vitamins?

9. Which dog was first bred as the 'imperial lion dog'?

10. Which English garden designer coined the term 'landscape gardening'?

11. In which country is the Firth of Thames?

12. Who is the godfather of Marina Mowatt?

13. Of which bird family is the quail the smallest species?

14. The US Medal of Honor depicts which goddess?

15. Which composer did Clara Wieck marry in 1840?

16. What is the English name for the Dutch port Vlissingen?

17. What do we call the bulbous plant *Allium cepa*?

18. The word 'budget' is derived from which language's word for leather bag?

19. What type of monkey is the Barbary ape?

20. In the film world, who were Harry, Albert, Sam and Jack?

ANSWERS: 1 Gibraltar, 2 Ice hockey, 3 Piano, 4 On Her Majesty's Secret Service, 5 Ultra heat treated, 6 Pakistan, 7 Orpheus, 8 B, 9 Pekingese, 10 Humphrey Repton, 11 New Zealand, 12 Prince Charles, 13 Partridge, 14 Minerva, 15 Robert Schumann, 16 Flushing, 17 Onion, 18 French, 19 Macaque, 20 The Warner Brothers.

Entertainment

1. Which city was the main location for the detective series *Spender*?

2. Which famous comedienne/writer is married to Geoffrey Durham, alias The Great Suprendo?

3. Which British singer had a hit with *Steam*?

4. In the comedy series *Are You Being Served?*, who played mincing Mr. Humphries?

5. Which *Disclosure* star appeared as prosecuting counsel in the film *A Few Good Men*?

6. Which ex-Beatle had a US No 1 hit in 1974 with *You're Sixteen*?

7. Which Hole singer was given a suspended jail sentence for attacking a member of a rival band?

8. Which legendary US actor played Rhett Butler in the original *Gone with the Wind*?

9. Which long-enduring Scottish songstress had a hit with *Independence*?

10. Who plays grumpy Victor Meldrew in *One Foot in the Grave*?

11. Which Brian De Palma thriller starred John Lithgow?

12. Which heavy metal band released a single entitled *Heaven Is*?

13. Which actress plays Sharon in *Birds of a Feather*?

14. Which Canadian rock star had a successful 1992 album called *Waking up the Neighbours*?

15. Who starred as the Easterner out West in the classic 1958 cowboy film *The Big Country*?

16. Which character was played by Pauline Moran in *Agatha Christie's Poirot*?

17. Which Jamaican vocalist had a UK No 1 hit with *The Israelites* in 1969?

18. Which female rock singer played Aunty Entity in *Mad Max Beyond Thunderdome*?

19. Who presents *Whose Line Is It Anyway*?

20. Who had a 1982 No 1 with the Rodgers/Hammerstein tune *Happy Talk*?

ANSWERS: *1 Newcastle, 2 Victoria Wood, 3 Peter Gabriel, 4 John Inman, 5 Demi Moore, 6 Ringo Starr, 7 Courtney Love, 8 Clark Gable, 9 Lulu, 10 Richard Wilson, 11 Raising Cain, 12 Def Leppard, 13 Pauline Quirke, 14 Bryan Adams, 15 Gregory Peck, 16 Miss Lemon, 17 Desmond Dekker, 18 Tina Turner, 19 Clive Anderson, 20 Captain Sensible.*

General Knowledge

1.   What does the Mohs scale measure?

2.   With which art forms is Norman Rockwell associated?

3.   From which drink is Calvados distilled?

4.   Which actress was born Emilie Charlotte le Breton?

5.   What is Europe's largest inland port?

6.   Which group of plants has blue-green, yellow-green and golden-brown varieties?

7.   Of which church are the sacred writings called the *Divine Principle*?

8.   In which TV series did Lionel Stander play Max?

9.   Whom did Idi Amin depose in 1971?

10. Of which ocean is the Beaufort Sea a section?

11. What do we call an invertebrate whose body is divided into head, thorax and abdomen?

12. In which country did the mazurka originate?

13. Who jokingly insulted Prince Charles at the British Comedy Awards in 1994?

14. Which colonel administrator was responsible for the acquisition and foundation of Singapore?

15. By what other name is Israel's Lake Tiberias known?

16. Who was the first monk to become archbishop of Westminster?

17. Who wrote the novel *Flamingo Feather* in 1955?

18. Which volcano buried Pompeii in AD 79?

19. Whose father was Robert I, known as The Devil?

20. In which city is *Romeo and Juliet* set?

General Knowledge

1. What was Charles Sherwood Stratton's nickname?

2. In which religion are the Veda the most sacred scriptures?

3. Where did Body Shop's Anita Roddick open her first shop?

4. Who wrote the musical *Oliver!*?

5. Of what is the predatory crown-of-thorns a variety?

6. Which North African capital is known in Arabic as Tarabolus al-Gharb?

7. What type of creature is a mara?

8. Over how many days is a decathlon held?

9. Which '30s film star married three oil millionaires?

10. In which county is the village of Stilton?

11. What is neutralised by degaussing?

12. Which mime artist created the clown-harlequin Bip?

13. On which island is Hanois lighthouse, the only remaining manned rock tower?

14. What is the common name for Marburg disease?

15. What do we call a fibrous skeleton of the fruit of *Luffa cylindrica*?

16. Which religious group was established by Mary Baker Eddy in 1879?

17. In which country was the Rosetta Stone discovered in 1799?

18. Who is singer Tara Newley's mother?

19. What is petrol called in America?

20. Who wrote the tragedy *Medea*?

General Knowledge

1. What do we call the scavenger bird *Corvus corax*?

2. What is the capital of Australia's Northern Territory?

3. What are the alloy pewter's two main constituents?

4. What is the Scottish national symbol?

5. What is the capital of Chechnya?

6. What is the official residence of the Chancellor of the Exchequer?

7. What was boxer Joe Louis's nickname?

8. Which cotton fabric is named after the Iraqi city Mosul?

9. What is the name of the Atlantic-Pacific sea route around the north of Canada?

10. Which Broadway award is named after actress and producer Antoinette Perry?

11. Of which African country is Brazzaville the capital?

12. Which Greek letter represents the ratio of the circumference of a circle to its diameter?

13. Which Norwegian composer had the middle name Hagerup?

14. With which sport is the English Leander Club associated?

15. Which French author wrote *The Human Comedy* series of novels?

16. What type of animal is a porcupine?

17. Which poet laureate wrote *The Fair Penitent*?

18. Membership of which body allows MPs to be called Right Honourable?

19. What nationality was Ivor Novello?

20. Who directed the controversial film *Natural Born Killers*?

ANSWERS: 1 *Raven*, 2 *Darwin*, 3 *Tin and lead*, 4 *Thistle*, 5 *Grozny*, 6 *11 Downing Street*, 7 *The Brown Bomber*, 8 *Muslin*, 9 *Northwest Passage*, 10 *Tony award*, 11 *Congo*, 12 *Pi*, 13 *Edward Grieg*, 14 *Rowing*, 15 *Balzac*, 16 *Rodent*, 17 *Nicholas Rowe*, 18 *Privy Council*, 19 *Welsh*, 20 *Oliver Stone*.

Entertainment

Your rating: ● 0-5   Buy a TV   ● 6-10   Keep at it
            ● 11-15   Join a quiz team   ● 16-20   Enter Telly Addicts

1. Who played the marshal awaiting a midday fate in *High Noon*?
2. Which Italian band had a Top 10 hit with a single entitled *Open Your Mind*?
3. Which university city was the setting for *Inspector Morse*?
4. Who directed *Bram Stoker's Dracula*?
5. Which US vocalist/composer had a US No 1 hit in 1974 with *Laughter in the Rain*?
6. Which TV soap, set in Spain, was not a great success for the BBC?
7. Which actress starred in the 1961 film *Breakfast at Tiffany's*?
8. Which *Brookside* character is played by Diane Burke?
9. At which historical location was *The Last Emperor* filmed?
10. Which British band had a No 1 hit, in 1964, with *Needles and Pins*?
11. Chalet-maid Peggy in *Hi-De-Hi!* was played by which bespectacled comedienne?
12. Which manic US actor provided the voice for the Genie in Disney's film *Aladdin*?
13. Which affectionately-named band had a Top 10 hit with *Sweet Harmony*?
14. What was the name of the rubbish receptacle made famous in *3-2-1*?
15. Which actress co-starred with Joe Pesci in *The Public Eye*?
16. Which band had a US No 1 hit with *I Just Died in Your Arms* in 1986?
17. Which actress links the comedy shows *Waiting for God* and *One Foot in the Grave*?
18. Which rock star played the King of the Goblins in Jim Henson's 1986 film *Labyrinth*?
19. Which singer joined Rapination for their single *Love Me The Right Way*?
20. Who was the questionmaster of *University Challenge* from 1962?

ANSWERS: 1 *Gary Cooper*, 2 *Usura*, 3 *Oxford*, 4 *Francis Ford Coppola*, 5 *Neil Sedaka*, 6 *Eldorado*, 7 *Audrey Hepburn*, 8 *Katie Rogers*, 9 *The Forbidden City*, 10 *The Searchers*, 11 *Su Pollard*, 12 *Robin Williams*, 13 *The Beloved*, 14 *Dusty Bin*, 15 *Barbara Hershey*, 16 *Cutting Crew*, 17 *Janine Duvitski*, 18 *David Bowie*, 19 *Kim Mazelle*, 20 *Bamber Gascoigne*.

- 97 -

General Knowledge

1. What is the Greek word for 'hot'?

2. What was the European Recovery Programme of 1948-52 better known as?

3. In which American state was Davy Crockett born?

4. What was the profession of Mrs Patrick Campbell, who died in 1940?

5. On what part of a suit of armour would you find a beaver?

6. What is the dried outer covering of the nutmeg called?

7. What is Hans Lippershey credited with having invented in 1608?

8. Which jazz trumpeter recorded the album *Bitches' Brew*?

9. Who was Secretary General of the UN from 1972-81?

10. In which year was the Victoria Cross instituted?

11. In which country is the state of Uttar Pradesh?

12. Who directed the film *Jules et Jim*?

13. What sort of animal is a tarpon?

14. What nationality is the avant-garde composer Karlheinz Stockhausen?

15. Which physicist discovered alpha, beta and gamma rays?

16. What is the capital of Haiti?

17. Which king constructed the Hanging Gardens of Babylon?

18. In which century did the poet John Milton live?

19. What is the symbol used for the element magnesium?

20. In which year did Steve McQueen die?

General Knowledge

1. Which singer was called the Empress of the Blues?

2. Who wrote the opera *Parsifal*?

3. What is a member of the Society of Jesus called?

4. Which singer and actress was born Frances Gumm?

5. What is the parliament building in Northern Ireland called?

6. What is pemmican?

7. About which leader's life has his physician Li Zhisui written a book?

8. What do we call the central part of a church between the choir and the entrance?

9. What was the period 1811-20 called in Britain?

10. Of which country is Massawa the chief port?

11. What did Christopher Cockerell invent in 1959?

12. Who wrote the book *Perestroika* in 1987?

13. Which Thomas Hardy novel is subtitled '*A Pure Woman*'?

14. Which lake's German name is Bodensee?

15. What is Fats Domino's real first name?

16. Of what is a naevus a type?

17. To which country do the Azores belong?

18. With which instrument is Ravi Shankar chiefly associated?

19. What animal has Indian, African black and broad-lipped varieties?

20. Which Hollywood star was the son of the actor Osgood Perkins?

ANSWERS: 1 Bessie Smith, 2 Richard Wagner, 3 Jesuit, 4 Judy Garland, 5 Stormont, 6 Dried meat, 7 Chairman Mao, 8 Nave, 9 The Regency, 10 Ethiopia, 11 Hovercraft, 12 Mikhail Gorbachev, 13 Tess of the D'Urbervilles, 14 Lake Constance, 15 Antoine, 16 Birthmark, 17 Portugal, 18 Sitar, 19 Rhinoceros, 20 Anthony Perkins.

General Knowledge

1. By which letters do we remember the Nazi 'protective squadron'?

2. What is the North American name for an elk?

3. What relation was Pliny the Younger to Pliny the Elder?

4. Of which calendar was Thermidor the eleventh month?

5. What is the Poet Laureate's annual stipend?

6. Which motor-racing team were the first winners of the Constructor's Championship in 1958?

7. To which family of trees does the avocado belong?

8. What is COBOL?

9. What do we call the biennial herb *Petroselinum crispum*?

10. Of which country is Dakar the capital?

11. Of what is the farad a unit?

12. Who created the *Secret Seven*?

13. What do the letters LED stand for?

14. Which of the Seven Wonders of the World has been found underwater?

15. The record for which type of dancing is 15.25 cm?

16. Into which ocean does the Limpopo flow?

17. What do we call a mammal of the genus Erinaceus?

18. Of what is semiotics the study?

19. What is hydrophobia more commonly called?

20. Whose play *Hedda Gabler* was first produced in 1891?

ANSWERS: 1 SS, **2** Moose, **3** Nephew, **4** French Revolutionary, **5** 70 pounds, **6** Vanwall, **7** Laurel, **8** A computer language, **9** Parsley, **10** Senegal, **11** Electrical capacitance, **12** Enid Blyton, **13** Light-Emitting Diode, **14** Pharos of Alexandria, **15** Limbo, **16** Indian, **17** Hedgehog, **18** Signs and symbols, **19** Rabies, **20** Henrik Ibsen.

Entertainment

1. Which actress played Emma Peel in *The Avengers*?
2. Who played vampire-hunter Van Helsing in *Bram Stoker's Dracula*?
3. Which duo from Holland had a No 1 hit with a single called *No Limit*?
4. Sting and Elton John interpreted the songs of which sombre folk singer on the album *Tower Of Song*?
5. Who had a Top 5 hit in 1981 with *Vienna*?
6. Who played the role of Madge Bishop in *Neighbours*?
7. Which US band had a No 1 hit with *Good Vibrations* in 1964?
8. Who played the starring role in Visconti's 1971 film *Death in Venice*?
9. Who starred as *Zorba the Greek* in 1964?
10. Which Welshman had a Top 20 hit with a cover version of the Beatles' *All You Need Is Love*?
11. Who co-starred with Marlon Brando in the 1972 film *Last Tango in Paris*?
12. Who played Donal Davoren in the BBC adaptation of Sean O'Casey's *The Shadow of a Gunman*?

13. Which Australian celebrity had a Top 10 hit with a cover of *Stairway to Heaven*?
14. Which *Mork and Mindy* star played Helen Knable in the comedy *Stay Tuned*?
15. Who played Det. Sgt. Mike Jardine in the drama series *Taggart*?
16. Who had a US No 1 hit in 1974 with a single entitled *I Shot the Sheriff*?
17. The film *Danzon* was made in which country?
18. Which renowned comedian played Lurcio in *Up Pompeii*?
19. What creature was saved by the USS Enterprise in *Star Trek IV: The Voyage Home*?
20. Who duetted with Marilyn Martin on the 1985 US No 1 Hit *Separate Lives*?

General Knowledge

1. Who wrote the novel *The History of Tom Jones*?

2. Of what is encephalitis the inflammation?

3. Which veteran TV cook died in December 1994?

4. Which country's parliament is the Folketing?

5. What was a highwayman without a horse called?

6. Of which country is Cape Byron the eastern extremity?

7. What do we call a cloud of gas and dust in space?

8. Which king was the intended victim of the Gunpowder Plot?

9. With which type of drama is the late John Osborne associated?

10. Which town is the administrative centre of the Highland region?

11. Of what is Soweto a contraction?

12. Where has Norwegian Liv Arnesen become the first woman to reach alone?

13. Which scavenger may be brown, striped or spotted?

14. What nationality was General Blücher, Wellington's ally at Waterloo?

15. Which *Monty Python* star has written the novel *Hemingway's Chair*?

16. With which art-form is 'Grandma' Moses associated?

17. Of which city is Spandau a suburb?

18. With which art form is the American Virgil Thomson associated?

19. What would someone with dysphagia have difficulty doing?

20. In which country is the Ruahine mountain range?

ANSWERS: 1 Henry Fielding, 2 The brain, 3 Fanny Cradock, 4 Denmark, 5 Footpad, 6 Australia, 7 Nebula, 8 James I, 9 'Kitchen sink' drama, 10 Inverness, 11 South West Township, 12 South Pole, 13 Hyena, 14 Prussian, 15 Michael Palin, 16 Painting, 17 Berlin, 18 Music, 19 Swallowing, 20 New Zealand.

General Knowledge

1. What type of animal is a prairie dog?

2. How are birds of the order *Strigiformes* known?

3. Which prime minister adopted the three day week policy?

4. Of which American river is the Red River a tributary?

5. What sort of creature is a pratincole?

6. By which judicial procedure may a US president be brought to trial?

7. Who wrote *The Naked Lunch* in 1959?

8 Which two countries comprise Iberia?

9. To which family of fishes does the burbot belong?

10. In Greek mythology, who was the father of Icarus?

11. Of whom was the Colossus of Rhodes a statue?

12. Which sport's two forms are the snatch and the clean and jerk?

13. Which element accounts for 70 per cent of the sun?

14. By what familiar name is royal nanny Alexandra Legge-Bourke known?

15. What is known as 'the garden resort of Wales'?

16. What do the letters VHF stand for?

17. In which age was the Minoan civilization?

18. Who wrote several novels featuring the poet Enderby?

19. As governor of which prison was John Marriott sacked in January 1995?

20. What name did Portuguese dancer Maria de Carmo Miranda da Cunha assume?

ANSWERS: *1 A rodent, 2 Owls, 3 Edward Heath, 4 Mississippi, 5 A bird, 6 Impeachment, 7 William Burroughs, 8 Spain and Portugal, 9 Cod, 10 Daedalus, 11 Apollo, 12 Weightlifting, 13 Hydrogen, 14 Tiggy , 15 Colwyn Bay, 16 Very high frequency, 17 Bronze Age, 18 Anthony Burgess, 19 Parkhurst, 20 Carmen Miranda.*

General Knowledge

1. Who was Surveyor of the Queen's Pictures from 1945 to 1972?

2. What is a tonka?

3. To which family of mammals does the vicuna belong?

4. Which planet's year is equivalent to 84 of our years?

5. Which country's national assembly is the Cortes?

6. In the *Arabian Nights*, who escapes from the Old Man of the Sea?

7. What is the USA's Beaver State?

8. What type of tree is the sweet bay?

9. What nationality was philosopher Baruch Spinoza?

10. Of which planet is Deimos a moon?

11. In which ocean did the mutiny on the Bounty take place?

12. What type of animal is a marmoset?

13. Which religion is divided between the Digambaras and the Swetambaras?

14. In which country is the Grande Dixence dam?

15. Of which country is Cape York Peninsula the most northerly mainland point?

16. What sort of creature is split and cooked to make a spitchcock?

17. In which Cornish town was a surgeon suspended for having his theatre sister remove someone's appendix?

18. What do we call the biennial *Pastinaca sativa*?

19. Who is best known as the author of the *Doctor* books?

20. The troy pound is used for weighing what?

ANSWERS: *1 Anthony Blunt, 2 South American tree, 3 Camel, 4 Uranus, 5 Spain, 6 Sinbad, 7 Oregon, 8 Laurel, 9 Dutch, 10 Mars, 11 Pacific, 12 Monkey, 13 Jainism, 14 Switzerland, 15 Australia, 16 An eel, 17 Truro, 18 Parsnip, 19 Richard Gordon, 20 Precious metals and gems.*

Entertainment

1. Who played Zoe Callender in the popular comedy series *May to December*?
2. In which 1990 film did Gerard Depardieu and Andie McDowell have a marriage of convenience?
3. Which former Roxy Music member has had a Top 20 hit with *I Put A Spell On You*?
4. In which late 60's series did a superhuman trio work for an agency called *'Nemesis'*?
5. Who played the title role of Agatha Christie in the 1979 film *Agatha*?
6. Which keyboards player had a US No 1 in 1985 with *Miami Vice Theme*?
7. What is the name of Lady Jane's lovely residence in *Lovejoy*?
8. In which film did Robin Williams and Joan Cusack play brother and sister?
9. Which US group had a UK and US No 1 hit in 1966 with *I'm A Believer*?
10. Who played Col. Hannibal Smith in *The A Team*?
11. Which French actress starred with Jeremy Irons in the film *Damage*?
12. Which member of Guns 'n Roses played guitar on Michael Jackson's single *Give In To Me*?
13. Which US soul singer duetted with Lulu on the single *I'm Back for More*?
14. Who played Michelangelo in the 1965 epic Hollywood saga *The Agony and The Ecstasy*?
15. *Animal Nitrate* was a Top 10 hit for which leathery-sounding band?
16. Who played weather girl Suzanne Stone in *To Die For*?
17. Who directed the film *Malcolm X*?
18. Which US vocal/instrumental duo had a US No 1 hit with *Rich Girl*, in 1977?
19. Which food broadcaster/author had an ancestor involved in The Mutiny on the Bounty?
20. In which 1986 film did Ally Sheedy and Steve

General Knowledge

1. Which mountains traditionally separate Europe from Asia?

2. What type of creature is a sandhopper?

3. In which soap did Herman's Hermits' Peter Noone briefly appear?

4. Which US author's debut novel was *The Naked and the Dead*?

5. Which actor was the father of Sarah Siddons?

6. What do we call the extinct African volcano Kirinyaga?

7. Whose Press Secretary is Alastair Campbell?

8. What nationality was dancer Dame Ninette de Valois?

9. Which city was at the centre of the 1995 Japanese earthquake?

10. Who designed Marble Arch?

11. What is patchouli?

12. What type of bird is a budgerigar?

13. Which *Clockwork Orange* star kills Captain Kirk in *Star Trek: Generations*?

14. To which group of islands do North and South Uist belong?

15. Which Italian conductor has been appointed music director of the Royal Philharmonic Orchestra?

16. Who was England's last Plantagenet king?

17. A marimba is a bass variety of which instrument?

18. What sort of fruit is a spanspek?

19. What is the Australian town Coober Pedy famous for mining?

20. Who is Speaker of the US House of Representatives?

ANSWERS: *1 Urals, 2 Crustacean, 3 Coronation Street, 4 Norman Mailer, 5 Roger Kemble, 6 Mount Kenya, 7 Tony Blair, 8 Irish, 9 Kobe, 10 John Nash, 11 A fragrant shrub, 12 Parakeet, 13 Malcolm McDowell, 14 Outer Hebrides, 15 Daniele Gatti, 16 Richard II, 17 Xylophone, 18 Melon, 19 Opals, 20 Newt Gingrich.*

General Knowledge

1. How is the convolvulus genus of plants also known?

2. Which charitable organisation has re-designed its poppy logo?

3. On which part of the body is a lobotomy performed?

4. In Greek mythology, from whose blood is the winged horse Pegasus supposed to have sprung?

5. Which Irish drink has lost its royal warrant?

6. What was the capital of the Confederacy in the US Civil War?

7. Who was the first Hollywood legend to star on a US postage stamp?

8. In which year was the GLC abolished?

9. What is the medical specialty concerned with the study of disease processes called?

10. Which American actor's real surname is Matuschanskavasky?

11. In the Christian church, what is another name for the Lord's Supper?

12. Which hat is named after a former Moroccan capital?

13. What bears the inscription Decus et tutamen, 'an ornament and a safeguard'?

14. What would we normally call ortho-sulpho benzimide?

15. Which *Beyond The Fringe* satirist died in January 1995?

16. Which musical post was first held by Nicholas Lanier in 1626?

17. Which spirit is named from the Dutch for 'burnt wine'?

18. Who quit as Radio 1's top disc jockey in 1995?

19. In which county is Greenham Common?

20. Which famous children's novel was written by Johanna Spyri?

ANSWERS: *1 Bindweed, 2 British Legion, 3 The brain, 4 Medusa, 5 Guinness, 6 Richmond, Virginia, 7 Marilyn Monroe, 8 1986, 9 Pathology, 10 Walter Matthau, 11 Eucharist, 12 Fez, 13 One pound coin, 14 Saccharin, 15 Peter Cook, 16 Master of the King's Musick, 17 Brandy, 18 Steve Wright, 19 Berkshire, 20 Heidi.*

General Knowledge

Your rating: ● 0-5 Join a library   ● 6-10 Keep at it
                ● 11-15 Join a quiz team   ● 16-20 Enter Mastermind

1. Which actor is married to ex-Pan's People dancer Babs?

2. To which family of fish does the bream belong?

3. Which ruler's daughter is Xiao Rong?

4. How many symphonies did Brahms write?

5. What is another name for common heather?

6. How many ares are there in a hectare?

7. Which Kirov Ballet star defected in 1979?

8. Student John Gillard drove 200 miles from Wakefield to crash into the gates of which building?

9. Which Verdi opera is based on the Dumas novel *The Lady of the Camellias*?

10. What was J Arthur Rank's first name?

11. What does the acronym 'laser' stand for?

12. What do the initials a.m. stand for?

13. Who wrote *The Chimes* in 1844 in Genoa?

14. What type of bath did its inventor design for his 15-month-old rheumatoid arthritic son?

15. Which soldier received a life sentence for killing a joy-rider in West Belfast?

16. What is a sidewinder?

17. Who is fifth in line to the throne?

18. What is a tamarack?

19. What is sometimes called the fourth estate?

20. Who wrote *A Town Like Alice* in 1949?

ANSWERS: 1 *Robert Powell*, 2 *Carp*, 3 *Deng Xiaoping*, 4 *Four*, 5 *Ling*, 6 *100*, 7 *Natalia Makarova*, 8 *Buckingham Palace*, 9 *La Traviata*, 10 *Joseph*, 11 *Light Amplification by Stimulated Emission of Radiation*, 12 *Ante meridiem*, 13 *Charles Dickens*, 14 *The jacuzzi*, 15 *Private Lee Clegg*, 16 *A rattlesnake*, 17 *Princess Beatrice*, 18 *A coniferous tree*, 19 *The press*, 20 *Nevil Shute*.

Entertainment

1. In which fictitious northern town would you find *Coronation Street*?
2. Which US singer had a No. 1 hit in 1960 with *Only The Lonely*?
3. Which American sport was the subject of the 1984 film *The Natural*?
4. Who played the role of James Hadleigh squire of Melford Park in *Hadleigh*?
5. Which London band had a Top 5 hit with *Deep*?
6. Who played the huge Russian boxer Ivan Drago in *Rocky IV*?
7. Who played Arthur Daley in *Minder*?
8. Which US vocal group had a US No. 1 with a cover version of *One Bad Apple* in 1971?
9. What profession is Gerard Depardieu's character in the 1992 film *Tous Les Matins du Monde*?
10. Who had a Top 3 hit with a double 'A' side single *Little Bird/Love Song For A Vampire*?
11. Who played George Cowley controller of C15 in *The Professionals*?
12. Which nail-studded demon is played by Doug Bradley in *Hellraiser III*?
13. Which British vocalist had a US No. 1 hit in 1986 with *Higher Love*?
14. Who directed and starred in *Sharky's Machine*?
15. Which Hollywood actor directed the film *A River Runs Through It*?
16. Which Rolling Stones song did Rod Stewart take into the Top 20?
17. Which aeronautical-sounding children's variety show was presented by Mickey Hutton?
18. Who played Scarlett O'Hara in the classic 1939 film *Gone With The Wind*?
19. Which former *Treasure Hunt* star edited a children's book in Hong Kong?
20. Which member of a famous showbiz family played Pamela Lynch in the comedy series *Watching*?

General Knowledge

1. On which island is the fishing port of Peel?

2. To which actress is composer Carl Davis married?

3. Who refers to God as the 'Great Architect of the Universe'?

4. Which British motorcycle manufacturer has relaunched its Thunderbird?

5. What type of drug is reserpine?

6. Which engraver produced the series *A Rake's Progress* in 1735?

7. Who instigated the Great Leap Forward of 1958-1962?

8. Which sea did the Romans call mare nostrum?

9. Which French chemist developed the rabies vaccine?

10. What nationality was the artist Sidney Nolan?

11. Which gender of gnat draws blood?

12. Of which group of islands is Mount Apo the highest peak?

13. Which *Archers* part is played by Trevor Harrison?

14. What was known until July 1940 as the Local Defence Volunteers?

15. Whose double murder trial was presided over by Judge Lance Ito?

16. What do the initials ECG stand for?

17. What is the capital of Tibet?

18. Calamine is a form of which metal?

19. In which country is the river port Fray Bentos?

20. What is measured in ohms?

ANSWERS: *1 Isle of Man, 2 Jean Boht, 3 Freemasons, 4 Triumph, 5 A tranquilliser, 6 William Hogarth, 7 Mao Zedong, 8 Mediterranean, 9 Louis Pasteur, 10 Australian, 11 Female, 12 Philippines, 13 Eddie Grundy, 14 Home Guard, 15 OJ Simpson, 16 Electrocardiogram, 17 Lhasa, 18 Zinc, 19 Uruguay, 20 Electrical resistance.*

General Knowledge

1. Which great British actor's middle name was Kerr?

2. What is the collective name for the first five books of the Old Testament?

3. Which Greek actress died of lung cancer in March 1994?

4. What is the name of Seurat's technique of painting with dots?

5. Which pop group had a hit with *Morningtown Ride*?

6. Which African leader was called 'the Lion of Judah'?

7. Which composer was nicknamed 'the Waltz King'?

8. With which US political party is Tammany Hall associated?

9. Which military vehicle was invented by Ernest Swinton?

10. Which sleepy character was invented by Washington Irving in 1819?

11. Who scored the only goal in Terry Venables's first match as England manager?

12. Whose first wife was Frances Nisbet?

13. What did I A Richards and C K Ogden devise?

14. What type of animal is the dik-dik?

15. What is the judicial capital of the Republic of South Africa?

16. Which country was ruled by dictator Kim Il-Sung?

17. Which car firm's name means 'people's car'?

18. Which film actress achieved fame in *The Torrent* in 1926?

19. To which literary group did Virginia Woolf belong?

20. What do children get from the tree *Aesculus hippocastanum*?

ANSWERS: 1 *Laurence Olivier*, 2 *Pentateuch*, 3 *Melina Mercouri*, 4 *Pointillism*, 5 *The Seekers*, 6 *Haile Selassie*, 7 *Johann Strauss II*, 8 *Democrats*, 9 *Tank*, 10 *Rip Van Winkle*, 11 *David Platt*, 12 *Horatio Nelson*, 13 *Basic English*, 14 *Antelope*, 15 *Bloemfontein*, 16 *North Korea*, 17 *Volkswagen*, 18 *Greta Garbo*, 19 *Bloomsbury Group*, 20 *Conkers*.

General Knowledge

1. Of which range is Mount Toubkal the highest mountain?

2. Which dynasty's family home is at Hyannis Port?

3. How old was Anna Paquin when she won an Oscar?

4. Which Thomas Mann novel is set in a Swiss sanatorium?

5. Which Italian monk was born Giovanni di Bernardone?

6. Which British animator has won two Oscars?

7. Of which band was Brian Jones an original member?

8. In British folklore, which fairy rules over men's dreams?

9. Whose palace of Nonsuch was excavated at Epson in 1959?

10. In which city did Lady Thatcher pass out during a speech?

11. What type of acid does a car battery contain?

12. What is the capital of Burgundy, famous for its mustard?

13. What tree provides the majority of a koala's diet?

14. Whose film *Alexander Nevsky* forms part of an uncompleted trilogy?

15. Which jockey has ridden the most National Hunt winners?

16. How many Inns of Court are there in London?

17. How is deuterium oxide better known?

18. In which country is the port of Arica?

19. How many Oscars did *Schindler's List* win?

20. In which art gallery is the *Venus de Milo*?

ANSWERS: 1 *Atlas*, 2 *Kennedys*, 3 *Eleven*, 4 *The Magic Mountain*, 5 *St Francis of Assisi*, 6 *Nick Park*, 7 *The Rolling Stones*, 8 *Queen Mab*, 9 *Henry VIII*, 10 *Santiago*, 11 *Sulphuric*, 12 *Dijon*, 13 *Eucalyptus*, 14 *Sergei Eisenstein*, 15 *John Francome*, 16 *Four*, 17 *Heavy water*, 18 *Chile*, 19 *Seven*, 20 *Louvre*.

Entertainment

1. Who is the author of *A Year in Provence*?
2. Which actress played the role of Michaela Odone in *Lorenzo's Oil*?
3. Which US singer had a No 1 hit in 1974 with *Annie's Song*?
4. What was the name of the TV show where two teams of stars played charades?
5. Who played the role of 007 in the 1967 James Bond film *Casino Royale*?
6. Which US band had a Top 20 hit with *The Sidewinder Sleeps Tonite*?
7. Who was the Scottish presenter of *The Snow Show*?
8. Which martial arts teacher starred in the action film *Under Siege*?
9. Which UK band had a Top 10 hit with *I Feel You*?
10. Who played the role of Charles Ingalls in *Little House on the Prairie*?
11. *A Simple Twist of Fate* featured which *Roxanne* star?
12. Which vocalist, in collaboration with Queen, had a No 1 hit with *Under Pressure* in 1981?
13. Who was the first woman to be seen on Channel 4?
14. Who was the US director of the violent films *The Wild Bunch* and *Straw Dogs*?
15. Which hirsute-sounding Jamaican singer had a hit with *Oh Carolina*?
16. Who played glamorous witch Samantha in *Bewitched*?
17. Which US actor played the title role in the film *Bad Lieutenant*?
18. Which US vocalist had a US No 1 hit in 1961 with *Take Good Care Of My Baby*?
19. What type of cartoon animal is *Scooby Doo*?
20. Who played ruthless gangster Bonnie Parker in the 1967 film *Bonnie and Clyde*?

ANSWERS: *1 Peter Mayle, 2 Susan Sarandon, 3 John Denver, 4 Give Us A Clue, 5 David Niven, 6 REM, 7 Muriel Gray, 8 Steven Seagal, 9 Depeche Mode, 10 Michael Landon, 11 Steve Martin, 12 David Bowie, 13 Carol Vorderman, 14 Sam Peckinpah, 15 Shaggy, 16 Elizabeth Montgomery, 17 Harvey Keitel, 18 Bobby Vee, 19 A dog, 20 Faye Dunaway.*

General Knowledge

1. On which animal does Britain's largest flea live?

2. Which Welsh buccaneer became deputy-governor of Jamaica?

3. Where is Norilsk, the world's most northerly industrial city?

4. Which evangelical movement was founded by John Wesley in 1739?

5. Who is the central character of Homer's *Iliad*?

6. In cockney slang, what is a rozzer?

7. What is a chow chow?

8. Which sport was invented by Dr James Naismith in 1891?

9. What is the subject of the Surgeon's Photograph of 1934?

10. Of what is eugenics the study?

11. On which island is Tokyo?

12. Which South American revolutionary was known as The Liberator?

13. Who formed the Free French in the UK in WW2?

14. Which Gothic horror story is subtitled *The Modern Prometheus*?

15. Which OT prophet was carried to heaven in a fiery chariot?

16. For which fish is Canada's Fraser River famous?

17. Which multi-millionaire owns Wolverhampton Wanderers?

18. In Scandinavian mythology, who were the three goddesses of fate?

19. In which country is the yuan the standard monetary unit?

20. Which peninsula contains much of Denmark?

ANSWERS: *1 Mole, 2 Sir Henry Morgan, 3 Siberia, 4 Methodism, 5 Achilles, 6 A policeman, 7 Dog, 8 Basketball, 9 The Loch Ness Monster, 10 Selective breeding, 11 Honshu, 12 Simon Bolivar, 13 General de Gaulle, 14 Frankenstein, 15 Elijah, 16 Salmon, 17 Sir Jack Hayward, 18 Norns, 19 China, 20 Jutland.*

General Knowledge

1. Which scientist was US ambassador to France 1776-85?

2. Where is the seat of the secretariat of the European Parliament?

3. Who became director of the FBI in 1924?

4. Of what nationality was the astronomer Nicolaus Copernicus?

5. Of what was Goebbels minister in the Third Reich?

6. Who made the golden calf?

7. Which animal's fur is called musquash?

8. What sort of creature possesses a sensillum?

9. In which US state is Palo Alto?

10. Who wrote *The Mill on the Floss* in 1860?

11. Which disorder is also called word blindness?

12. What is a dunlin?

13. What is the name of the newest Womble?

14. Which singer was born Declan McManus?

15. Which US President was assassinated in Buffalo?

16. To which family does the lovebird belong?

17. Which comedienne posed nude for Esquire magazine?

18. Which art-form is regulated in the US by the Hays Office?

19. Of what is Ceres the largest known example?

20. According to Arthurian legend, who was Sir Galahad's father?

ANSWERS: 1 Benjamin Franklin, 2 Luxembourg, 3 J Edgar Hoover, 4 Polish, 5 Propaganda, 6 Aaron, 7 Muskrat, 8 Insect, 9 California, 10 George Eliot, 11 Dyslexia, 12 A bird, 13 Alderney, 14 Elvis Costello, 15 William McKinley, 16 Parrot, 17 Dawn French, 18 Films, 19 Asteroid, 20 Sir Lancelot.

General Knowledge

1. Whose husband was King Prasutagus?

2. Of which country is the Orszaggyles the national assembly?

3. Which heavyweight boxer collapsed after his defeat by Herbie Hide?

4. Which *Mr Moto* star was born Laszlo Loewenstein?

5. Where was the first Test match between England and Australia played in 1880?

6. Who is the Greek counterpart of the Roman Jupiter?

7. In which country did kung fu originate?

8. Which fruit comes from the plant *Rubus idaeus*?

9. Which condition was treated by the Kenny method?

10. Who won a director's Oscar for *The Last Emperor*?

11. Which Bizet opera was based on a story by Prosper Merimee?

12. Who wrote the film *The Misfits* for Marilyn Monroe?

13. Where is the counterpart of London's Cleopatra's Needle?

14. Of what is a dyne a unit?

15. Which country is immediately north of Panama?

16. What is the full form of i.e.?

17. How is the herb *Artemisia dracunculus* better known?

18. Of which US state is Helena the capital?

19. Which mammal's most commonly-seen variety is the bottlenosed?

20. Whose voice does Plato use in *The Republic*?

ANSWERS: *1 Boudicca, 2 Hungary, 3 Michael Bentt, 4 Peter Lorre, 5 The Oval , 6 Zeus, 7 China, 8 Raspberry, 9 Poliomyelitis, 10 Bernardo Bertolucci, 11 Carmen, 12 Arthur Miller, 13 Central Park, New York, 14 Force, 15 Costa Rica, 16 Id est, 17 Tarragon, 18 Montana, 19 Dolphin, 20 Socrates.*

Sports

1. Which golfer won the 1995 US Masters?
2. Which Brazilian footballer managed Peru in the 1970 World Cup?
3. Who was the 1964 women's 100m Olympic champion?
4. Which Nigerian striker scored two goals against Spurs in the 1995 F.A. Cup semi-final?
5. Which England cricketer was the most prolific batsman from any country in the 1983 World Cup?
6. At which sport does Chen Xinhua compete?
7. How many players are there in an Australian Rules Football team?
8. How many teams comprised the first English football league in 1888?
9. At Cheltenham 1995, which horse became the least experienced horse ever to win a Champion Hurdle?
10. Who won the men's singles title at the 1995 US Open?
11. Who beat James Wattana in the 1994 World snooker championship?
12. Which famous England soccer captain died in February 1993?
13. Which baseball player was known as 'the Yankee Clipper'?
14. Which golfer won the 1994 US Women's Open?
15. Who was men's long jump gold winner at the 1964 Olympics?
16. Which Australian male won the 1982 Junior singles title at Wimbledon?
17. Which World Cup player joined Crystal Palace from Aston Villa for £300,000 in 1995?
18. Who won the 1994 Stanley Cup?
19. For which national Rugby Union side has Maurice Field played?
20. Which teams contested the 1994 Italian Cup final?

General Knowledge

1.   Which English king made the Homburg fashionable?

2.   As which bird is the Holy Spirit usually depicted?

3.   To which mountain range does Ben Nevis belong?

4.   Which war was ended by the Treaty of Paris in 1856?

5.   What is a monkey puzzle?

6.   What was Walter Lantz's most famous cartoon creation?

7.   Which singer-songwriter was born Robert Zimmerman?

8.   In which city is the Bridge of Brotherhood and Unity?

9.   Who wrote *The Doll's House*?

10.   What is the brightest star in the constellation Lyra?

11.   In which bay is the island of Capri?

12.   Which soprano was born Helen Porter Mitchell?

13.   Where were the Plymouth Brethren founded?

14.   In which Austrian city was Mozart born?

15.   What was the Beatles' own record label called?

16.   Which city's Roman name was *Durovernum*?

17.   Which Royal's middle names are Elizabeth Alice Louise?

18.   Which Radio 4 show did Kenneth Robinson present for 15 years?

19.   Of what is the tog a unit of measurement?

20.   Of which country was Victor Emmanuel proclaimed king in 1861?

ANSWERS: 1 Edward VII, 2 White dove, 3 Grampians, 4 Crimean, 5 A tree, 6 Woody Woodpecker, 7 Bob Dylan, 8 Sarajevo, 9 Henrik Ibsen, 10 Vega, 11 Bay of Naples, 12 Nellie Melba, 13 Dublin, 14 Salzburg, 15 Apple, 16 Canterbury, 17 Princess Anne, 18 Start the Week, 19 Thermal insulation, 20 Italy.

General Knowledge

1. Which annual publication was first published in 1700 as *Voices of the Stars*?

2. What did Ben Carson and Roger Staughton invent?

3. Which 'absurdist' playwright died in March 1994?

4. Which US city was designed by French engineer Pierre L'Enfant?

5. What is the BBC's 24-hour news-and-sport radio network called?

6. Who wrote the classic US satirical novel *Main Street*?

7. What is sangaree?

8. What is the capital of Zimbabwe?

9. Which king of France did Marie Antoinette marry?

10. What is a devil's coach-horse?

11. Which London theatre was founded in 1818 as the Coburg?

12. Who described the poorest of the poor as the lumpenproletariat?

13. Which Lost Generation novelist wrote *Manhattan Transfer*?

14. What is the administrative centre of Dorset?

15. What did Andy Bryant undergo with the help of self-hypnosis?

16. In Greek mythology, what were the fifty daughters of Doris called?

17. From what is the antibiotic melitin extracted?

18. Who, according to the Bible, said 'Ecce Homo'?

19. What does the soya bean product TVP stand for?

20. When was the cricket World Cup first held?

ANSWERS: 1 *Old Moore's Almanac*, 2 CS gas, 3 Eugene Ionesco, 4 Washington DC, 5 Radio 5 Live , 6 Sinclair Lewis, 7 A spiced drink, 8 Harare, 9 Louis XVI, 10 A beetle, 11 Old Vic, 12 Karl Marx, 13 John Dos Passos, 14 Dorchester, 15 A vasectomy, 16 Nereids or nereides, 17 Honey-bee poison, 18 Pontius Pilate, 19 Textured vegetable protein, 20 1975.

General Knowledge

- 0-5   Join a library
- 11-15   Join a quiz team
- 6-10   Keep at it
- 16-20   Enter Mastermind

1. What is the name of the sequel to Milton's *Paradise Lost*?

2. Which avant-garde New York rock group featured Lou Reed and John Cale?

3. Whose vice-president was Richard Nixon?

4. Of which group of islands is Espiritu Santo the largest?

5. What position would we call that of the Taoiseach?

6. Which British tennis-player won the 1994 Korean Open?

7. By what name do we know the spider *Latrodectus mactans*?

8. Who is the current Poet Laureate?

9. Which former Bishop of London has become a Roman Catholic priest?

10. In which African country is Abuja?

11. Goths were divided into Visigoths and which other group?

12. What was founded in 1903 as the first English garden city?

13. In Christianity and Judaism, what are the highest order of angels called?

14. Which poet won the 1948 Nobel prize for literature?

15. Which clan conspired with the English in the Glencoe massacre?

16. Where was the British Unknown Soldier buried in 1920?

17. Of what is stinkhorn a species?

18. Which incendiary liquid is a mixture of naphthenic and palmitic acids?

19. What is the oldest British university?

20. What is the hybrid between a blackberry and a raspberry called?

ANSWERS: 1 Paradise Regained, 2 Velvet Underground, 3 Dwight Eisenhower, 4 New Hebrides, 5 Prime minister (of Ireland), 6 Jeremy Bates, 7 Black Widow, 8 Ted Hughes, 9 Dr Graham Leonard, 10 Nigeria, 11 Ostrogoths, 12 Letchworth, 13 Seraphim, 14 TS Eliot, 15 Campbells, 16 Westminster Abbey, 17 Fungus, 18 Napalm, 19 Oxford, 20 Loganberry.

- 120 -

Entertainment

1. Who sang the title song in the classic 1952 movie musical *Singing' in the Rain*?
2. Which Country and Western star wrote the No 1 hit *I Will Always Love You*?
3. From which planet did alien Mork arrive on a fact-finding mission in *Mork and Mindy*?
4. Which heavy metal band released an album called *The X Factor*?
5. Which US vocalist/guitarist had a hit in 1972 with *My Ding-A-Ling*?
6. Which former *Dr Who* plays Prof Geoffrey Hoyt in *Medics*?
7. What type of pet does Clint Eastwood own in the film *Every Which Way But Loose*?
8. Which Heavy Metal band had a Top 10 hit with *Fear Of The Dark*?
9. Which *Absolutely Fabulous* actress played Lydia Bennet in the BBC adaptation of *Pride and Prejudice*?
10. Which silent movie star performed her final role in the 1987 film *The Whales of August*?
11. Which UK band had a No 1 with *House of The Rising Sun* in 1964?
12. Who played Eliot Ness in the TV series *The Untouchables*?
13. What's the surname of the pop star brothers who played *The Krays* in the 1990 film?
14. Which charity received the proceeds from sales of *Stick It Out*, by Right Said Fred?
15. Which drama series chronicled the life of a group of women held in a Japanese POW camp?
16. Al Pacino's character in *Scent of a Woman*, has what physical disability?
17. Which actress played Jennifer half of the *Hart to Hart* husband and wife detective team?
18. Which flamboyant ex-civil servant played Elizabeth I in *Orlando*?
19. Which group had a No 1 in 1986 with *Don't Leave Me This Way*?
20. Who played Krystal Carrington in *Dynasty*?

- 121 -

General Knowledge

1. What was Viscount Montgomery of Alamein's first name?

2. Which post did David Owen hold in the Labour Government from 1977-1979?

3. The best-known form of which game is called 8-ball?

4. Which actor played Lord Bellamy in *Upstairs, Downstairs*?

5. Which condition was also called the king's evil?

6. Which comic actor's first talking film was *Monsieur Verdoux*?

7. What, in 1959, became London's first new theatre in 200 years?

8. What is the name of the 2-day holiday at the start of the Jewish New Year?

9. Who was Queen Elizabeth II's father?

10. Which partnership wrote *My Fair Lady* and *Paint Your Wagon*?

11. Which delicacy comes in American, Norwegian and spiny varieties?

12. Which composer was Richard Wagner's father-in-law?

13. How is the laughing jackass also known?

14. What was Thomas Edison's middle name?

15. Who was Lynne Frederick's first husband?

16. Which Yorkshire town includes the remains of the castle where Richard II died?

17. What type of edible plant is laver?

18. What is a skink?

19. In which sport are the Swaythling and Corbillon Cups contested?

20. Which dreamer was the creation of US humorist James Thurber?

ANSWERS: *1 Bernard, 2 Foreign Secretary, 3 Pool, 4 David Langton, 5 Scrofula, 6 Charlie Chaplin, 7 Mermaid, 8 Rosh Hashanah, 9 George VI, 10 Lerner and Loewe, 11 Lobster, 12 Franz Liszt, 13 Kookaburra, 14 Alva, 15 Peter Sellers, 16 Pontefract, 17 Seaweed, 18 A lizard, 19 Table tennis, 20 Walter Mitty.*

General Knowledge

1. Who was born Maria Eva Duarte?

2. Of which bird is the European redwing a variety?

3. The border between which two US states is known as Tornado Alley?

4. How many cards are there in a tarot deck?

5. In which US state are the towns Norman and Enid?

6. Who passed Kew Gardens to the nation in 1840?

7. In which mythology was Marduk the creator of Earth and humans?

8. Which sea bird is also called the solan goose?

9. What is the study of crops and soils called?

10. In which country was Alcoholics Anonymous set up in 1934?

11. Which London boxer died after a title fight in 1994?

12. Which coin was first minted in Florence in 1252?

13. What is the official residence of the presidents of France?

14. Of what is copra the dried kernel?

15. Who, as minister of health, inaugurated the NHS?

16. At which racetrack were Ayrton Senna and Roland Ratzenberger killed?

17. Which club overthrew the Girondists in the French Revolution?

18. What do we call the large wild cat *Acinonyx jubatus*?

19. How is Jerusalem's Western Wall also known?

20. Which order of knighthood's motto is *Honi soit qui mal y pense*?

ANSWERS: *1 Evita Perón, 2 Thrush, 3 Texas and Oklahoma, 4 78, 5 Oklahoma, 6 Queen Victoria, 7 Babylonian, 8 Gannet, 9 Agronomy, 10 USA, 11 Bradley Stone, 12 Florin, 13 Elysée Palace, 14 Coconut, 15 Aneurin Bevan, 16 San Marino, 17 Jacobins, 18 Cheetah, 19 Wailing Wall, 20 Order of the Garter.*

General Knowledge

1. What is the USA's equivalent of the Epsom Derby?

2. Who was the first woman, according to Greek mythology?

3. Which former Middle East empire's capital was Nineveh?

4. What sort of creature is a bluetongue?

5. Which Australian port is at the mouth of the Swan river?

6. Which martial art's name is Japanese for 'gentle way'?

7. Of what is the *Sequoiadendron giganteum* the world's largest?

8. Which war opened with the Battle of Lexington and Concord?

9. What was Zaire called before 1971?

10. What is the BBC's teletext service called?

11. In the *Arabian Nights*, how many journeys did Sinbad make?

12. What is the administrative capital of Bolivia?

13. Which US state is nicknamed the Beehive State?

14. What is the Lord Chancellor's seat in the House of Lords called?

15. What is the capital of Rwanda?

16. Which drug yields both morphine and codeine?

17. Which architect designed London's Royal Exchange?

18. What is the longest river in Europe?

19. Who was the Roman god of fire and destruction?

20. Which Canadian territory's capital is Whitehorse?

ANSWERS: *1 Kentucky Derby, 2 Pandora, 3 Assyrian, 4 A lizard, 5 Fremantle, 6 Judo, 7 Tree, 8 US Independence, 9 Congo, 10 Ceefax, 11 7, 12 La Paz, 13 Utah, 14 Woolsack, 15 Kigali, 16 Opium, 17 Sir Christopher Wren, 18 Volga, 19 Vulcan, 20 Yukon.*

Entertainment

1. What is the name of the amateur sleuth played by Angela Lansbury in *Murder She Wrote*?
2. Which US rock band had a hit with a cover version of Harry Chapin's *Cat's in the Cradle*?
3. Which US playwright wrote *A Streetcar Named Desire*?
4. *Have I Got News For You* captain Ian Hislop is editor of which satirical magazine?
5. Which Motown vocal group had a No 1 in 1966 with *Reach Out I'll Be There*?
6. Which American actress played the title role in the 1980 film *Private Benjamin*?
7. Who was the presenter of the children's zoo programme *Animal Magic*?
8. Which cool-sounding character had a Top 10 hit with *Informer*?
9. Who played the title role in Danny DeVito's film, *Hoffa*?
10. Which British composer had his famous choral work *War Requiem* televised?
11. Which British group had a US No 1 in 1987 with *Throwing It All Away*?
12. Who played the title role in the 1988 black comedy *Beetlejuice*?
13. What was the collective name for the bevy of girls who adorned *The Benny Hill Show*?
14. Whose *Constant Craving* produced a hit single?
15. Who starred with Madonna in the 1985 film *Desperately Seeking Susan*?
16. To which branch of the police force did detectives Regan and Carter belong in *The Sweeney*?
17. Which British vocalist had a UK No 1 with *I Love You Love Me Love* in 1973?
18. Which TV personality was senior lecturer in botany at Durham University?
19. Which actress played the role of Alexis in *Dynasty*?
20. What was the name of the lion cub raised by the Adamsons in the 1966 film *Born Free*?

General Knowledge

1. Who wrote *Brideshead Revisited* in 1945?

2. On which Hebridean island is Fingal's Cave?

3. Which *A-Team* star died in 1994?

4. Which British coin was discontinued in 1961?

5. Which ceremonial office is held by the Lordship of Scrivelsby, Lincolnshire?

6. Who wrote the classic jazz number *Round Midnight*?

7. What did the Fayed brothers call the shark in Harrods' food hall?

8. Who made his US film debut as Christ in *The Greatest Story Ever Told*?

9. Which Indian state's name is Sanskrit for 'five rivers'?

10. Who is *University Challenge*'s new host?

11. Which artist painted the ceiling of the Banqueting House in Whitehall?

12. Which golfer was noted for wearing all-black outfits?

13. Which island includes New York boroughs Queens and Brooklyn?

14. Who wrote *A Brief History of Time* in 1988?

15. Which present-day city was the capital of the Byzantine and Ottoman Empires?

16. Which organs are affected by asbestosis?

17. Which author is married to Jonathan Dimbleby?

18. To which country do the Stewart and Chatham Islands belong?

19. Who is manager of Middlesbrough football club?

20. What type of animal is a capuchin?

General Knowledge

1. What type of tree is the tamarack?

2. Whose autobiography is called *The Tale of My Life*?

3. On which day does Martinmas fall?

4. At what age, according to the Old Testament, did Moses die?

5. Which ocean contains the Norwegian Sea?

6. Which millionairess tennis player was charged with drug possession in 1994?

7. Whose office is at 12 Downing Street?

8. Of what nationality is the novelist Nadine Gordimer?

9. Which religious victims are named from the Greek for 'witness'?

10. In which country was dramatist Eugene Ionesco born?

11. Which political leader's middle name is Rolihlahla?

12. Which US weekly magazine was founded in 1925 by Harold Ross?

13. What type of creature is the bushmaster?

14. Which river flows through Lake Constance?

15. In which year was the first EC passport introduced?

16. What is the official report of the proceedings of the British Parliament called?

17. What was the first English commemorative medal?

18. Who wrote *Sinister Street* and *Whisky Galore*?

19. In which country is El Lliama volcano, which erupted in 1994?

20. What is the highest rank in the RAF?

ANSWERS : *1 Larch, 2 Hans Christian Andersen, 3 11th November, 4 120, 5 Arctic, 6 Jennifer Capriati, 7 Government Whips, 8 South African, 9 Martyrs, 10 Romania, 11 Nelson Mandela, 12 The New Yorker, 13 A snake, 14 Rhine, 15 1978, 16 Hansard, 17 Armada Medal, 18 Sir Compton Mackenzie, 19 Chile, 20 Marshal.*

General Knowledge

1. Who received £4m to play Fred's mother-in-law in *The Flintstones*?

2. In which country did King Farouk abdicate in 1952?

3. Which Beatles song was covered by 1,186 performers in its first ten years?

4. What type of animal is the blackcap?

5. On which Scottish island was John Smith buried?

6. On what date does Epiphany fall?

7. Which artform uses labanotation?

8. Which food sustained the Israelites in the wilderness?

9. In which country is Doi Inthanon the highest mountain?

10. In which year was the Suez Crisis?

11. Of what is a pascal a unit?

12. Which Hindu festival's name means 'garland of lamps'?

13. What do the initials RIBA stand for?

14. Which Red Indian tribe has the largest reservation in the USA?

15. What does the legal term 'sub judice' mean?

16. Where are the annual Diamond Challenge Sculls held?

17. Which royal turned down the part of Boadicea in a Ken Russell film?

18. What, in ancient Greece, was a rhyton?

19. What type of pet is the Mongolian jird?

20. What is the fruit of the *Prunus armeniaca* tree?

ANSWERS: 1 Liz Taylor, 2 Egypt, 3 Yesterday, 4 A bird, 5 Iona, 6 January 6, 7 Dance, 8 Manna, 9 Thailand, 10 1956, 11 Pressure, 12 Diwali, 13 Royal Institute of British Architects, 14 Navajo, 15 Under a judge, 16 Henley, 17 The Duchess of York, 18 A drinking vessel, 19 Gerbil, 20 Apricot.

Entertainment

1. Which American drama series focuses on the life-guards of Los Angeles County?
2. Which French actress starred in the film *Indochine*?
3. Which group had a hit with a re-release of their song *Young at Heart*?
4. Which British actor starred as a San Francisco child psychiatrist in *Nine Months*?
5. Which actor battles terrorists in *Under Siege*?
6. Which British group had a No 1 hit in 1964 with *Needles and Pins*?
7. Which former *Blue Peter* presenter co-hosted *Travel UK* with Chris Packham?
8. Which Viennese philosopher was the subject of a film starring Karl Johnson?
9. Which US vocalist had a US No 1 with *Shakedown* taken from *Beverley Hills Cop II* in 1987?
10. Which American actor links the TV series *Star Trek* and *T J Hooker*?
11. Which tragic singer gave one of her best performances in the 1944 musical *Meet Me in St Louis*?
12. Which film starred Robin Williams as a doctor and Robert De Niro as a patient?
13. In which fictitious Scottish village is *Doctor Finlay* set?
14. Which Rolling Stone had a Top Twenty Hit in 1981 with *(Si Si) Je Suis Un Rock Star*?
15. Who had a Top 5 hit with *Mr Loverman*?
16. Who played Del in *Only Fools and Horses*?
17. Which German artiste gained international acclaim following her role in *The Blue Angel* in 1930?
18. Which British group had a No 1 hit with *Skweeze Me Pleeze Me* in 1973?
19. Which actress plays Vera Duckworth in *Coronation Street*?
20. Which 60's playwright was the subject of the 1987 film *Prick up your Ears*?

General Knowledge

1. What is the Roman name for Odysseus?

2. Of which mountain range is Mount McKinley the highest?

3. Which John Travolta film won the Palme d'Or at Cannes in 1994?

4. What is the smallest US state?

5. Of which religion is a Parsee or Parsi a follower?

6. Which boxer retired after twice losing to Steve Collins?

7. Which race is the blue riband of the English horse-racing season?

8. Which film company took over MGM in the '70s?

9. Which town in Greater Manchester includes Old Trafford cricket ground?

10. Which Hollywood star's first name is Eldred?

11. In which county is the ship-burial site Sutton Hoo?

12. What is the edible fruit of the bush *Ribes uva-crispa*?

13. Which English bridge was the world's longest single-span suspension bridge when completed in 1980?

14. Which Crazy Gang member was born Robert Winthrop?

15. Where, in Norse mythology, did the principal gods live?

16. Tony Blair's wife Cherie is the daughter of which actor?

17. Which town is the headquarters of the UK Civil Service Commission?

18. Which bird's ancient name was ouzel or ousel?

19. What is the capital of Italy's Lazio region?

20. Of which branch of biology was Gregor Mendel a founder?

ANSWERS: 1 Ulysses, 2 Rockies, 3 Pulp Fiction, 4 Rhode Island, 5 Zoroastrianism, 6 Chris Eubank, 7 The Derby, 8 United Artists, 9 Stretford, 10 Gregory Peck, 11 Suffolk, 12 Gooseberry, 13 Humber Bridge, 14 Bud Flanagan, 15 Asgard, 16 Tony Booth, 17 Basingstoke, 18 Blackbird, 19 Rome, 20 Genetics.

General Knowledge

1. How many players are there in a Rugby League team?

2. Which island's parliament is called the Chief Pleas?

3. Which *Coronation Street* star turned his libel battle into a board game?

4. Who was the last viceroy of India?

5. Which political leader's first names are Jeremy John Durham?

6. Whose novel *Dr Zhivago* was first published in Italy in 1957?

7. What type of animal is a tarsier?

8. What is the meaning of the title of Wagner's opera *Gotterdammerung*?

9. Which volcano's name is Aztec for 'smoking mountain'?

10. Which disease used to be called consumption?

11. In which S American city did Erich Honecker die?

12. To which organisation did the ship *Rainbow Warrior* belong?

13. Who founded the Church of Scientology in 1954?

14. Which countries were joined in the Act of Union of 1707?

15. Who wrote *The Firm* and *The Pelican Brief*?

16. By what name is tetanus or trismus also known?

17. Which composer wrote *The Pines of Rome*?

18. Of which group of islands is Naxos the largest?

19. Whose departure closed the musical *Piaf*?

20. Who wrote *Our Man in Havana*?

General Knowledge

1. Who became South Africa's first executive state president in 1984?

2. Which increasingly-common medical condition is treated with a bronchodilator?

3. From which flower is orrisroot obtained?

4. Of which bird is the ptarmigan a variety?

5. How many milliemes are in a Tunisian dinar?

6. Which school featured in a series of films by Sidney Gilliat?

7. Who founded the Society of Friends?

8. When was the Domesday Book completed?

9. To which church do the Moonies belong?

10. Which choirboy had a hit with *Walking In The Air*?

11. On which river does Ipswich lie?

12. With which art form is Pina Bausch connected?

13. Which European capital is divided by the Attila line?

14. In biology, what do two gametes merge to form?

15. What is the biggest British vessel ever lost at sea?

16. To which English king was Hans Holbein the Younger court painter?

17. After which battle is the East Sussex town Battle named?

18. Who is the latest James Bond?

19. Of what is the morel a type?

20. Which sea lies between Italy and Greece?

ANSWERS: 1 P.W. Botha, 2 Asthma, 3 Iris, 4 Grouse, 5 One thousand 6 St. Trinian's, 7 George Fox, 8 1086, 9 Unification Church, 10 Aled Jones, 11 Orwell, 12 Dance, 13 Nicosia, 14 A zygote, 15 Derbyshire, 16 Henry VIII, 17 Hastings, 18 Pierce Brosnan, 19 Mushroom, 20 Ionian.

Entertainment

Your rating: ● 0-5　　**Buy a TV**　　　　　　● 6-10　　**Keep at it**
　　　　　　　　　　● 11-15　**Join a quiz team**　　● 16-20　**Enter Telly Addicts**

1. What was the name of the lion in the children's series *The Chronicles of Narnia*?
2. Who starred with his real-life daughter in the 1973 film *Paper Moon*?
3. Which American female singer starred with Danny de Vito in the 1986 film *Ruthless People*?
4. Which comedy drama series starred Ray Brooks as a compulsive gambler?
5. What type of animal was Shere Khan in the Disney classic *The Jungle Book*?
6. Which James Bond film starred Steven Berkoff as Russian General Orlov?
7. Who played Annie Mayle in *A Year in Provence*?
8. Which American comedian starred in the 1948 comedy *The Paleface*?
9. Which American group had a US No 1 hit in 1964 with *Rag Doll*?
10. Which star of *Brush Strokes* played the title role in the comedy series *Mulberry*?
11. Which Oscar-winning star of *Misery* appeared in the film *Used People*?
12. Who is the lead singer of Simply Red?
13. What sci-fi TV drama was about an Earth invasion by carnivorous lizards disguised as humans?
14. Which former *Monty Python* member starred in the film *Splitting Heirs*?
15. Which British group's only No 1 hit was a single called *Down, Down* in 1974?
16. What was the name of Gomez and Morticia's son in *The Addams Family*?
17. What fictitious school and its ghastly girls was at the centre of several 50's comedy films?
18. Who had a Top 10 hit with a song called *Show Me Love*?
19. Which flowery character is played by Patricia Routledge in *Keeping Up Appearances*?
20. Which wrestling star played the title role in the film *Mr Nanny*?

ANSWERS: *1 Aslan, 2 Ryan O'Neal, 3 Bette Midler, 4 Big Deal, 5 A tiger, 6 Octopussy, 7 Lindsay Duncan, 8 Bob Hope, 9 Four Seasons, 10 Karl Howman, 11 Kathy Bates, 12 Mick Hucknall, 13 V, 14 Eric Idle, 15 Status Quo, 16 Pugsley, 17 St. Trinian's, 18 Robin S, 19 Hyacinth Bucket, 20 Hulk Hogan.*

General Knowledge

1. Which two of Wagner's opera titles are father and son?

2. At what Beaufort number does smoke rise vertically?

3. Of which element is charcoal a form?

4. What was 12-year-old Vicki van Meter the youngest female pilot to cross?

5. Who painted *The Anatomy Lesson of Dr Tulp*?

6. What is the British equivalent of America's Bureau of Consumer Protection?

7. Who was the second man on the moon?

8. With which medical disorder may one have Jacksonian fits?

9. Which controversial TV playwright died in June 1994?

10. Of which country was Rafael Callejas elected president in 1989?

11. To which collection of stories does *How The Leopard Got His Spots* belong?

12. Which city is at the centre of the Asian dollar market?

13. Which former tennis star took Harry Carpenter's place at Wimbledon?

14. Which silk fabric's name is derived from the Persian for 'spun'?

15. Who was Henry VIII's last wife?

16. Who is the chief god of Scandinavian mythology?

17. What nationality was Mata Hari?

18. Of which country are the Chatham Islands part?

19. What sort of creature is a knot?

20. What do the letters J.P. stand for?

ANSWERS: 1 *Parsifal and Lohengrin*, 2 0, 3 *Carbon*, 4 *The Atlantic*, 5 *Rembrandt*, 6 *Office of Fair Trading*, 7 *Edwin "Buzz" Aldrin*, 8 *Epilepsy*, 9 *Dennis Potter*, 10 *Honduras*, 11 *Just So Stories*, 12 *Singapore*, 13 *Sue Barker*, 14 *Taffeta*, 15 *Catherine Parr*, 16 *Odin*, 17 *Dutch*, 18 *New Zealand*, 19 *A sandpiper*, 20 *Justice of the Peace*.

General Knowledge

1. Which country was rocked by the Recruit scandal?

2. Which soccer hero received a knighthood in the 1994 Queen's Birthday Honours list?

3. What does an entomologist study?

4. What is the capital of New Mexico?

5. In which sport is play started by a 'bully'?

6. What is the US's oldest educational institution?

7. Which country's largest lake is Lake Garda?

8. What is a maduro?

9. Which genus of tree includes the peach, the apricot and the cherry?

10. Of which war was the Battle of Crecy the first important battle?

11. What is the highest mountain on the continent of Europe?

12. With which genre is author Michael Moorcock associated?

13. Which order of chivalry did Princess Anne receive in 1994?

14. Which alcoholic drink is used in making lobster Newburg?

15. Which element has the Latin name plumbum?

16. Who became a Dame and received a Tony award within 48 hours in 1994?

17. What is the first name of baby care writer Dr Spock?

18. Which tennis player banned her father from attending Wimbledon?

19. In which ocean are the Maldives?

20. Which organisation's agents were nicknamed G-Men?

ANSWERS: 1 Japan, 2 Bobby Charlton, 3 Insects, 4 Santa Fe, 5 Hockey, 6 Harvard University, 7 Italy, 8 A cigar, 9 Prunus, 10 Hundred Years' War, 11 Elbrus, 12 Science fiction, 13 Order of the Garter, 14 Sherry, 15 Lead, 16 Diana Rigg, 17 Benjamin, 18 Mary Pierce, 19 Indian, 20 FBI.

General Knowledge

Your rating: ● 0-5   Join a library   ● 6-10   Keep at it
               ● 11-15 Join a quiz team   ● 16-20 Enter Mastermind

1.   Who is Frank Richards's most famous creation?

2.   With which disease is oncology concerned?

3.   Which unit of distance is 1.852 km long?

4.   Who wrote the foreword for the surprise best-seller *The Catechism*?

5.   Which recent Australian PM was nicknamed 'the Prefect'?

6.   In which country is the Ijsselmeer lake?

7.   Which violinist was often acccompanied by his sister Hephzibah?

8.   Who wrote *The Bostonians*?

9.   Which *Naked Gun* star was involved in a real-life police pursuit?

10. In which county is the seaside resort Herne Bay?

11. Who was the Greek sun god?

12. Of what is Moscow's Tsar Kolokol the world's largest example?

13. Which casino game was adapted from the game hazard?

14. How many valves does a bugle have?

15. Which Jewish festival commemorates the exodus from Egypt?

16. What is the largest living lizard?

17. With which country did Germany sign the Anti-Comintern Pact in 1936?

18. In Greek mythology, who was overthrown by his son Zeus?

19. What is Susan Mayoss-Hurd the first woman priest to have?

20. Which Italian word for 'little book' is used to denote an opera text?

ANSWERS: *1* Billy Bunter, *2* Cancer, *3* Nautical mile, *4* The Pope, *5* Malcolm Fraser, *6* Netherlands, *7* Yehudi Menuhin, *8* Henry James, *9* O J Simpson, *10* Kent, *11* Helios, *12* Bell, *13* Craps, *14* None, *15* Passover, *16* Komodo Dragon, *17* Japan, *18* Cronus, *19* A baby, *20* Libretto.

Entertainment

1. Which New Zealand writer created TV's *Inspector Alleyn*?

2. Who co-starred with Eric Idle in the 1990 comedy film *Nuns on the Run*?

3. Which UK duo had three UK No 1 hits in 1984 including *Freedom* and *Last Christmas*?

4. Which star of *El C.I.D.* also played Prof. Plum in the murder game series *Cluedo*?

5. Which Fritz Lang 1926 classic silent firm was revamped/restored for a 1984 re-release?

6. Which 'precious' vocal trio had a Top 10 hit with their single *Don't Walk Away*?

7. Which country is the main setting for the film *Cold Fever*?

8. Which actress played the title role in the Oscar-nominated film *Educating Rita*?

9. Which American vocalist/composer had a US No 1 hit with *Lean On Me* in 1972?

10. Which British vocalist had a UK No 1 hit in 1989 with *You'll Never Stop Me Loving You*?

11. Which actress played the title role in the 1986 film *Peggy Sue Got Married*?

12. Which American trio had a 1969 US No 1 hit with *Leavin' On A Jet Plane*?

13. Which actor played the role of 'Jody' in the US sitcom *Soap*?

14. Which actress co-starred with Dustin Hoffman in the film *Accidental Hero*?

15. Which global-sounding group had a Top 20 hit with *Is it Like Today*?

16. Which Labour MP played the title role in the 1971 TV series *Elizabeth R*?

17. What is the name of the 'Man-cub' hero of Disney's classic film *Jungle Book*?

18. Which singer featured with Sub Sub on the Top 5 hit *Ain't No Love (Ain't No Use)*?

19. What is the name of the fictitious stately home at which TV's *The Riff Raff Element* was set?

20. Who played defence lawyer Frank Dulaney in the film *Body of Evidence*?

ANSWERS: *1 Ngaio Marsh, 2 Robbie Coltrane, 3 Wham!, 4 John Bird, 5 Metropolis, 6 Jade, 7 Iceland, 8 Julie Walters, 9 Bill Withers, 10 Sonia, 11 Kathleen Turner, 12 Peter, Paul & Mary, 13 Billy Crystal, 14 Geena Davis, 15 World Party, 16 Glenda Jackson, 17 Mowgli, 18 Melanie Williams, 19 Tundish Hall, 20 Willem Dafoe.*

General Knowledge

1. To which country did Bosnia belong from 1463 to 1878?

2. Which atomic particle is negatively charged?

3. Of which country was Haile Selassie regent, king and finally emperor?

4. In which US state is Dodge City?

5. Which equestrian event's name is French for 'the training of horses'?

6. Who discovered the respiratory effects of laughing gas?

7. Which organs are affected by nephritis?

8. With which form of entertainment is Hal Prince associated?

9. In which city is Madison Square Garden?

10. Whose half-sister is singer Roslyn Kind?

11. What is a line of equal temperature on a map called?

12. Of which race was Goliath champion?

13. Which Italian region includes Naples and Capri?

14. Which decorative work's name is derived from the Arabic for 'striped cloth'?

15. Which singer was known as Lady Day?

16. Lincoln is a breed of which animal?

17. On which day is Thanksgiving Day held in the USA?

18. In which country is the Orange River?

19. In which country is the CERN nuclear research organisation based?

20. Who wrote *Little Lord Fauntleroy* in 1886?

General Knowledge

1. On which Hebridean island did Prince Charles overshoot the runway on landing?

2. Where is the St. Leger run?

3. Of which gland is a goitre an enlargement?

4. How many Inns of Court are there in England?

5. In biology, what is a group of families called?

6. What is the Peak District's highest point?

7. Of what animal are *mississipiensis* and *sinensis* the two varieties?

8. Which novelist created Svengali?

9. Which king converted Leeds Castle to a palace?

10. On silverware, what do the letters EPNS stand for?

11. Who played the title role in *Batman Forever*?

12. Which European peninsula is named after the Turkish for 'mountains'?

13. Which English philosopher was made a citizen of the French Republic in 1792?

14. Of what is the condor a variety?

15. Which flag is also known as Old Glory?

16. Since the Common Market began in 1957, which language has had to be used at its press briefings?

17. Which substances do Boyle's and Charles's laws concern?

18. After which Norse god is Wednesday named?

19. Which magazine coined the term nouvelle cuisine in 1975?

20. At which football ground did Eric Cantona attack a fan in 1995?

ANSWERS: *1 Islay, 2 Doncaster, 3 Thyroid, 4 Four, 5 Order, 6 Kinder Scout, 7 Alligator, 8 George Du Maurier, 9 Henry VIII, 10 Electroplated nickel silver, 11 Val Kilmer, 12 Balkans, 13 Jeremy Bentham, 14 Vulture, 15 Stars and Stripes, 16 French, 17 Gases, 18 Odin, 19 Harpers and Queen, 20 Selhurst Park.*

General Knowledge

1. Whose novel *Madame Bovary* was published in 1857?

2. Which anaesthetic was discovered by Justus, Baron Von Liebig?

3. In which country was the Great Trek of 1836-37 made?

4. Of what is the Ivy League an eight-member group?

5. Which shrub has common and hedge varieties?

6. What do we call the mammal *Oryctolagus cuniculus*?

7. Which composer's most famous piece is *Carnival of the Animals*?

8. How was Arthur Marx better known?

9. Of which tree is the ironbark a species?

10. Which best-selling author and naturalist died in January 1995?

11. Where is the annual British Showjumping Derby held?

12. Which great circle may be terrestrial or celestial?

13. In which US state is the Corning Museum of Glass, reputedly the world's finest collection?

14. Who directed *The Wild Bunch* in 1969?

15. For which motor racing team did Nigel Mansell drive (briefly) in 1995?

16. Which book of stories inspired Baden Powell to form the Wolf Cub division of the Boy Scout movement?

17. Which astronomical feature may be spiral, barred or elliptical?

18. Whose traditional sign is three gold balls?

19. Which Christian festival commemorates the coming of the Magi?

20. What is skua?

ANSWERS: 1 *Gustave Flaubert*, **2** *Chloroform*, **3** *South Africa*, **4** *Universities*, **5** *Privet*, **6** *Rabbit*, **7** *Camille Saint-Saens*, **8** *Harpo*, **9** *Eucalyptus*, **10** *Gerald Durrell*, **11** *Hickstead*, **12** *The equator*, **13** *New York*, **14** *Sam Peckinpah*, **15** *McLaren*, **16** *The Jungle Book*, **17** *Galaxy*, **18** *Pawnbroker*, **19** *Epiphany*, **20** *A sea-bird*.

Entertainment

1. Which actress played Elsie Tanner for 24 years in *Coronation Street*?
2. Which American actor played the title role in *Sommersby*?
3. Which British group had UK No 1s with *Start* in 1980 and *Beat Surrender* in 1982?
4. Which controversial pop singer starred in *Body of Evidence*?
5. Which cartoon character was played by Robin Williams in his first major film in 1980?
6. Which group had a Top 10 hit with a track called *U Got 2 Know*?
7. At which sporting venue is the World Snooker Championship held?
8. Which Australian actor has appeared in *Neighbours*, *Home and Away* and *Bugs*?
9. Which American group had a US and UK No 1 hit with *Three Times A Lady* in 1978?
10. Which star of *The Professionals* also appeared as *The Chief*?
11. Which film marked Billy Crystal's debut as a director?
12. Which American vocal duo had a US No 1 hit in 1963 with *Surf City*?
13. Who played Jamie Diadoni in Alan Bleasdale's *Jake's Progress*?
14. Which *EastEnders* character is played by Caroline Paterson?
15. Which former 'Communard' joined *Voice of the Beehive* on *Gimme Shelter*?
16. Which actress played the title role in *Connie* and Sable Colby in *Dynasty*?
17. Who was the villainous Korean henchman of Auric *Goldfinger* in the 1964 Bond film?
18. Which member of a famous musical family sang *That's The Way Love Goes*?
19. Which actor played *Father Brown* in the 1974 series about Chesterton's clerical sleuth?
20. Which precocious child actress starred in the 1936 musical *Stowaway*?

General Knowledge

1. What was the pen name of author Amandine Aurore Lucie Dupin?

2. What does a natural trumpet not have?

3. In which US state is Black Rock Desert?

4. In Greek mythology, of what was Aeolus the god?

5. What was the Gestapo's nickname for WW2 nurse Nancy Wake?

6. What is a razor-fish?

7. What do the letters CH stand for, when appended to a name?

8. Who was the first British-born astronaut to walk in space?

9. Which US presidential home did Eisenhower name after his grandson?

10. In the Old Testament, who caused Samson's hair to be cut off?

11. What is the largest species of antelope?

12. For which film did Dustin Hoffman win his first Best Actor Oscar?

13. What is the female counterpart of the male spirit incubus?

14. Which plants have an organ called a holdfast?

15. Which poet's novel *The Memoirs of a Midget* appeared in 1921?

16. In which country was the explosive Semtex originally manufactured?

17. Of which group of creatures is the porpoise the smallest member?

18. In the New Testament, whom did Jesus raise from the dead?

19. Which organisation's military HQ is at Chievres, Belgium?

20. Which king married Princess Caroline of Brunswick in 1795?

General Knowledge

1. How is a leucocyte more commonly known?

2. What is the name of the Russian space station visited by the shuttle Atlantis?

3. In which city was the first underground train line opened, in 1863?

4. What do the letters UHF stand for?

5. Which *Virginian* star lost his fight against cancer in 1995?

6. What is a jerboa?

7. What nationality was the pioneering sixteenth-century astronomer Tycho Brahe?

8. Which physician coined the word vaccination?

9. Which tribe did Crazy Horse lead?

10. Which aircraft safety device was invented by British engineer James Martin?

11. Which actress's daughter is Isabella Rossellini?

12. What is a conger?

13. In Greek legend, who was Electra's brother?

14. Of which city's council was Derek Hatton deputy leader?

15. Of whom is George Frampton's statue in Kensington Gardens?

16. Gyres are large-scale rotations of what?

17. Of what is the dogfish a species?

18. Which space probe made the first fly-by of Venus?

19. What was Jerome K Jerome's middle name?

20. In which US state were the Mormons founded?

ANSWERS: 1 White blood cell, 2 Mir, 3 London, 4 Ultra high frequency, 5 Doug McClure, 6 Rodent, 7 Danish, 8 Edward Jenner, 9 Sioux or Dakota, 10 Ejector seat, 11 Ingrid Bergman, 12 An eel, 13 Orestes, 14 Liverpool, 15 Peter Pan, 16 Ocean water, 17 Shark, 18 Mariner 2, 19 Klapka, 20 New York.

General Knowledge

1. Who wrote the libretto for Stravinsky's opera *The Rake's Progress*?

2. What type of creature is an argonaut?

3. What may be real, complex or rational?

4. For what is the panther another name?

5. On which river is Indianapolis?

6. In which country is Sucre?

7. What is the name of the sun's faint halo, visible at solar eclipses?

8. In which Irish county are Macgillycuddy's Reeks?

9. What is fescue?

10. Which best-selling thriller writer died in February 1995?

11. What nationality was the composer Heitor Villa-Lobos?

12. The Khyber Pass connects Pakistan and which other country?

13. Which court was abolished by the Long Parliament in 1641?

14. Which *Carry On* star was born James Smith?

15. What parts of speech are 'they' and 'them'?

16. What do we call *Pongo pygmaeus*?

17. Which former sex symbol described Jill Phipps as the 'Joan of Arc of veal'?

18. Of what is the bar a unit?

19. Which Roman slave is associated with a lion?

20. What is the name of the channel separating Tasmania from Australia?

ANSWERS: 1 W H Auden, **2** Octopus, **3** Numbers, **4** Leopard, **5** White River, **6** Bolivia, **7** Corona, **8** County Kerry, **9** A grass, **10** Patricia Highsmith, **11** Brazilian, **12** Afghanistan, **13** The Star Chamber, **14** Jim Dale, **15** Pronouns, **16** Orang-utan, **17** Brigitte Bardot, **18** Pressure, **19** Androcles, **20** Bass Strait.

Sports

1. Which rugby union side are known as 'the Pumas'?
2. To which club did Norwich City sell Ruel Fox?
3. Who won the 1994 NBA finals?
4. Which golfer won the Peugeot Spanish Open for the third time in 1995?
5. Who was the 1964 men's 100m Olympic champion?
6. In 1995, which former England football manager attempted a citizen's arrest after a fan spat at him?
7. Which British heavyweight beat Tommy Morrison in October 1995?
8. Which national football team has been managed by Bryan Hamilton?
9. When did Steve Davis win his first World Championship snooker title?
10. What sport does Gillian Gowers compete at?
11. Which football team play at St. Andrews?
12. In 1995, which Premiership team signed Ruud Gullit?
13. Which two cricket teams competed in the 1994 Benson & Hedges Cup final?
14. Which golfer won the 1995 British Masters title at Colingtree Park?
15. In which city was Monica Seles stabbed in 1993?
16. Who scored five goals for Russia against Cameroon in the World Cup?
17. Which Chicago Bulls basketball player was fined $5,000 for wearing non-conforming shoes?
18. What nationality is tennis player Yayuk Basuki?
19. Which country won the Rugby Union World Cup in 1995?
20. Which second division team defeated Manchester United 3-0 at Old Trafford in 1995?

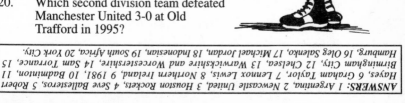

General Knowledge

1. In Greek mythology, who was rejected by Narcissus and pined away, leaving only her voice?

2. Edda is the name given to two collections of early literature from which country?

3. What is a jota?

4. What is the smallest territorial subdivision in Christian church administration?

5. With whom did Lord Alfred Douglas have a scandalous affair?

6. Who invented a typewriter and a rifle that bear his name?

7. Which animal's head did the Egyptian goddess Sekhmet have?

8. On which lake is the port of Milwaukee?

9. What is commemorated in the Jewish festival of Purim?

10. Which band won a record four categories at the 1995 Brit Awards?

11. Which cartoonist and illustrator created the schoolgirls of St. Trinian's?

12. Which king's eldest son was the Black Prince?

13. What is the capital of the Lorraine region?

14. Of which bird is the tragopan a type?

15. Which band's drummer did *Baywatch* star Pamela Anderson marry?

16. What, in economics, may be fixed or circulating?

17. On the southern flank of which mountain is Delphi?

18. Which boxer underwent surgery to remove a blood clot after his fight with Nigel Benn?

19. Of what are bort, balas and carbonado varieties?

20. Where did Billy Butlin open his first camp?

ANSWERS: 1 Echo, 2 Iceland, 3 Spanish dance, 4 Parish, 5 Oscar Wilde, 6 Philo Remington, 7 Lioness, 8 Lake Michigan, 9 Story of Esther, 10 Blur, 11 Ronald Searle, 12 Edward III, 13 Nancy, 14 Pheasant, 15 Motley Crue, 16 Capital, 17 Parnassus, 18 Gerald McClennan, 19 Diamonds, 20 Skegness.

General Knowledge

1. Of which bird is the fantail a type?

2. Which screenwriter won Oscars for *Dr Zhivago* and *Lawrence of Arabia*?

3. What is the chief city of Japan's Kinki region?

4. What was US animator Willis H O'Brien's most famous character?

5. Who walked out of the West End play *Cell Mates* in 1995?

6. By which first name is saxophonist Theodore Walter Rollins better known?

7. Which animal is the source of mohair?

8. Of what nationality was artist René Magritte?

9. What is the capital of the Indian state Maharashtra?

10. In which ocean would one find flying fish?

11. Which organ is attacked by the fluke parasite?

12. In which ocean is the Marianas Trench?

13. How is the spearfish better known?

14. From which plant is the drug mescalin obtained?

15. Who, in the Old Testament, was Ruth's mother-in-law?

16. In which present-day country would Mesopotamia be?

17. Who lost his position as Greek PM due to the 'Koskotas Affair'?

18. Which veteran US actor was born Joe Yule?

19. What is the common name for the pest insect Bemisia tabaci?

20. Where is the pituitary gland located?

ANSWERS: *1 Dove, 2 Robert Bolt, 3 Osaka, 4 King Kong, 5 Stephen Fry, 6 Sonny, 7 Angora goat, 8 Belgian, 9 Bombay, 10 Atlantic, 11 Liver, 12 Pacific, 13 Martin, 14 The mescal or peyote cactus, 15 Naomi, 16 Iraq, 17 Andreas Papandreou, 18 Mickey Rooney, 19 Whitefly, 20 The brain.*

General Knowledge

Your rating: ● 0-5 Join a library   ● 6-10 Keep at it
              ● 11-15 Join a quiz team   ● 16-20 Enter Mastermind

1. What was Louis Blériot the first to fly over in 1909?

2. Who directed the 1979 film *Raging Bull*?

3. Which branch of mathematics is named after the latin for pebble?

4. In which country is town of Rosetta, where the Stone was found?

5. What is the technical name for hives or nettle rash?

6. Which pop star was born Bernard Jewry?

7. Against which country did the UK wage the Opium Wars?

8. Which chart-topper was created by Michael Leggo?

9. Of which US state is Salem the capital?

10. Who was the last king of Rome, 534-510 BC?

11. What is the adopted first name of Mary Elizabeth Spacek?

12. In which US state does the Cajun community live?

13. Who is said to have used the shamrock to illustrate the doctrine of the Holy Trinity?

14. Of which age was the Mesolithic the middle period?

15. What date is Armistice Day?

16. Who became chancellor of West Germany in 1969?

17. What, in the football world, is the fashionable term for an illegal payment?

18. Which Italian poet's surname was Alighieri?

19. Which Royal took part in the 21-mile Desert Challenge Endurance Ride?

20. In architecture, Composite is one of the five types of what?

ANSWERS: *1 English Channel, 2 Martin Scorsese, 3 Calculus, 4 Egypt, 5 Urticaria, 6 Alvin Stardust, 7 China, 8 Mr Blobby, 9 Oregon, 10 Tarquin (Lucius Tarquinius Superbus), 11 Sissy, 12 Louisiana, 13 St Patrick, 14 Stone Age, 15 November 11, 16 Willy Brandt, 17 A bung, 18 Dante, 19 Princess Anne, 20 Column.*

Entertainment

1. Who had a No 1 in 1977 with *So You Win Again*?
2. *Alive* is a film about survivors of a plane crash in which mountain range?
3. Who joined Queen on the No. 1 hit *Somebody To Love* from the EP *Five Live*?
4. Which *EastEnders* character was played by Nicola Stapleton?
5. Which former Monty Python member starred in the 1986 comedy film *Clockwise*?
6. Who duetted with Phil Collins on the 1985 US No. 1 hit single *Separate Lives*?
7. In which fictitious Yorkshire village is the drama series *Heartbeat* set?
8. Which Irish actor co-starred with Andie McDowell in the film *Ruby Cairo*?
9. Which British band had a Top 5 hit with *Regret*?
10. Who has presented *The Vibe* and *Dear Dilemma*?
11. Who played the role of Billy The Kid in the 1988 cowboy film *Young Guns*?
12. Which American band had a US No. 1 hit with *Babe* in 1979?
13. Which actress plays Nora Batty, light of Compo's life, in TV's *Last of the Summer Wine*?
14. Who directed the 1985 film *Brazil*?
15. Which former Led Zeppelin member released a solo single entitled *29 Palms*?
16. Which football team was the subject of the Channel 4 documentary *Yours for a Fiver*?
17. Which actress starred as Olive Oyl in the 1980 film *Popeye*?
18. Which American vocalist had a US No. 1 hit in 1961 with *Runaround Sue*?
19. Which *Sale of the Century* host played the role of Reverend Green in the TV series *Cluedo*?
20. Who wrote the epic novel from which the classic 1939 film *Gone With The Wind* was adapted?

LONDON BOROUGH OF WALFORD

ALBERT SQUARE

General Knowledge

1. What is the capital of Australia's Northern Territory?

2. Which common Latin phrase means 'and the rest'?

3. What was the name of the first space station?

4. What are pewter's two main constituents?

5. Who was the mother of Napoleon II?

6. Of what is a cantaloupe a variety?

7. To what did Joseph Vissarionovich Djugashvili change his name?

8. Which silent film actress was born Gladys Smith?

9. In which modern-day country is the site of the Sumerian civilisation?

10. Which mythical creature is half-lion, half-eagle?

11. Which church was founded by John Knox?

12. Which Natural History Museum exhibit is the largest animal the world has ever known?

13. Which darts player is nicknamed 'the Crafty Cockney'?

14. What type of tree is the pecan?

15. In which ocean are the Cape Verde group of islands?

16. Of which animal are Berkshire and Tamworth varieties?

17. Which equestrian centre was built at the Sussex home of Douglas Bunn?

18. Who wrote the play *Quality Street*?

19. Which school did Prince William start at in September 1995?

20. The pineal gland is an outgrowth of which organ?

ANSWERS: 1 *Darwin*, 2 *Et cetera*, 3 *Salyut 1*, 4 *Tin and lead*, 5 *Marie Louise*, 6 *Melon*, 7 *Joseph Stalin*, 8 *Mary Pickford*, 9 *Iraq*, 10 *Griffin*, 11 *Church of Scotland*, 12 *Blue Whale*, 13 *Eric Bristow*, 14 *Hickory*, 15 *Atlantic*, 16 *Pig*, 17 *Hickstead*, 18 *J M Barrie*, 19 *Eton*, 20 *The brain*.

General Knowledge

1. What is the commonest volcanic igneous rock?

2. Who directed *The Great Gatsby* and *Room at the Top*?

3. Which city's baseball players are the Dodgers?

4. To which family of birds does the jackdaw belong?

5. What does *pro tem* mean?

6. Which US president gave amnesty to those who had resisted the draft for the Vietnam War?

7. Which unit of measurement is derived from the Arabic 'quirrat', meaning seed?

8. In which field did ex-Barings employee Nick Leeson deal?

9. In which sport was Heather McKay British Open champion for 16 successive years?

10. Which official represents the crown in matrimonial, probate and admiralty cases?

11. Who composed the oratorio *The Beatitudes*?

12. An excess of crystals of which acid in the tissues causes gout?

13. What is a matamata?

14. Which West German chancellor was called the 'Old Fox'?

15. What is Britain's busiest container port?

16. What type of animal is a Tasmanian tiger?

17. Whose last two drama series are *Karaoke* and *Cold Lazarus*?

18. Of which metal is limonite an ore?

19. The word 'gypsy' is a corruption of which other word?

20. Which veteran singer's *Unplugged* album won him a Grammy in 1995?

ANSWERS: *1 Basalt, 2 Jack Clayton, 3 Los Angeles, 4 Crow, 5 For the time being, 6 Gerald Ford, 7 Carat, 8 Derivatives, 9 Squash, 10 The Queen's Proctor, 11 César Franck, 12 Uric acid, 13 S American turtle or terrapin, 14 Konrad Adenauer, 15 Felixstowe, 17 A marsupial, 17 Dennis Potter, 18 Iron, 19 Egyptian, 20 Tony Bennett.*

General Knowledge

1. Which sailing vessel is named after the Tamil for 'tied log'?

2. Which part of the body is affected by amoebiasis?

3. Which recent Chancellor of the Exchequer is a Shetlander?

4. Of which county is the spa town Matlock the administrative centre?

5. Who won an Oscar for directing *The Treasure of the Sierra Madre*?

6. Of what is quartz a crystalline form?

7. What was the name of the ferry in the Zeebrugge disaster of 1987?

8. What replaced Dawson as capital of Canada's Yukon Territory in 1953?

9. Which island is separated from the mainland by the Palk Strait?

10. What type of drug is scopolamine, or hyoscine?

11. Which discredited US politician gave his name to the practice of making unsupported accusations?

12. Which language was devised in 1887 by Dr Ludwig L Zamenhof?

13. Which German school of architecture was founded by Walter Gropius?

14. Which insect has common, American and German varieties?

15. Which Dutch banking group paid £1 for Barings bank?

16. Which oceans are connected by the Strait of Magellan?

17. What is a ginkgo?

18. Which empire succeeded the Seljuk Empire?

19. Which bird is nicknamed the 'butcher-bird'?

20. Believers in voodoo retain membership of which church?

Entertainment

1:   Who has presented *Game for a Laugh* and *You've Been Framed*?
2.   Which actress played the role of disenchanted Helen Odom in the film *Rich in Love*?
3.   Which Swedish group had a hit with their single entitled *All That She Wants*?
4.   Which *Soldier, Soldier* recruit is played by Shaun Dingwall?
5.   Which veteran 'tough guy' actor won an Oscar for his role in the 1965 spoof Western *Cat Ballou*?
6.   Which country star released the album *Something Special*?
7.   Who played Charlene Robinson in *Neighbours*?
8.   Which Rome landmark links three romances together in the 1954 film *Three Coins in the Fountain*?
9.   Who is the lead singer of Scottish band *Simple Minds*?
10. Which actress plays the role of Raquel Wolstenhulme in *Coronation Street*?
11. Who made his starring debut in the title role of the 1939 film *The Invisible Man*?
12. Which American vocal duo had a No 1 hit in 1965 with *You've Lost That Loving Feeling*?
13. Who played Nina in *Truly Madly Deeply*?
14. Who played the title role in the 1944 Oscar-winning Jerome Kern/Ira Gershwin musical *Cover Girl*?
15. Which singer featured with Shabba Ranks on his remixed single *Housecall*?
16. Which actress played the role of Dr Kate Rowan in the TV drama series *Heartbeat*?
17. Which *Ghostbusters* star played weatherman Phil Connors in the film *Groundhog Day*?
18. Which former member of *Lovin' Spoonful* had a US No 1 hit in 1976 with *Welcome Back*?
19. Who provided the voice for the baby in *How to Be a Little S*d*?
20. Which half of a famous comedy duo played a harassed writer in the TV series *Colin's Sandwich*?

General Knowledge

1. What may be glacial, barrier, crater or tectonic?

2. On the outskirts of which city is the Defence Procurement HQ, the largest office block in Western Europe?

3. The Old Court House in Richmond-upon-Thames was which architect's last home?

4. By what name is the dunnock more commonly known?

5. Who is the only man to have been head of both MI5 and MI6?

6. Which branch of philosophy is concerned with human values?

7. Which obsolete title of the Japanese emperor meant 'honourable palace gate'?

8. Is colour blindness more common in men or women?

9. Which island's capital is Port Louis?

10. Whose story *Heart of Darkness* was published in 1902?

11. What produces sound in an aeolian harp?

12. What is the Sea of Galilee also called?

13. Whom did the Greeks defeat in the Battle of Salamis of 480 BC?

14. In which constellation is Aldebaran the brightest star?

15. With whom did William Powell co-star in the *Thin Man* films?

16. Which city was probably named after Jan Meyer, its first mining commissioner?

17. Whose poetry included the sonnet '*No man is an island*'?

18. What is a pipit?

19. Who was US president during WWI?

20. Who was lead singer with Big Brother and the Holding Company?

ANSWERS: *1 Lakes, 2 Bristol, 3 Sir Christopher Wren, 4 Hedge sparrow, 5 Sir Dick White, 6 Ethics, 7 Mikado, 8 Men, 9 Mauritius, 10 Joseph Conrad, 11 Wind, 12 Lake Tiberias, 13 The Persians, 14 Taurus, 15 Myrna Loy, 16 Johannesburg, 17 John Donne, 18 A bird, 19 Woodrow Wilson, 20 Janis Joplin.*

General Knowledge

1. Okra is the edible fruit of which plant?

2. Which European country's first king was St Stephen?

3. Of what is the bonito a small species?

4. What is a boobook?

5. What does the acronym NAAFI stand for?

6. What is the most southerly point of England called?

7. Who designed London's National Westminster Tower?

8. Which war poet wrote the autobiography *Memoirs of a Foxhunting Man*?

9. In which US state is the winter resort Palm Beach?

10. With which sport is the National Homing Union concerned?

11. What is the translation of the Latin phrase 'tempus fugit'?

12. Which literary layout was designed in 1873 by Christopher Sholes?

13. In which country is the autonomous region Navarre?

14. Of which fruit is the cayenne a smoother-skinned variety?

15. What is made more regular by defibrillation?

16. In which ocean is the Sargasso Sea?

17. To what is the formula translation computer-programming language abbreviated?

18. In the stock market, what is the opposite of a bull?

19. Which Greek dramatist wrote over 80 plays, including *Andromache*?

20. To which city does the former village Donnybrook now belong?

ANSWERS: 1 Hibiscus, **2** Hungary, **3** Tuna, **4** An owl, **5** Navy, Army and Air Force Institutes, **6** Lizard Point, **7** Richard Seifert, **8** Siegfried Sassoon, **9** Florida, **10** Pigeon racing, **11** Time flies, **12** Qwerty keyboard, **13** Spain, **14** Pineapple, **15** Heartbeat, **16** Atlantic, **17** Fortran, **18** A bear, **19** Euripides, **20** Dublin.

General Knowledge

1. What type of drug is usually used to relieve allergies?

2. Where was Orlando Gibbons appointed organist in 1623?

3. In cricket, what do the letters lbw stand for?

4. What is affected by the disease chorea?

5. With which author is the illustrator John Tenniel usually associated?

6. Of which metal is cinnabar the only important ore?

7. What were the targets of the Combination Laws of 1799 and 1800?

8. In geology, for what is the darcy a unit?

9. What replaced estate duty in 1974, to be replaced in turn by inheritance tax in 1986?

10. The sloe is the fruit of which plant?

11. Which US separatist movement was founded in 1966 by Huey Newton and Bobby Seale?

12. In which year did London last stage the Olympics?

13. To which family of birds does the African oxpecker belong?

14. To which Judy Garland musical has Sir Andrew Lloyd Webber bought the rights?

15. According to legend, who was the brother of Morgan le Fay?

16. What nationality, originally, were the Komi people?

17 Which diamond is named after the Persian for 'mountain of light'?

18. Whom did Ron Atkinson replace at Coventry City?

19. Which Welsh county contains the Brecon Beacons National Park?

20. Which king married Princess Charlotte Sophia of Mecklenburg-Strelitz?

ANSWERS: 1 Antihistamine, 2 Westminster Abbey, 3 Leg before wicket, 4 Nervous system, 5 Lewis Carroll, 6 Mercury, 7 Trade unions, 8 Permeability, 9 Capital transfer tax, 10 Blackthorn, 11 Black Panther Party, 12 1948, 13 Starlings, 14 A Star is Born, 15 King Arthur, 16 Finnish, 17 Koh-I-noor, 18 Phil Neal, 19 Powys, 20 George III.

Entertainment

1. Which town was home to *The Flintstones*?
2. Which star of TV's *Cheers* co-starred with Demi Moore in the film *Indecent Proposal*?
3. Which presenter of *The Clothes Show* was married to Sandie Shaw?
4. Which star of *2point4 Children* played Agatha Troy in *The Inspector Alleyn Mysteries*?
5. Which cockney actor played video game hero Mario in the film *Super Mario Bros*?
6. Which singer had a UK No 1 hit with *I Feel Love* in 1977?
7. Which member of the legal profession was the creator of crotchety TV barrister *Rumpole of the Bailey*?
8. Which star of TV's *Cagney and Lacey* played Clint Eastwood's partner in the 1976 film *The Enforcer*?
9. Which group had a Top 10 hit with a single entitled *Believe in Me*?
10. Which former 'Goon' narrated the children's TV programme *Wolves, Witches and Giants*?
11. Who played the attorney helping Jodie Foster to seek justice in the 1988 film *The Accused*?
12. Who was the lead singer of *The Animals*?
13. Which English county is the setting for the TV drama series *Peak Practice*?
14. Which US actress co-starred with Bill Murray in *Groundhog Day*?
15. Which American teenager had a No 1 hit with *I Think We're Alone Now*?
16. Which former Labour Deputy Leader offered personal views on the party in the TV series *Fight Again*?
17. Which 1972 film was about a fishing party attacked by psychopathic hillbillies?
18. Which female vocalist released a single entitled *I Don't Wanna Fight*?
19. Which former RAF pilot wrote the book from which the 1954 film *The Dam Busters* was adapted?
20. Which daughter of a famous TV quizmaster has presented *Songs of Praise*?

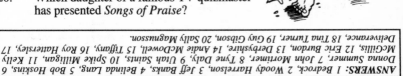

ANSWERS: *1 Bedrock, 2 Woody Harrelson, 3 Jeff Banks, 4 Belinda Lang, 5 Bob Hoskins, 6 Donna Summer, 7 John Mortimer, 8 Tyne Daly, 9 Utah Saints, 10 Spike Milligan, 11 Kelly McGillis, 12 Eric Burdon, 13 Derbyshire, 14 Andie McDowell, 15 Tiffany, 16 Roy Hattersley, 17 Deliverance, 18 Tina Turner, 19 Guy Gibson, 20 Sally Magnusson.*

General Knowledge

1. Which port is France's chief Mediterranean naval station?

2. Which TV presenter's first job was as Noel Edmonds's chauffeur?

3. Which study of selective breeding is named after the Greek for 'well-born'?

4. What colour flowers does the shrubby herb rue produce?

5. For which shrub is furze another name?

6. What is soca?

7. Of which material is viscose the most common type?

8. Which film star was born Lucille Le Sueur?

9. What is a hoatzin?

10. Who was the wealthy last king of Lydia?

11. What do the two carotid arteries supply with blood?

12. What does Japanese religious cult Aum Shinrikyo's name mean?

13. Which English king was nicknamed 'the Unready'?

14. Which element accounts for about 78 per cent of our atmosphere?

15. What is a samoyed?

16. What is the trade name of the heat-resistant plastic PTFE?

17. In which year was the Cuban Missile Crisis?

18. Which radio and TV star lost his fight against Aids in April 1995?

19. What is America's highest peacetime civilian honour?

20. To which city did the PLO move its HQ in 1982?

ANSWERS: 1 Toulon, 2 Mike Smith, 3 Eugenics, 4 Yellow, 5 Gorse, 6 Latin Caribbean music, 7 Rayon, 8 Joan Crawford, 9 A tropical bird, 10 Croesus, 11 The head and neck, 12 Sublime Truth, 13 Ethelred II, 14 Nitrogen, 15 Breed of dog, 16 Teflon, 17 1962, 18 Kenny Everett, 19 Presidential Medal of Freedom, 20 Tunis.

General Knowledge

1. Which Labour baroness was responsible for founding the Open University?

2. Which unexplained phenomenon is named after the German for 'noisy ghost'?

3. Which public school was founded by Kurt Halin in 1935?

4. What was 'Capability' Brown's actual first name?

5. Which March 1995 agreement saw the dismantling of borders between seven European countries?

6. What are Macgillycuddy's Reeks?

7. In which state is Mount McKinley, North America's highest peak?

8. What type of creature is a dasyure?

9. With which subject is author Elizabeth David associated?

10. Of which Dutch province is Leeuwarden the capital?

11. How are singing trio Joy, Teddie and Babs better known?

12. Which occupation did Geronimo take up in his last years?

13. What is esparto?

14. In which year was the European Satellite Ariane launched?

15. Who is the patron saint of Cornwall and its nationalist movement?

16. Which planet's largest moon is Triton?

17. Who published his Stenographic Soundhand system in 1837?

18. Who wrote the tone poem *An American in Paris*?

19. Which unit is equal to the mass in grams of 9,000 metres of yarn?

20. On whose play was Debussy's opera *Pelléas et Mélisande* based?

General Knowledge

1. In which year was the North Atlantic Treaty first signed?

2. Which disorder, known as the 'royal disease', has been suggested as the basis of vampire legends?

3. By what name, after a Surrey town, do we know hydrated magnesium sulphate?

4. After which canton is Switzerland named?

5. The flour of which grain is used to make black bread?

6. Of which African country is Libreville the capital?

7. Of which country is Steep Point the most westerly extremity?

8. What do the initials of the meat substitute TVP stand for?

9. What do we call the Eurasian mammal *Meles meles*?

10. In which county is Ilfracombe?

11. Against whom did Britain wage the War of 1812?

12. Of which flower is polyanthus a garden variety?

13. The entrance to which sea is guarded by rocks called the Pillars of Hercules?

14. Which sport do the Edmonton Oilers play?

15. Who was the first footballer to be knighted?

16. Whose fourth husband was Lord Seymour of Sudeley?

17. The Ainu are an aboriginal people of which country?

18. After which Austrian novelist is masochism named?

19. Where was the first battle of the English Wars of the Roses fought?

20. What does the Latin phrase *bona fide* mean?

ANSWERS: 1 1949, 2 Porphyria, 3 Epsom salts, 4 Schwyz, 5 Rye, 6 Gabon, 7 Australia, 8 Textured vegetable protein, 9 Badger, 10 Devon, 11 USA, 12 Primrose, 13 Mediterranean, 14 Ice hockey, 15 Stanley Matthews, 16 Catherine Parr, 17 Japan, 18 Leopold von Sacher-Masoch, 19 St Albans, 20 In good faith.

Entertainment

Your rating: ● 0-5   Buy a TV   ● 6-10   Keep at it
● 11-15 Join a quiz team   ● 16-20 Enter Telly Addicts

1. Which star of *The Manageress* played Helen West in the TV thriller *A Question of Guilt*?
2. Which star of TV's *Star Trek* appeared in the spoof film *Loaded Weapon 1*?
3. Which Birmingham reggae band had a hit with *(I Can't Help) Falling In Love With You*?
4. Which actor played US Marshal Matt Dillon in the classic TV cowboy series *Gunsmoke*?
5. Who co-starred with Jean-Claude Van Damme in the film *Nowhere To Run*?
6. Which British group had a hit with the single *All Right Now*?
7. Which star of *Fawlty Towers* played Nat Silver in the TV comedy series *Every Silver Lining*?
8. Which star of *A Fish Called Wanda* co-starred with Mel Gibson in the 1992 film *Forever Young*?
9. Which ex-Soft Cell member joined Bronski Beat on their 1985 hit single *I Feel Love*?
10. Who played the eponymous hero of *Wayne's World*?
11. Which regular of many Woody Allen films starred in the 1987 comedy film *Baby Boom*?
12. Which vocalist had a No 1 hit in 1960 with *Three Steps To Heaven*?
13. Which former star of *Bergerac* played the role of Janet in *Rides*?
14. Which film starring Wesley Snipes is set aboard a hijacked aeroplane?
15. Which soul diva had a hit with a single entitled *Express*?
16. Which comedy duo presented the TV game show *Shooting Stars*?
17. Who played the NY cop assigned to guard Mimi Rogers in the 1987 film *Someone To Watch Over Me*?
18. Which American band had a hit with their single *In These Arms*?
19. Who played the monster in the 1931 film of Mary Shelley's classic horror story *Frankenstein*?
20. In which Australian city was the TV documentary series *Sylvania Waters* filmed?

ANSWERS: 1 *Cherie Lunghi*, 2 *William Shatner*, 3 *UB40*, 4 *James Arness*, 5 *Rosanna Arquette*, 6 *Free*, 7 *Andrew Sachs*, 8 *Jamie Lee Curtis*, 9 *Marc Almond*, 10 *Mike Myers*, 11 *Diane Keaton*, 12 *Eddie Cochran*, 13 *Louise Jameson*, 14 *Passenger 57*, 15 *Dina Carroll*, 16 *Vic Reeves and Bob Mortimer*, 17 *Tom Berenger*, 18 *Bon Jovi*, 19 *Boris Karloff*, 20 *Sydney*.

General Knowledge

1. How many archbishops does the Church of England have?
2. What do the initials GATT stand for?
3. For which film did Burl Ives win a Best Supporting Actor Oscar?
4. In which sea is the Dogger Bank?
5. Which New Testament figure supposedly built Britain's first Christian church at Glastonbury?
6. Of which union is Doug McAvoy leader?
7. Of which drug is crack a derivative?
8. What is a lory?
9. Bets on whose match with Jimmy White were suspended after match-fixing claims?
10. Which French fortification system was built 1929-36 and outflanked by the Germans in 1940?
11. Which French sports stadium is home to the national rugby union team?
12. What type of plantlife is smut?
13. In botany, to which family of plants do the two rape species belong?
14. What do the initials RPI stand for?
15. Which 54-year-old singer released his first album for 20 years in 1995?
16. In which country is the port of Helsinger?
17. Who wrote the piano piece *Pavane pour une infante défunte* in 1899?
18. Which engineer and inventor designed the Clifton Suspension Bridge?
19. What was the first artificial satellite?
20. In which US city are the remains of the Alfred Murrah Federal Block?

ANSWERS: *1 Two, 2 General Agreement on Tariffs and Trade, 3 The Big Country, 4 North Sea, 5 St Joseph of Arimathaea, 6 NUT, 7 Cocaine, 8 An Australasian parrot, 9 Peter Francisco, 10 Maginot Line, 11 Parc des Princes, 12 Parasitic fungus, 13 Mustard, 14 Retail Price Index, 15 Gene Pitney, 16 Denmark, 17 Maurice Ravel, 18 Isambard Kingdom Brunel, 19 Sputnik 1, 20 Oklahoma City.*

General Knowledge

1. What is the more common name for the blister beetle?

2. To which family of fish does the pollack belong?

3. Which sport contests the Melbourne Cup?

4. Which character did Jacques Tati play in several of his films?

5. Which denomination bank note did the Bank of England introduce in 1752 and withdraw in 1945?

6. What carries along and deposits the rocky debris moraine?

7. Of which secret police was the OGPU a former name?

8. Which island had the catamaran Saint-Malo just left when it hit a submerged rock in 1995?

9. What is the name for the classification of living organisms?

10. Who wrote *The History of the Decline and Fall of the Roman Empire*?

11. Which of Marlon Brando's nine children committed suicide in April 1995?

12. At the mouth of which river is the Nore sand bank?

13. To which instrument is the basset horn most closely related?

14. Which Canadian city was founded by French explorer Samuel de Champlain?

15. Which character actor started in music hall as the Prince of the Wideboys?

16. What is the meaning of 'non sequitur'?

17. Which rugby league team's players are known as the Cougars?

18. Of which mineral is amethyst a variety?

19. Which king's wife was Phillipa of Hainault?

20. In which county is Wookey Hole?

ANSWERS: *1 Spanish fly, 2 Cod, 3 Horse Racing, 4 Monsieur Hulot, 5 £1000, 6 A glacier, 7 KGB, 8 Jersey, 9 Taxonomy, 10 Edward Gibbon, 11 Cheyenne, 12 Thames, 13 Clarinet, 14 Quebec, 15 Arthur English, 16 It does not follow, 17 Keighley, 18 Quartz, 19 Edward III, 20 Somerset.*

General Knowledge

1. Which music hall queen was known as the last of the Red Hot Mommas?

2. Of which organ is hepatic the related adjective?

3. What is a gaur?

4. Which US state is nicknamed the Pelican State?

5. Who moved from the CBI to take over as deputy governor of the Bank of England?

6. Which study is named from the Greek for 'house'?

7. What is the English equivalent of the Scottish provost?

8. Which book did Hitler write in prison?

9. What is a wheatear?

10. What is the young of the herring called?

11. Of which team is Barry Fry manager?

12. What is an erythrocyte more commonly called?

13. Who wrote *Uncle Tom's Cabin*?

14. With which geometric shape is Pythagoras's theorem concerned?

15. Which country was divided by the 38th parallel in 1945?

16. Which race carried out the Sack of Rome in AD 410?

17. Which dance legend died in April 1995?

18 Which vegetable may be globe or Jerusalem?

19. Of which European country is Wim Kok premier?

20. A caryatid is a pillar in the shape of what?

ANSWERS: 1 Tessie O'Shea, 2 Liver, 3 Asiatic wild ox, 4 Louisiana, 5 Howard Davies, 6 Ecology, 7 Mayor, 8 Mein Kampf, 9 Small migratory bird, 10 Whitebait, 11 Birmingham City, 12 Red blood cell, 13 Harriet Beecher Stowe, 14 Triangle, 15 Korea, 16 The Goths, 17 Ginger Rogers, 18 Artichoke, 19 Netherlands, 20 A woman.

Entertainment

1. *As It Happens* is the autobiography of which TV presenter and fitness fanatic?
2. Which magical nanny was played by Julie Andrews?
3. Which group had a No. 1 hit in 1985 with *Shout*?
4. Which drama series was based around a haulage company called Hammonds?
5. Which British actor starred as a Cabinet Minister in the film *Damage*?
6. Which female vocalist had a Top 5 hit with *When I'm Good And Ready*?
7. What is the numeric title of the TV series featuring real-life emergencies?
8. Who starred with Ellen Barkin in the 1987 film *The Big Easy*?
9. Which amphibian-sounding group had a US No.1 in 1967 with *Happy Together*?
10. Which actress links *Maigret* and *The Beiderbecke Affair*?
11. Which famous French singer starred in the 1958 Oscar-winning musical *Gigi*?
12. Which Top 20 hit for Arrested Development was named after an American state?
13. Which female pop star appeared in the comedy baseball movie *A League of Their Own*?
14. Which actress played con man evangelist Steve Martin's sidekick in the film *Leap of Faith*?
15. Which star of *Coronation Street* had a Top 20 hit with *One Voice*?
16. Who had a Top Ten Hit in 1980 with *My Perfect Cousin*?
17. Which English actress won an Oscar for her performance in *Howard's End*?
18. Who duetted with Barbra Streisand on *You Don't Bring Me Flowers* in 1978?
19. Which metropolis were Dorothy and her friends trying to reach in *The Wizard of Oz*?
20. Which star of *Mapp and Lucia* played Miss Farnaby in *Mulberry*?

General Knowledge

1. As what creature is the southern constellation Dorado represented?

2. What is the personal expenditure of the British monarch called?

3. In which state of the USA is Fort Knox?

4. Which team did Jurgen Klinsmann join from Tottenham Hotspur?

5. Whose first novel was *Where Angels Fear to Tread*?

6. Which composer had a theatre built at Bayreuth?

7. What is the smallest US state?

8. What is the smallest British bird?

9. Who made a maximum break in the 1995 World Snooker Championship?

10. Of which gas is marsh gas a form?

11. Which English town was the first place chosen for development as a 'new town'?

12. Which vegetable has the Agriculture Ministry warned should be peeled if eaten raw?

13. In which US state is the active volcano Mount Redoubt?

14. What was the name given to the leaders of the faction that tried to seize power in China after Mao's death?

15. Of which other warm ocean current is the North Atlantic Drift a continuation?

16. What does the acronym SALT stand for?

17. Which city is home to the Metropolitan Opera Company?

18. Of which fish is the shanny the most common British species?

19. What is a cithara?

20. In philosophy, what is the name of the concept that the whole is greater than the sum of its parts?

General Knowledge

1. Which team's only FA Cup win was in 1988?

2. Which bird is often called the hedge sparrow?

3. In which field do the French award the Prix Goncourt?

4. Which feature of prison life has returned to America after a 50-year absence?

5. Who wrote *Auld Lang Syne*?

6. In which war did the Tet Offensive take place?

7. Which part of speech may be transitive or intransitive?

8. Which Texan city is named after the general who won Texas' independence from Mexico?

9. Which herbaceous plant is more commonly called monkshood?

10. On which river is Balmoral Castle?

11. Who is France's president?

12. For which type of stitch is petit point another name?

13. What do the letters IQ stand for?

14. What type of bird is the yaffle?

15. Of which island is Snaefell the highest mountain?

16. Which pop group was founded by Brian Wilson?

17. Which acid is also called oil of vitriol?

18. Which new 'classless' honour was Corporal Wayne Mills the first to receive?

19. Of which game bird are the grey and French varieties the most common in the UK?

20. What was James Dean's last film?

ANSWERS: *1 Wimbledon, 2 Dunnock, 3 Literature, 4 The chain gang, 5 Robert Burns, 6 Vietnam War, 7 Verb, 8 Houston, 9 Aconite, 10 Dee, 11 Jacques Chirac, 12 Tent stitch, 13 Intelligence quotient, 14 Woodpecker, 15 Isle of Man, 16 The Beach Boys, 17 Sulphuric acid, 18 Conspicuous Gallantry Cross, 19 Partridge, 20 Giant.*

General Knowledge

1. In which county is Charnwood Forest?

2. In computing, what does CPU stand for?

3. What is a monotreme?

4. Who wrote *The Use of Lateral Thinking* in 1967?

5. Who beat Arsenal to win the 1995 European Cup-winner's Cup?

6. Which genre was established by Horace Walpole's *The Castle of Otranto*?

7. To which film is *Fierce Creatures* the sequel?

8. What is the plant *Rhus radicans* more commonly called?

9. Which senior ecclesiastical post did the Most Rev Derek Worlock hold?

10. Which is larger, a crayfish or a lobster?

11. Which Romanian gymnast won three gold medals at the 1976 Olympics?

12. Which deadly virus caused the city of Kikwit to be declared a disaster zone?

13. Which famous Gibson guitar was named after the adopted name of Lester Polfuss?

14. On which unit is the avoirdupois system of weights based?

15. What was Oswald Mosley's BUF?

16. How many pedals does a harp have?

17. Who directed *Bullets over Broadway*?

18. Which branch of philosophy studies valid reasoning and argument?

19. To which family of animals does the skunk belong?

20. Which cricketer married Sir James Goldsmith's daughter Jemima?

Entertainment

1. Which British actress played the title role in the movie *Carrington*?
2. Which singer had hits in the 1980's with *Young Turks* and *Baby Jane*?
3. Which star of the film *10* was featured in the classical music programme *Orchestra*?
4. Which rapper covered Third World's *Now That We've Found Love*?
5. Who presented *Notes And Queries*?
6. Which *London's Burning* star featured in the movie *Cliffhanger*?
7. Who ex-*Blue Peter* man presented the canine challenge *Superdogs*?
8. Who was The Smith's lead singer?
9. Which *Rain Man* star appeared in *Marathon Man*?
10. Which character does Derek Thomson play in *Casualty*?
11. Which TV personality has presented *Crackerjack* and *The Price Is Right*?
12. Which husband-and-wife team starred in *Born Yesterday*?
13. Which band had a chart hit with *You're In A Bad Way*?
14. Who starred as *Lawrence Of Arabia* in 1962?
15. Which medical comedy featured Duncan Preston as Dr Jonathan Haslam?
16. Who was The Police's drummer?
17. Which *Omen* star featured in Spielberg's *Jurassic Park*?
18. Which *EastEnders* character, played by Sian Martin, was married to Phil before Cathy?
19. Which actor was *Falling Down* after *Romancing The Stone*?
20. Which British singer returned to the limelight with *If I Can't Have You*?

General Knowledge

1. In mathematics, what may be arithmetic, geometric or weighted?
2. Which British writer's novels include *The Millstone* and *The Radiant Way*?
3. Which musical term, from the Italian for 'robbed', refers to a loose treatment of tempo?
4. In polyandry, of what does a woman have more than one at the same time?
5. Whose album was *Made In England*?
6. What is seismology the study of?
7. Which disease used to be known as infantile paralysis?
8. Which country uncharacteristically won the 1995 Eurovision Song Contest?
9. Which fictional William Combe cleric was first seen *In Search of the Picturesque* in 1809?
10. In which city did New York-born Al Capone establish his criminal organisation?
11. In the French Revolution, who were the tricoteuses?
12. Which football team were 1995 Premiership champions?
13. How many fluid ounces are there in a pint?
14. Which seaside resort had Britain's first no-smoking beaches?
15. Which French philosopher's materialism is most articulately expressed in *D'Alembert's Dream*?
16. Which Scottish village was 'virtually bought' by disgraced Scotland Yard financier Anthony Williams?
17. What sort of street means 'bottom of the bag' in French?
18. Which sport is played by the Detroit Red Wings and the New England Whalers?
19. What do we call the largest and most luminous type of star known?
20. Who wrote the opera *The Love of Three Oranges* in 1921?

ANSWERS: 1 *The mean*, 2 *Margaret Drabble*, 3 *Rubato*, 4 *Husband*, 5 *Earthquakes*, 7 *Polio*, 8 *Norway*, 9 *Doctor Syntax*, 10 *Chicago*, 11 *Women knitting by the guillotine*, 12 *Blackburn Rovers*, 13 *20*, 14 *Bournemouth*, 15 *Diderot*, 16 *Tomintoul*, 17 *Cul-de-sac*, 18 *Ice-hockey*, 19 *Supergiant*, 20 *Prokofiev*.

General Knowledge

1. Of what is the torr a unit of measurement?

2. In which country was the 1995 Rugby World Cup contested?

3. What may be civil, limited or total?

4. Which Russian spacecraft were named after their word for 'east'?

5. What record number of points did civil servant Kevin Ashman score on Mastermind?

6. What is the waratah, the symbol of New South Wales?

7. Which former Israeli PM was born in Kiev?

8. What are Lloyd's of London's syndicate members more commonly called?

9. What type of creature is a tope?

10. In medicine what do we call treatment given to relieve symptoms rather than cure the underlying cause?

11. Which film company was founded in 1912 as the Famous Players Film Company?

12. Which country has had five kings called Olaf?

13. Which Italian painter's real name was Jacopo Robusti?

14. What type of creature is a vole?

15. Which US president introduced the New Deal to counter the depression of 1929?

16. What is a margay?

17. Which unit of distance represents roughly 5.87 million million miles?

18. Which English king's queen was Margaret of Anjou?

19. What is the oldest city in the Netherlands?

20. Which ultimately fatal disease prompted Harold Wilson to quit as PM in 1976?

ANSWERS: *1 Pressure, 2 South Africa, 3 War, 4 Vostok, 5 41, 6 Shrub or tree, 7 Golda Meir, 8 Names, 9 A shark, 10 Palliative, 11 Paramount studios, 12 Norway, 13 Tintoretto, 14 Rodent, 15 F D Roosevelt, 16 A small wild cat, 17 Light year, 18 Henry VI, 19 Maastricht, 20 Alzheimer's.*

General Knowledge

1. On which king was the title Defender of the Faith conferred by Pope Leo X?

2. What was Johnny Morris's long-running TV show called?

3. Which acid has the formula HNO3?

4. What is hyssop?

5. Which FA Cup-winning footballer received a 3-month jail sentence for head-butting?

6. Which city is built on the site of the Aztec capital Tenochtitlan?

7. Which actor was artistic director of the Royal Court Theatre 1972-5?

8. What does a public bill become, on being passed?

9. In Arab countries, what is a fellah?

10. What is a Dandie Dinmont?

11. Who was sacked from *Tomorrow's World* in a row over advertising?

12. What nationality is cube-maker Erno Rubik?

13. Which seafood is named from the Italian for 'shrimps'?

14. Who directed the film *Ed Wood*?

15. Where would one find a coleoptile?

16. Where was Robert the Bruce crowned in 1306?

17. Which post has Judge Stephen Tumim left after eight years?

18. In which continent do common swallows spend the winter?

19. Which king's daughter was the first to bear the title princess royal?

20. In which country is Rogers Pass?

ANSWERS: 1 Henry *VIII*, **2** Animal Magic, **3** Nitric acid, **4** A herb, **5** Duncan Ferguson, **6** Mexico City, **7** Albert Finney, **8** An act of Parliament, **9** A peasant farmer, **10** A breed of terrier, **11** Carol Vorderman, **12** Hungarian, **13** Scampi, **14** Tim Burton, **15** On a blade of grass, **16** Scone, **17** Chief Inspector of Prisons, **18** Africa, **19** Charles I, **20** Canada.

Sports

1. In 1995, who did Alan Sugar agree to allow into White Hart Lane after a two-year ban?
2. Who lost the 1994 Australian Open men's Singles tennis final?
3. At which sport do the Nottingham Panthers compete?
4. Which Italian football team paid Paris St-Germain £4.5m for George Weah?
5. Which West Indies cricketer scored 147 on his county debut for Warwickshire?
6. What nationality is tennis player Patrick Rafter?
7. How often is the Ryder Cup held?
8. What is a mawashi?
9. Which Manchester United player was sent off in the 1995 F.A. Cup semi-final against Crystal Palace?
10. In which year did Tracy Austin last play at Wimbledon?
11. Who scored twice for Milan in the 1994 European Cup Final?
12. Which tennis star co-authored a novel called *The Total Zone* in 1995?
13. Who rode Flakey Dove for his 1,000th winner in Britain?
14. In the 1995-96 season, which Ukrainian football team was expelled from the Champions League?
15. Which British boxer is nicknamed the *Dark Destroyer*?
16. In which country was England rugby forward Steve Ojomoh born?
17. At which equestrian event is George Bowman a specialist?
18. Who is the famous father of Indy 500 driver Jacques Villeneuve?
19. Who is the manager of Wimbledon FC?
20. Who beat Pete Sampras in the 1994 French Open tennis championship?

ANSWERS: 1 *Terry Venables,* **2** *Todd Martin,* **3** *Ice hockey,* **4** *AC Milan,* **5** *Brian Lara,* **6** *Australian.* **7** *Every two years,* **8** *A sumo wrestler's fighting belt,* **9** *Roy Keane,* **10** *1982,* **11** *Daniele Massaro,* **12** *Martina Navratilova,* **13** *Richard Dunwoody,* **14** *Dynamo Kiev,* **15** *Nigel Benn,* **16** *Nigeria,* **17** *Carriage-driving,* **18** *Gilles Villeneuve,* **19** *Joe Kinnear,* **20** *Jim Courier.*

General Knowledge

1. What is a korrigum?

2. Which Scottish football team are nicknamed the Diamonds?

3. What is the MMC, established in 1973 under the Fair Trading Act?

4. In which field did John Maynard Keynes become famous?

5. In which US state is the fishing port of Monterey?

6. Which former heavyweight champion made a record 25 successful defences of his title?

7. What do we now call the fabric serge de Nîmes?

8. Which ancient people's first emperor was Manco Capac?

9. The Gulf of Finland is the eastern arm of which sea?

10. What sort of creature is a dotterel?

11. Which fashion designer, made a CBE in 1984, died in 1995?

12. Which 'monument' is named after the Greek for 'empty tomb'?

13. Which landmark stands in the Champ de Mars?

14. What is a jarrah?

15. Which Welsh market town has the highest tides in Britain?

16. How is London's Central Criminal Court better known?

17. What are the closest attendants of the Queen called?

18. Which football club did Dutch veteran Ruud Gullit join in 1995?

19. On which river are Uganda's Owen Falls?

20. Which island's capital is Godthaab?

General Knowledge

1. At which racecourse is the Queen Elizabeth Stakes run?

2. Which ballet dancer was born Margaret Hookham?

3. Which warm, dry wind is named after the American Indian for 'snow-eater'?

4. In which country did the Long March of 1934-5 take place?

5. Of which theatrical genre is Congreve's *The Way of the World* an example?

6. Laudanum is an alcoholic solution of which drug?

7. Who wrote the philosophical work *The Leviathan* in 1651?

8. Which country's motto is 'nemo me impune lacessit'?

9. Which US president used atom bombs against Japan?

10. In which country did the satsuma originate?

11. To which animal family does the guanaco belong?

12. With which crime was Townsend Thoresen Ltd the first to be charged in Britain?

13. Which religion is based on the ideas of Marcus Garvey?

14. Which rodent has an 'edible' variety, so-called due to its popularity at Roman feasts?

15. Where was Lord Wilson buried?

16. Under which emperor was St Paul executed?

17. What is abnormally curved in scoliosis?

18. Who returned to tennis with an exhibition match against Martina Navratilova in 1995?

19. What is the capital of France's Midi-Pyrenees region?

20. What is a plane's equivalent to a ship's voyage recorder?

General Knowledge

1.   Of which mountain is Maclear's Beacon the highest point?

2.   Which French president quelled the Paris student demonstrations of 1968?

3.   What is the capital of Austria's Tirol province?

4.   What does an epidemic become on spreading across many countries?

5.   Where is the world's longest pleasure pier?

6.   Followers of which religion try to pursue the Noble Eightfold Path?

7.   Which group of islands off the NW coast of Africa have Funchal as the capital?

8.   Which porcelain was first produced under King Charles III of Naples in about 1740?

9.   Which race was held on a Saturday in 1995, the first time since 1953?

10. In which year was America's Declaration of Independence?

11. What do we call the perennial plant *Allium sativum*?

12. What is the largest species of cat in the Americas?

13. Which type of creature is a quetzal?

14. Which TV personality was born Caterina Irene Elena Maria Imperiali del Principi di Francavilla?

15. Which martial art's most popular form is called 'beautiful spring-time'?

16. Which sporting body was formed in 1787 following the folding of the White Conduit Club?

17. Who scored England's winning drop goal to put Australia out of the 1995 Rugby World Cup?

18. Of what is limnology the study?

19. Which band's original singer was Syd Barrett?

20. Where would one find a caldera?

ANSWERS: 1 Table Mountain, 2 Charles De Gaulle, 3 Innsbruck, 4 Pandemic, 5 Southend, 6 Buddhism, 7 Madeira, 8 Capodimonte, 9 The Derby, 10 1776, 11 Garlic, 12 Jaguar, 13 A bird, 14 Katie Boyle, 15 Kung fu, 16 MCC, 17 Rob Andrew, 18 Lakes, 19 Pink Floyd, 20 At the top of a volcano.

Entertainment

Your rating: ● 0-5 Buy a TV ● 6-10 Keep at it
● 11-15 Join a quiz team ● 16-20 Enter Telly Addicts

1. Which actor played Rodney in *Only Fools and Horses*?
2. What is the name of Bob Marley's son, whose band is the Melody Makers?
3. Which classic comedy series set in a Yorkshire village stars Bill Owen and Peter Sallis?
4. Who went from *The Big Breakfast* to *Don't Forget Your Toothbrush*?
5. Which *On The Waterfront* star played alongside Matthew Broderick in *The Freshman*?
6. Which rock band's tour was called *I'll Sleep When I'm Dead*?
7. Which director made *The Bridge on the River Kwai* and *A Passage to India*?
8. Which character does Dieter Brummer play in *Home and Away*?
9. Who sang *Unforgettable* and *Mona Lisa* in the '50's?
10. Which Western starred Sharon Stone and Gene Hackman?
11. Which film about films starred *Roseanne's* John Goodman?
12. Who played Sherlock Holmes in the 1939 version of *Hound of the Baskervilles*?
13. Who duetted with George Michael on the track *Days Of Our Lives* from Queen's No 1 EP *Five Live*?
14. Which singing ex-boxer had hits with *Wishing Well* and *Sign Your Name*?
15. Who played Siegfried in the long-running TV series *All Creatures Great and Small*?
16. Who was the lead singer of Culture Club?
17. Which film based on a Franz Kafka novel starred *Twin Peaks'* Kyle Maclachlan?
18. Which *Rocky III* star played B. A. Baracus in *The A-Team*?
19. Which *Fabulous Baker Boys* star appeared with Kiefer Sutherland in *The Vanishing*?
20. Who plays Jack Duckworth in *Coronation Street*?

General Knowledge

1. In which city was the US detective Allan Pinkerton born?

2. Where is the highest tidal point of the Thames?

3. Which New Zealand rugby player is nicknamed The Whale?

4. Who wrote a series of novels about a writer, *Nathaniel Zuckerman*?

5. Which legendary river is believed to be the present-day Fiumicino?

6. Which city is the headquarters of the Mormon Church?

7. By which name is the fictional character Lord Greystoke better known?

8. What nationality was Britain's adopted tennis player Greg Rusedski?

9. Which producer of silent films was born Michael Sinnott?

10. With which instrument is jazz musician Art Blakey associated?

11. What is a cowrie?

12. Which impressionist painter's first forenames were Hilaire Germain?

13. Which sport is played by the Sheffield Steelers?

14. Which famous scientist was an inspector of patents in Berne?

15. Which North Sea island group's Longstone lighthouse was made famous by Grace Darling?

16. Which former Liverpool FC manager won one of the highest libel payouts ever awarded in Britain?

17. Which Arthurian Knight succeeded in his quest for the Holy Grail because of his virtue?

18. Which metal has been issued with a hallmark in the UK since 1913?

19. In which year did the closure of Palmer's shipyard in Jarrow cause the unemployed to march to London?

20. According to researchers, which London landmark was Hitler planning to put up in Berlin?

ANSWERS: 1 Glasgow, 2 Teddington, 3 Jonah Lomu, 4 Philip Roth, 5 Rubicon, 6 Salt Lake City, 7 Tarzan, 8 Canadian, 9 Mack Sennett, 10 The drums, 11 A mollusc, 12 Degas, 13 Ice Hockey, 14 Albert Einstein, 15 Farne, 16 Graeme Souness, 17 Sir Galahad, 18 Platinum, 19 1933, 20 Nelson's Column.

General Knowledge

1. Who is the Roman equivalent of the Greek god Poseidon?

2. What do we call the fruit *Actinidia chinensis*?

3. What sort of creature is a boomslang?

4. Which moon is the most volcanically active body in our solar system?

5. What is the name of the Russian parliament building?

6. For what is Old English another term?

7. Which language is spoken in Lusophone countries?

8. Which ancient game's name is Chinese for 'sparrows'?

9. Whose *The Red Badge of Courage* is the classic US novel of the American Civil War?

10. With regard to sleep, what do the initials REM stand for?

11. In which region of Spain did the ball game pelota originate?

12. Who has become Britain's 'first knight of pop'?

13. In which religion is satori the experience of sudden enlightenment?

14. Which is the largest of the Dodecanese Islands?

15. Which one-time possible husband to Princess Margaret died in 1995?

16. What is the first novel of Paul Scott's Raj Quartet?

17. With which instrument is Ravi Shankar chiefly associated?

18. Which mountaineer has become a member of the Order of the Garter?

19. What does heavy water contain to distinguish it from light water?

20. The island group *Tierra del Fuego* is divided between Argentina and which other country?

ANSWERS: 1 *Neptune,* **2** *Kiwi or Chinese Gooseberry,* **3** *A snake,* **4** *Io,* **5** *The White House,* **6** *Anglo-Saxon,* **7** *Portuguese,* **8** *Mah-jong,* **9** *Stephen Crane,* **10** *Rapid-eye-movement,* **11** *Basque region,* **12** *Cliff Richard,* **13** *Zen Buddhism,* **14** *Rhodes,* **15** *Peter Townsend,* **16** *The Jewel in the Crown,* **17** *Sitar,* **18** *Sir Edmund Hillary,* **19** *Deuterium,* **20** *Chile.*

General Knowledge

1. What are the counterparts of spring tides?

2. Of which country is Tirana the capital?

3. While making which film did Kim Basinger meet husband Alec Baldwin?

4. The perennial herb tansy has what colour flowerheads?

5. Who ran John Major's 1995 leadership campaign?

6. What did Ernest Swinton invent in 1916?

7. Which vegetable is commonly known as rutabaga in North America?

8. What is American Football's William Perry's nickname?

9. Who was the Roman goddess of the hearth?

10. Of which bird is the whooper a variety?

11. The lack of which vitamin causes rickets?

12. Which screen cowboy was born Leonard Slye?

13. Which country will host the 1999 Rugby World Cup?

14. Which US president beat Democrat Adlai Stevenson in two successive elections?

15. The aspen belongs to which family of trees?

16. Which motor-manufacturing city in Michigan shares its name with an 18th C. native American chief?

17. Which industrialist built the model village Port Sunlight in 1888?

18. What is a nilgai?

19. What nationality was actor Anthony Quinn?

20. What is taro, allegedly the secret behind All Black Jonah Lomu's success?

ANSWERS: 1 Neap tides, 2 Albania, 3 The Marrying Man (Too Hot To Handle), 4 Yellow, 5 Lord Cranborne, 6 The tank, 7 Swede, 8 The Refrigerator, 9 Vesta, 10 Swan, 11 Vitamin D, 12 Roy Rogers, 13 Wales, 14 Dwight Eisenhower, 15 Poplar, 16 Pontiac, 17 W H Lever, 18 An antelope, 19 Mexican, 20 A vegetable.

Entertainment

1. Which tale of the old West featured the Cartwrights on the Ponderosa ranch?
2. Which film starring Bridget Fonda was a re-make of Jean Luc Besson's *Nikita*?
3. Haddaway and Howard Jones both had hits with songs with which title?
4. Which brother of *The Monocled Mutineer* played Charlie in *The Upper Hand*?
5. Which romantic melodrama starred Marisa Tomei and Christian Slater?
6. Which actor played Leonard Swindley in *Coronation Street* and Captain Mainwaring in *Dad's Army*?
7. Who sang *Tease Me* with Chaka Demus?
8. Which actor starred in *Dangerous Liaisons* and *Alive*?
9. Which BBC soap-opera screened its final episode on Friday 9th July 1993?
10. Who has had hits with *You Are Not Alone* and *Will You Be There*?
11. Which BAFTA award-winning *Room With A View* actress starred in *A Fine Romance*?
12. Which TV comedienne has used the surnames Barr and Arnold?
13. Who directed *American Werewolf In London*?
14. Which disco diva had a No 1 with *I Will Survive* in 1979?
15. Which *Dirty Dancing* star played in surf-action film *Point Break*?
16. Which Spin Doctors song might have been about Charles and Andrew?
17. Which former Jam member had a hit with *Sunflower*?
18. Which *EastEnders* regular played Tucker in *Grange Hill*?
19. Which director made *Marnie* and *The 39 Steps*?
20. Which acting giant won an Oscar for his role as Atticus in *To Kill A Mockingbird*?

ANSWERS: *1 Bonanza, 2 The Assassin, 3 What Is Love?, 4 Joe McGann, 5 Untamed Heart, 6 Arthur Lowe, 7 Pliers, 8 John Malkovich, 9 Eldorado, 10 Michael Jackson, 11 Judi Dench, 12 Roseanne, 13 John Landis, 14 Gloria Gaynor, 15 Patrick Swayze, 16 Two Princes, 17 Paul Weller, 18 Todd Carty, 19 Alfred Hitchcock, 20 Gregory Peck.*

General Knowledge

1. How is singer Paul Hewson better known?

2. What is the longest river in Italy?

3. What is the SI unit of frequency?

4. Which port is known in its country's language as Abertawe?

5. Which fruit does the tree *Punica granatum* yield?

6. On the coast of which county are the North and South Forelands?

7. Which band won the 1995 Silver Clef Award?

8. What nationality was the painter El Greco?

9. Of which US state is Lansing the capital?

10. Of which king was St David an uncle?

11. Whose £1.5m sale to Chelsea angered Manchester United fans?

12. Which confectionery item is composed mainly of chicle, which comes from the sapodilla tree?

13. From which position did John Redwood resign to contest the Tory party leadership?

14. Who was the mother of Queen Elizabeth I?

15. What type of bird is a fulmar?

16. In which African capital did Egypt's President Mubarak survive an assassination attempt in 1995?

17. Who wrote the play *Volpone* in 1606?

18. Which photographic device was invented by Edwin Land in 1947?

19. What type of creature is a megamouth?

20. Who was disqualified from Wimbledon after hitting a ball girl with a ball?

ANSWERS: *1 Bono, 2 Po, 3 Hertz, 4 Swansea, 5 Pomegranate, 6 Kent, 7 Take That, 8 Spanish, 9 Michigan, 10 King Arthur, 11 Mark Hughes, 12 Chewing gum, 13 Welsh Secretary, 14 Anne Boleyn, 15 A petrel, 16 Addis Ababa, 17 Ben Jonson, 18 Polaroid camera, 19 Shark, 20 Tim Henman.*

General Knowledge

1. What colour flowers does the guelder rose have?

2. Which social upstart is named from the French for 'arrived'?

3. In which Asian capital did a department store collapse in 1995?

4. What is New Jersey's largest city?

5. Who was Britain's first Labour prime minister?

6. Which American walked off court at Wimbledon before his wife assaulted the umpire?

7. Of which empire was Nineveh the capital?

8. For which film did Margaret Rutherford receive an Oscar?

9. Which US poet and novelist wrote *The Bell Jar*?

10. Which major river splits to straddle the Camargue region?

11. Who has become the first American to be named the world's richest man?

12. Which city is known in its own country as Gravenhage?

13. Of which fish is *Salmo trutta* the common form?

14. Which Cabinet post disappeared in the 1995 reshuffle?

15. Which singer was born Annie Mae Bullock?

16. In mathematics, which diagram represents the relationships between sets?

17. Who took Sue Cook's place on *Crimewatch UK*?

18. What is the capital of the Seychelles?

19. Which country's commandos stormed the Rainbow Warrior II?

20. What kind of creature is a dipper?

ANSWERS: *1 White, 2 Parvenu, 3 Seoul, 4 Newark, 5 Ramsay MacDonald, 6 Jeff Tarango, 7 Assyrian, 8 The VIPs, 9 Sylvia Plath, 10 Rhone, 11 Bill Gates, 12 The Hague, 13 Trout, 14 Employment Secretary, 15 Tina Turner, 16 Venn diagram, 17 Jill Dando, 18 Victoria, 19 France, 20 A bird.*

General Knowledge

1. Which metallic element is represented by the symbol Tb?

2. In which country did the Red Brigades operate?

3. Who took over as Welsh Secretary in 1995, becoming the youngest Cabinet Minister since Harold Wilson?

4. In which city did a branch of the Tate Gallery open in 1988?

5. Which Welsh snooker player was 6 times world champion in the '70s?

6. Who has become known as the Butcher of Bosnia?

7. What registers lower than 7 on the pH scale?

8. Who was a losing singles finalist but a doubles champion at Wimbledon in 1995?

9. In Greek mythology, which animal's head did a chimera have?

10. For which football team did Ian Botham play?

11. What was the stage name of Thomas Terry Hoar-Stevens?

12. Which rock 'n' roll star's middle name was Aaron?

13. Which film producer is father to Loyd Grossman's wife Debbie?

14. What was the highest building in the world when it was built in Chicago in 1973?

15. For whom did the KGB use the codename Boar?

16. Of which country did Daniel Arap Moi become president in 1978?

17. Who was the vibraphone-player with the Modern Jazz Quartet?

18. How is lysergic acid diethylamide better known?

19. What is a dugong?

20. In Greek legend, which prince of Troy abducted Helen?

ANSWERS: 1 Terbium, **2** Italy, **3** William Hague, **4** Liverpool, **5** Ray Reardon, **6** Ratko Mladic, **7** Acid, **8** Arantxa Sanchez Vicario, **9** Lion, **10** Scunthorpe United, **11** Terry-Thomas, **12** Elvis Presley, **13** David Puttnam, **14** Sears Tower, **15** Winston Churchill, **16** Kenya, **17** Milt Jackson, **18** LSD, **19** A marine mammal, **20** Paris.

Entertainment

1. Which TV station had a "Dinosaur Weekend" as part of the *Jurassic Park* hype?
2. Which film starred Dennis Hopper and *Wild At Heart's* Nicholas Cage?
3. Who starred with Rodney Bewes as one of *The Likely Lads*?
4. Who had to *Pray* to get to No. 1 in the pop charts?
5. In which English county was the surfing movie *Blue Juice* set?
6. Which British dance outfit spent *One Night In Heaven*?
7. In which Clint Eastwood film did *The Crying Game's* Forest Whitaker play the starring role?
8. Which martial arts series featured David Carradine as a half-American hard-hitting Buddhist monk?
9. Which Cambridge professor has appeared in *Star Trek - The Next Generation*?
10. Which actress plays Helen Daniels in *Neighbours*?
11. Sonya Aurora Madan is lead singer with which band?
12. Who directed, produced and starred in *High Anxiety*?
13. Which *Only Fools and Horses* character was played by Buster Merryfield?
14. Which *Working Girl* starred in the detective movie *Close To Eden*?
15. Which former *Razzamatazz* presenter had a song scoring *In All The Right Places*?
16. Which long-running comedy featured Korean War medics BJ and Hawkeye?
17. How many No 1 hits did Michael Jackson have in the 80s?
18. Which masked rider has a horse named Silver?
19. Which group with dark hair sang the original chart hit *What's Up*?
20. Which *Coronation Street* character is played by Elizabeth Bradley?

General Knowledge

1. Which silent-film actress was known as the 'It' girl?

2. Of which Asian country did President Clinton announce diplomatic recognition in 1995?

3. What is an addax?

4. Of which vitamin is cyanocobalamin the chemical name?

5. In which sport did Denmark's team win the World Championships 1983-88?

6. Who resigned after 14 years as chairman and chief executive of the London Marathon?

7. Of which European plant is the woodbine another name for the common variety?

8. In which ocean do the Comoros islands lie?

9. What sort of creature is a bandy-bandy?

10. Which river does the Clifton Suspension Bridge cross?

11. In which country is Mount Kosciusko the highest peak?

12. Of which animal is the suslik a variety?

13. Which is larger, the metric or long ton?

14. In which country did the giro system of making payments originate?

15. How many months were there in the French Revolutionary Calendar?

16. Annual jumping competitions for which amphibians are held in Calaveras, California?

17. Which US president secured the Camp David Agreements for peace in the Middle East?

18. Which fictional character did Sancho Panza accompany?

19. Who would use a gurdwara as a place of worship?

20. From which illness did tenor Jose Carreras recover to resume his career in 1988?

ANSWERS: 1 Clara Bow, 2 Vietnam, 3 Antelope, 4 B12, 5 Speedway, 6 Chris Brasher, 7 Honeysuckle, 8 The Indian Ocean, 9 A snake, 10 Severn, 11 Australia, 12 Squirrel, 13 Long ton, 14 Austria, 15 Thirteen, 16 Bullfrogs, 17 Jimmy Carter, 18 Don Quixote, 19 A Sikh, 20 Leukemia.

General Knowledge

1. What is the largest island in the Indian Ocean?

2. Which racing circuit has a Maggotts Curve?

3. Of what is the Latin phrase 'mea culpa' an admission?

4. Who left Take That to pursue a solo career?

5. Of which animal is the numbat a variety?

6. Which country repealed its Pass Laws in 1986?

7. Which English-born cyclist won a stage of the 1995 Tour de France?

8. What was ceded by China to Britain under the 1842 Treaty of Nanking?

9. What do we call a narrow strip of land that connects two larger land masses?

10. What nationality is the poet Octavio Paz?

11. Which natural phenomenon ruins the Stealth Bomber's radar-invisibility?

12. Which European capital was called Christiania until 1924?

13. Which farm animal does a peccary resemble?

14. The name of which Australian opal-mining town translates as 'white man in a hole'?

15. Which golf course contains Hell Bunker and the Valley of Sin?

16. What is the name for the surgical removal of the spleen?

17. Which country's parliament is called the States General?

18. What were the Tatars called due to the wealth they gained by plunder?

19. Which religion received its name at the 1529 Diet of Spires?

20. Who was the first Christian martyr?

ANSWERS: *1 Madagascar, 2 Silverstone, 3 Guilt, 4 Robbie Williams, 5 Anteater, 6 South Africa, 7 Maximilian Sciandri, 8 Hong Kong, 9 Isthmus, 10 Mexican, 11 Rain, 12 Oslo, 13 Pig, 14 Coober Pedy, 15 St Andrews, 16 Splenectomy, 17 Netherlands, 18 Golden Horde, 19 Protestantism, 20 St Stephen.*

General Knowledge

1. On the coast of which English county is the Naze?

2. What did the Queen Mother have removed in hospital in 1995?

3. What type of creature is an onager?

4. Which US president immortalised the phrase 'if you can't stand the heat, get out of the kitchen'?

5. Which Christian festival celebrates Jesus's entry into Jerusalem?

6. What was the world's first public railway?

7. What is a tinamou?

8. At which Pacific port does the Trans-Siberian Railway terminate?

9. At which Grand Prix did Johnny Herbert get his first win?

10. Of which country was Victor Paz president 1952-56, 1960-64 and from 1985?

11. What sort of creature is a mud puppy?

12. Who wrote *Portnoy's Complaint* in 1969?

13. What nationality is the soprano Joan Sutherland?

14. Which tree bore fruit at Kew Gardens for the first time in more than 200 years in 1995?

15. Whose *A Modest Proposal* of 1729 suggested that children of the poor should be eaten?

16. Which space probe discovered ten new moons of Uranus in 1986?

17. What sort of creature is a frogmouth?

18. On which island is the port of Syracuse?

19. By what name was the Central Policy Review Staff 1970-83 popularly known?

20. To which archbishop of Canterbury was Terry Waite religious adviser?

ANSWERS: 1 *Essex,* **2** *A cataract,* **3** *A wild ass,* **4** *Harry Truman,* **5** *Palm Sunday,* **6** *Stockton and Darlington Railway,* **7** *An American bird,* **8** *Vladivostok,* **9** *1995 British Grand Prix,* **10** *Bolivia,* **11** *A salamander,* **12** *Philip Roth,* **13** *Australian,* **14** *Breadfruit tree,* **15** *Jonathan Swift,* **16** *Voyager 2,* **17** *A bird,* **18** *Sicily,* **19** *Think Tank,* **20** *Robert Runcie.*

Entertainment

1. Who had a No 1 hit in 1988 with *The Only Way Is Up*?
2. In *Coronation Street*, which brewery owns the Rovers Return?
3. Who directed and starred in *The Bridges Of Madison County*?
4. Which comedy actor plays *Mr Bean*?
5. Who played Butch in *Butch Cassidy and the Sundance Kid*?
6. Which queen of daytime TV got a black eye by 'bumping into a mantelpiece' in 1995?
7. Who played Sandy in the 1978 film *Grease*?
8. On which author's books were the Oscar-winning films *Room With A View* and *Howard's End* based?
9. Who sang lead vocals on the version of *Come Together* found on the War Child charity album *Help*?
10. What was Clare Huxtable's profession in *The Cosby Show*?
11. Which star of *The Crying Game* was also in the film *Bad Behaviour*?
12. Which Swedish band released a single called *Almost Unreal*?
13. Which Emmy-winning comedy series starred Burt Reynolds?
14. Which character did Jack Lord play in *Hawaii Five-O*?
15. How many James Bond films featured Sean Connery as 007?
16. Who has presented *Win, Lose or Draw* and *TV Heroes*?
17. How many of Simple Minds' albums reached No 1 in the 80's?
18. Who was the star of the various *Death Wish* films?
19. Which famous English director starred in dino-thriller *Jurassic Park*?
20. Which children's TV programme has been presented by Katy Hill and Peter Duncan?

ANSWERS: 1 *Yazz,* **2** *Newton and Ridley,* **3** *Clint Eastwood,* **4** *Rowan Atkinson,* **5** *Paul Newman,* **6** *Judy Finnigan,* **7** *Olivia Newton-John,* **8** *E.M. Forster,* **9** *Paul Weller,* **10** *Lawyer,* **11** *Stephen Rea,* **12** *Roxette,* **13** *Evening Shade,* **14** *Steve McGarrett,* **15** *7,* **16** *Danny Baker,* **17** *4,* **18** *Charles Bronson,* **19** *Richard Attenborough ,* **20** *Blue Peter.*

General Knowledge

1. What was the name of Nelson's flagship at Trafalgar?

2. Which fine parchment was made from the skin of the calf, kid or lamb?

3. Under which president did Cyrus Vance resign as secretary of state?

4. Who wrote a series of books featuring the Walkers and the Blacketts, including *Swallows and Amazons*?

5. Which is the only mainland US state to have been an independent republic?

6. What is the capital of Sierra Leone?

7. Which great American golfer played his last British Open in 1995?

8. Who is the Greek equivalent of the Roman Venus?

9. By what name is ascorbic acid more commonly known?

10. Which South Carolina town was the centre of the Susan Smith murder trial?

11. What is a rorqual?

12. Which Crusade of 1212 saw many of its participants sold into slavery at Marseille?

13. Which golfer won the 1995 British Open?

14. Which film actress was born Natasha Gurdin?

15. Which composer of marches wrote *The Stars and Stripes Forever* in 1897?

16. Which African country was known as Bechuanaland until 1966?

17. What did bricklayer Joseph Aspdin create and patent in 1824?

18. Which aristocrat is known for his numerous 'wifelets'?

19. Delphi is on the southern slopes of which mountain?

20. What is the more common name for the Mexican salamander?

ANSWERS: 1 *Victory*, 2 *Vellum*, 3 *Jimmy Carter*, 4 *Arthur Ransome*, 5 *Texas*, 6 *Freetown*, 7 *Arnold Palmer*, 8 *Aphrodite*, 9 *Vitamin C*, 10 *Union*, 11 *A whale*, 12 *Children's Crusade*, 13 *John Daly*, 14 *Natalie Wood*, 15 *Sousa*, 16 *Botswana*, 17 *Portland cement*, 18 *Marquess of Bath*, 19 *Mount Parnassus*, 20 *Axolotl*.

General Knowledge

1. Which Californian brine lake was created accidentally during irrigation works?
2. Who is the Greek counterpart of the Roman god, Dis?
3. Who won the 1995 Nobel prize for literature?
4. What was the name of the plane that dropped the bomb on Hiroshima?
5. In which city was the Freemasons' first Grand Lodge formed in 1717?
6. In which year was summer time introduced in the UK?
7. For which film did Sir John Mills receive an Oscar?
8. Of which county is Ipswich the administrative HQ?
9. Which acid is used in fizzy drinks and baking powders?
10. Which Jewish festival commemorates the recapture of the Temple of Jerusalem?
11. Who wrote *Take A Girl Like You*?
12. In 1995 who achieved the first hat-trick by an England bowler since Peter Loader in 1957?
13. Which Asian country is governed by the People's Great Assembly Ardyn Ih Hural?
14. What is the largest living bird?
15. Who wrote but didn't complete a *History of the World* while in the Tower of London?
16. To which city did the Royal Ballet move in 1989?
17. Which poet's middle name was Marlais?
18. On which island is Mount Ossa the highest peak?
19. What sort of creature is a screamer?
20. Who wrote the words of the *Ode to Joy*, the anthem of united Europe?

ANSWERS: 1 Salton Sea, 2 Pluto, 3 Seamus Heaney, 4 Enola Gay, 5 London, 6 1916, 7 Ryan's Daughter, 8 Suffolk, 9 Tartaric acid, 10 Hanukkah, 11 Kingsley Amis, 12 Dominic Cork, 13 Mongolia, 14 Ostrich, 15 Sir Walter Raleigh, 16 Birmingham, 17 Dylan Thomas, 18 Tasmania, 19 S American bird, 20 Schiller.

General Knowledge

1. Which prime minister introduced the three-day week?

2. To which family of birds does the linnet belong?

3. Which British athlete has become a grandad at 35?

4. Which country does the prefix Sino denote?

5. Who is the only person to have had five singles in the Top Twenty simultaneously?

6. In physics, what does the acronym GUT stand for?

7. On which island is the industrial port of Catania?

8. Which parts of speech may be demonstrative, personal or reflexive?

9. What was the South Pacific site of the first French nuclear test in 1995?

10. Who wrote *Around The World In Eighty Days*?

11. Whose album *La Carretera* went gold within 24 hours?

12. Where is the National Stud located?

13. What was the first capital of united Italy 1861-64?

14. Which sport has made Bernie Ecclestone a multi-millionaire?

15. What type of drug is gonadotrophin?

16. Which London museum was originally called the Museum of Ornamental Art?

17. To which family of trees does the tulip tree belong?

18. Of which electrical components are rheostats and potentiometers examples?

19. Of which 1995 film is Keiko the star?

20. Which Mercian king built a defensive earthwork along the Welsh border?

ANSWERS: *1 Edward Heath, 2 Finch, 3 Linford Christie, 4 China, 5 Ruby Murray, 6 Grand Unified Theory, 7 Sicily , 8 Pronouns, 9 Mururoa Atoll, 10 Jules Verne, 11 Julio Inglesias, 12 Newmarket, 13 Turin, 14 Motor racing, 15 Fertility drug, 16 Victoria and Albert, 17 Magnolia, 18 Resistors, 19 Free Willy 2, 20 Offa.*

Entertainment

1. Which *Good Life* actress starred in *Solo*?
2. Who sang the Motown hit *I Heard it Through the Grapevine*?
3. Who starred as *Dennis*?
4. In which city was rock band Chicago formed?
5. Which *Soap* star featured in the detective series *Pacific Station*?
6. Which TV funnyman created the character of Loadsamoney?
7. Which *EastEnders* character is played by Sid Owen?
8. Which singer was walking *Down That Road*?
9. Which actor starred as Robin in *Robin's Nest* and *Me and My Girl*?
10. Which star of *Awakenings* played a Chicago detective in *Mad Dog and Glory*?
11. What are the first names of comedy duo *Hale and Pace*?
12. Which group released the EP *Hang Your Head*?
13. What is the name of the hospital in *Casualty*?
14. For which group did Errol Brown sing in the 70s and 80s?
15. Which *Brookside* character is played by Sarah White?

16. Which muscular action star is nicknamed "Sly"?
17. Which Peter Cunnah fronted pop band released an album called *World*?
18. Which US rock band were *Nightswimming* in 1993?
19. Which actor was Dennis Waterman's guvnor in *The Sweeney*?
20. Which film about a continental bank job featured Michael Caine, Benny Hill and Noel Coward?

General Knowledge

1. In which county is Wytch Farm, the UK's largest onshore oilfield?

2. Who succeeded Paul Volcker as chair of the Federal Reserve Board in 1987?

3. Of what is the Tsar Kolokol the world's largest?

4. Under what name has Sheila Holland written over 100 Mills and Boon romances?

5. Which tennis player achieved the Grand Slam in 1962 and 1969?

6. Who made his name in 1962 with paintings of soup tins?

7. What sort of creature is a marabou?

8. In electronics what do the letters LCD stand for?

9. What was the stage name of Estelle Merle O'Brien Thompson?

10. In which festival is matza eaten?

11. Which star of *Moon over Miami* insured her legs for a million dollars as a publicity stunt?

12. In food additive code numbers, what does the E stand for?

13. Whose *Maple Leaf Rag* was the first instrumental sheet music to sell a million copies?

14. Which author of biographies is married to Harold Pinter?

15. What is the study of the motion of projectiles called?

16. In the pop world, how were Carl, Brian, Al, Dennis and Mike better known?

17. What is the second highest mountain in the Himalayas?

18. Which US political party was formed by Thomas Jefferson in 1792?

19. Which Briton broke the world triple jump record in 1995?

20. What is the capital of The Gambia?

ANSWERS: *1 Dorset, 2 Alan Greenspan, 3 Bell, 4 Charlotte Lamb, 5 Rod Laver, 6 Andy Warhol, 7 A stork, 8 Liquid crystal display, 9 Merle Oberon, 10 Passover, 11 Betty Grable, 12 European, 13 Scott Joplin, 14 Antonia Fraser, 15 Ballistics, 16 The Beach Boys, 17 Kangchenjunga, 18 Democrats, 19 Jonathan Edwards, 20 Banjul.*

General Knowledge

Your rating: ● 0-5 Join a library   ● 6-10 Keep at it
              ● 11-15 Join a quiz team ● 16-20 Enter Mastermind

1. What is chanterelle?

2. Whose autobiography is entitled *Fear of Fifty*?

3. With which country did Germany institute the 'pact of steel' in 1939?

4. Which band was fronted by Jerry Garcia?

5. Which insect has weaver and driver varieties?

6. How many furlongs make a mile?

7. What type of worm is *Hirudo medicinalis*?

8. The development of what in WW2 was code-named the Manhattan Project?

9. Which country is called Aotearoa in its native language?

10. With which art form is Jerome Robbins associated?

11. Which planet's largest satellite is Titan?

12. Which shrub is also known as furze or whin?

13. What is a brolga?

14. Who played Queen Elizabeth in the film *Fire Over England*?

15. In which country does the Blue Nile rise?

16. In which US state did Labour MP John Stonehouse stage his disappearance?

17. What type of insect is the greenfly?

18. In which sport was American Scott Hamilton world champion for four consecutive years?

19. Which lord did Quintin Hogg become?

20. Which BBC soap opera is advised by the National Farmers' Union?

ANSWERS: *1 An edible fungus, 2 Erica Jong, 3 Italy, 4 Grateful Dead, 5 Ant, 6 Eight, 7 Leech, 8 Atom bomb, 9 New Zealand, 10 Dance, 11 Saturn, 12 Gorse, 13 An Australian crane, 14 Flora Robson, 15 Ethiopia, 16 Florida, 17 An aphid, 18 Ice skating, 19 Lord Hailsham, 20 The Archers.*

General Knowledge

1. In which country is the Bridge on the River Kwai?

2. What type of writ is named after the Latin for 'under penalty'?

3. How is Karol Wojtyla better known?

4. What did Elisha Graves Otis develop and first install in the 1850s?

5. In which mountains does the river Liffey rise?

6. Who is the host of relaunched antiques quiz show *Going For A Song*?

7. Who defeated Hubert Humphrey to become US president?

8. From which mountain did Alison Hargreaves fail to return?

9. Which creature has diamondback and red-eared varieties?

10. Which insecticide was discovered in 1939 by Swiss chemist Paul Müller?

11. From which plant is linen and linseed oil obtained?

12. In which series of films does the character John Mclane feature?

13. Which ocean's greatest depth is Java Trench?

14. Which philosopher wrote *Ecce Homo* in 1888?

15. Which imperial liquid measure is equal to 4.546 litres?

16. In which country is the Tirol province?

17. What material was banned after the 1745 Jacobite rebellion until 1782?

18. What does the acronym SIDS stand for?

19. In which US state is Daytona Beach?

20. Which Scottish engineer has a unit of power named after him?

ANSWERS: 1 *Thailand*, 2 *Subpoena*, 3 *Pope John Paul II*, 4 *The lift*, 5 *Wicklow Mountains*, 6 *Michael Parkinson*, 7 *Richard Nixon*, 8 *K2*, 9 *Terrapin*, 10 *DDT*, 11 *Flax*, 12 *Die Hard*, 13 *Indian Ocean*, 14 *Nietzsche*, 15 *Gallon*, 16 *Austria*, 17 *Tartan*, 18 *Sudden Infant Death Syndrome*, 19 *Florida*, 20 *James Watt*.

Entertainment

1. Which singer had a hit with *Living on My Own*?
2. Which story of a motorist hounded by a murderous truck was Steven Spielberg's first film?
3. Which country is Arnold Schwarzenegger originally from?
4. Who plays Billy in *London's Burning*?
5. Who starred as 007 in *The Living Daylights*?
6. Who is the presenter of *Strange But True*?
7. Which *Aliens* director also made *The Terminator*?
8. Who played Johnny in *My Beautiful Laundrette*?
9. Who starred as the ultimate clumsy clot in *Some Mothers Do 'Ave 'Em*?
10. Who wanted to swap *Luv 4 Luv*?
11. Which film starred Hugh O'Conor as Neasden poisoner Graham Young?
12. Who had a Top Ten Hit in 1982 with *The Bitterest Pill (I Ever Had To Swallow)*?
13. What was the name of Buddy Holly's band?
14. Which well-known newsreader's brother starred in *Blott on the Landscape*?
15. Which US singer was seen swimming in *The River of Dreams*?
16. Which 80-year-old British comedian returned to Pinewood Studios after 25 years to make a new film?
17. Which wine expert presented a 10-part *Wine Course* on BBC2?
18. Which *Fatal Attraction* star won a best actress Emmy award for her TV role as a gay army officer?
19. Who had a number one in 1966 with *Strangers In The Night*?
20. Who played Captain Ahab in John Huston's film version of *Moby Dick*?

General Knowledge

1. Of which religion was John Wesley the founder?

2. Which present-day country was founded as Carthage by the Phoenicians?

3. In which country is Taupo the largest lake?

4. How long is the rope used in water skiing?

5. How long did Mike Tyson's comeback fight last?

6. Which 18th century agriculturist's major work was *Horse-Hoeing Husbandry*?

7. Which chat show queen spent £75,000 on her sick dog?

8. Which clergyman won the 1984 Nobel Peace Prize?

9. What is the largest draught horse in the world?

10. In which county is Wookey Hole?

11. What sort of creature is a caracal?

12. What is a depilatory used to eradicate?

13. Which US astronomer has a law, a constant and a telescope named after him?

14. Where did Charlie the dog kill Charlie the raven in 1995?

15. Who wrote the historical novel *I, Claudius*?

16. Which pioneering car was nicknamed Tin Lizzie?

17. On which island is the recently-active volcano Chance's Peak?

18. Which planet did Clyde Tombaugh discover in 1930?

19. Who presented his 32nd, and final, Last Night of the Proms in 1995?

20. What nationality was the graphic artist Escher?

ANSWERS: *1 Methodism, 2 Tunisia, 3 New Zealand, 4 75 feet/23 metres, 5 89 seconds, 6 Jethro Tull, 7 Oprah Winfrey, 8 Desmond Tutu, 9 Shire horse, 10 Somerset, 11 Lynx-type cat, 12 Hair, 13 Edwin Hubble, 14 Tower of London, 15 Robert Graves, 16 Model T, 17 Montserrat, 18 Pluto, 19 Richard Baker, 20 Dutch.*

General Knowledge

1. What is Britain's largest union?

2. Which jazz singer received a suspended sentence for shooting the boy next door?

3. What is inflamed in phlebitis?

4. Who wrote *The Song of Hiawatha* in 1855?

5. What type of reptile may be common or frilled?

6. In which US state is Roswell, site of the alleged UFO crash of 1947?

7. How is the trachea more commonly known?

8. In which resort is the Waterloo Hotel, site of an annual Crown Green Bowls tournament?

9. On what did Bruce Bursford attain a record speed of 207.9 mph?

10. The cultivation of which plant, introduced from Naples in the 16th century, still continues in Hitchin?

11. What do the letters DPP stand for?

12. Which economic phenomenon may be cost-push or demand-pull?

13. In which range is Dufourspitze the second highest peak?

14. Which sport is performed in Canadian singles and pairs?

15. Which organ has Larry Hagman had transplanted?

16. Which type of singing voice did Kathleen Ferrier have?

17. Which US State is called the Green Mountain State?

18. What is the name of France's national theatre which was founded in 1680?

19. Which sport ditched its amateur status in August 1995?

20. Of what are West, Bowell and Swift-Tuttle examples?

ANSWERS: 1 TGWU, 2 Nina Simone, 3 A vein, 4 Longfellow, 5 Lizard, 6 New Mexico, 7 Windpipe, 8 Blackpool, 9 A bicycle, 10 Lavender, 11 Director of Public Prosecutions, 12 Inflation, 13 Alps, 14 Canoeing, 15 Liver, 16 Contralto, 17 Vermont, 18 Comédie Française, 19 Rugby Union, 20 Comets.

General Knowledge

1. Which playwright's daughter Oona became Charlie Chaplin's fourth wife?

2. What is amatol?

3. Who painted *Olympia* and *Déjeuner sur l'herbe*?

4. What nationality was former UN secretary general Javier Pérez de Cuéllar?

5. To which family of fish does the anchovy belong?

6. Where was the UN's 1995 Global Conference on Women held?

7. Which divine food is named from the Greek for 'immortal'?

8. In which state of the USA can the dormant volcano Mount Shasta be found?

9. In Greek mythology, which three-headed dog guarded the entrance to Hades?

10. Who was the first archbishop of Canterbury?

11. Which novelist wrote *Little Lord Fauntleroy*?

12. How is the Welsh seaport Aberdaugleddau otherwise known?

13. What sort of creature is a chacma?

14. The Chaco War (1932-35) was between which two countries?

15. What sort of creature is a miller's thumb?

16. How many syllables are in a Japanese haiku?

17. The Augrabies Falls can be found in which country?

18. Which novelist and airman wrote *Le Petit Prince*?

19. What was General Custer's first name?

20. Who was the sixth wife of Henry VIII of England?

Sports

1. Who won the 1994 African Nations Cup in football?
2. Who saved three penalties against Sampdoria in the 1995 European Cup-Winners' Cup semi-final?
3. Which Leeds captain was omitted from England's 1995 World Cup Rugby League squad despite his record 46 caps?
4. At what sport did Nancy Liebermann-Cline successfully compete?
5. Which football team plays at Bramall Lane?
6. Who won the men's 400m in the 1992 Olympic games?
7. At what weight did boxer Robert McCracken win the British title?
8. Who won the 1994 women's world snooker championship?
9. Which player broke his jaw and cheekbone in the 1993 Lions tour of New Zealand?
10. How many times have the hosts won the football World Cup?
11. Who won the men's giant slalom Alpine skiing title at the 1994 Olympics?
12. Who took the cycling world one-hour track record from Chris Boardman?
13. Which team sold Les Ferdinand to Newcastle United?
14. In which sport was Bernie Parent a goalie?
15. Which sport does Sam Panapa play?
16. Who was the first British woman to climb Mount Everest?
17. Who won the men's race in the 1993 London marathon?
18. At what sport was Karl Maier a world champion in the 1980's?
19. From which team did Middlesbrough sign Brazilian

ANSWERS: 1 Nigeria, 2 David Seaman, 3 Garry Schofield, 4 Basketball, 5 Sheffield United, 6 Quincy Watts, 7 Light-middleweight, 8 Allison Fisher, 9 Scott Hastings, 10 Five times, 11 Markus Wasmeier, 12 Graeme Obree, 13 QPR, 14 Ice hockey, 15 Rugby league, 16 Rebecca Stephens, 17 Eamonn Martin, 18 Speedway, 19 Sao Paulo, 20 Greece.

General Knowledge

Your rating:
- **0-5** Join a library
- **11-15** Join a quiz team
- **6-10** Keep at it
- **16-20** Enter Mastermind

1. Who was president of South Korea 1963-79?

2. In which country is the tourist centre of Zermatt?

3. What sort of creature is a rudd?

4. Who wrote *Lost Horizon* and *Goodbye, Mr. Chips*?

5. Which British Pre-Raphaelite painted *Christ in the House of His Parents*?

6. In which sea does the island of Rügen lie?

7. What sort of creature is a chafer?

8. In which country can the Ruapehu volcano be found?

9. *Equus* and *Amadeus* were written by which English playwright?

10. Which British actress played Eliza in the 1938 film version of *Pygmalion*?

11. Who was Ghana's first president 1960-66?

12. What is the capital of Jordan?

13. Which element is represented by the symbol Rb?

14. Who was prime minister of the UK 1908-16?

15. Who wrote *The Day of the Locust* and *A Cool Million*?

16. Which Egyptian actor starred in *Dr Zhivago*?

17. In which former Soviet republic is the port Odessa?

18. What sort of creature is a nematode?

19. How is nitrous oxide familiarly known?

20. Which radical feminist wrote *Sexual Politics* and *Sita*?

ANSWERS: *1 Park Chung-Hee, 2 Switzerland, 3 A fish, 4 James Hilton, 5 John Everett Millais, 6 The Baltic, 7 A beetle, 8 New Zealand, 9 Peter Shaffer, 10 Wendy Hiller, 11 Kwame Nkrumah, 12 Amman, 13 Rubidium, 14 Herbert Asquith, 15 Nathanael West, 16 Omar Sharif, 17 Ukraine, 18 A worm, 19 Laughing gas, 20 Kate Millett.*

- 202 -

General Knowledge

1. What sort of creature is a grunt?

2. In the New Testament, who was the first Christian martyr?

3. Tokugawa Keiki was the last to hold which Japanese military title?

4. In which ocean can the Minch be found?

5. Which Welsh novelist wrote *How Green Was My Valley*?

6. What is the capital of Uganda?

7. Chalcedony is a form of which mineral?

8. Charon is a satellite of which planet?

9. Of which country is N'djamena the capital?

10. Which country was ruled by Jomo Kenyatta 1964-78?

11. A stere is equal to how many cubic metres?

12. What is the largest of the Solomon Islands?

13. What sort of creature is a wisent?

14. Who was the Roman equivalent of the Greek goddess Athena?

15. What was the name of the Angevin, Lancastrian, and Yorkist Kings of England (1154-1485)?

16. How is the tympanic membrane familiarly known?

17. Which bespectacled silent movie comedian starred in *The Freshman*?

18. What sort of creature is a planarian?

19. What is the Jewish ceremonial trumpet known as shofar made of?

20. Which Chinese dynasty succeeded the Mongol Yüan dynasty?

General Knowledge

1. Which son of Percival in Arthurian legend inspired a Wagner opera?

2. What is a dodder?

3. With which musical instrument was Charlie Mingus associated?

4. In which county is the shingle headland of Dungeness?

5. What is palaeography the study of?

6. Which grandson of William the Conqueror ruled England 1135-54?

7. What sort of creature is a whydah?

8. Which French poet wrote the autobiographical novel *La Fanfarlo*?

9. What is the largest inlet on the USA's Atlantic coast?

10. Who was US President 1909-13?

11. Which US tennis player won the Wimbledon women's singles title eight times 1927-38?

12. Which city in NW England was a Roman fortress named Deva?

13. What is batik?

14. What is the largest of the Mariana Islands?

15. With which musical instrument is Isaac Stern associated?

16. Who wrote the classic gothic novel *Vathek*?

17. Which forest is the setting for Shakespeare's *As You Like It*?

18. What is the last book of the Old Testament?

19. Which German philosopher wrote *The Phenomenology of Mind*?

20. What is a mesquite?

ANSWERS: 1 Lohengrin, 2 A plant, 3 Double-bass, 4 Kent, 5 Ancient handwriting, 6 Stephen, 7 A bird, 8 Baudelaire, 9 Chesapeake Bay, 10 William Taft, 11 Helen Wills (Moody), 12 Chester, 13 A dyed cloth, 14 Guam, 15 The violin, 16 William Beckford, 17 Forest of Arden, 18 The Book of Malachi, 19 Hegel, 20 A tree.

Entertainment

1. Which series tracing the development of Christianity was narrated by Bamber Gascoigne?

2. Which *Blues Brothers* star played one of the *Coneheads* in the zany alien film?

3. Which British film veteran played Sir James Menzies in *Strathblair*?

4. Which member of the *Rhythm Nation* had a chart hit with *If*?

5. Who played the cantankerous old dad in *Steptoe and Son*?

6. Which *Frantic* star played Richard Kimble in the film version of *The Fugitive*?

7. Which *Eastenders* star sang *Looking Up*?

8. Which *Batman* star played the manic ghost in *Beetlejuice*?

9. Which actor went from *The Good Life* to *Ever Decreasing Circles*?

10. Which supermodel made a guest appearance in *Absolutely Fabulous*?

11. Which character does Philip Middlemiss play in *Coronation Street*?

12. Which rap stars of *House Party* had their own children's TV cartoon show?

13. Who played the title role in *Dolores Claiborne*?

14. Who played loud-mouthed bigot Alf Garnett in *Till Death Us Do Part*?

15. Which Motown legend released an album entitled *Take Me Higher*?

16. Who played the incompetent Detective Frank Drebin in cult comedy series *Police Squad*?

17. Which group had No 1. hits with *It's a Sin* and *West End Girls*?

18. Who played feisty headmistress Dorothy Burke in *Neighbours*?

19. What is the name of Whoopi Goldberg and Ted Danson's film about a genetic mix-up?

20. Who played Hutch in *Starsky and Hutch*?

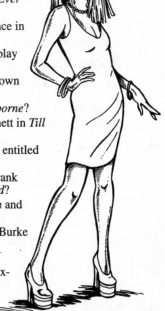

General Knowledge

1. Which German poet wrote *Prometheus* and *Faust*?

2. What is obsidian?

3. Which Roman Catholic religious order was founded in 1084 by St Bruno?

4. Which African republic was known as Nyasaland?

5. What sort of creature is a muntjac?

6. Which Nazi broadcaster was known as Lord Haw-Haw?

7. The name of which Irish political party means 'Ourselves'?

8. Which Greek novelist wrote *Zorba the Greek*?

9. In which European country is the town of Genk?

10. What sort of creature is a weever?

11. Which composer wrote the humorous orchestral *Divertissement*?

12. What is a hornbeam?

13. Which British philanthropist founded St Christopher's Hospice, London in 1967?

14. Who was the first Bourbon King of France?

15. In verse, which metrical foot consists of an unstressed syllable followed by a stressed syllable?

16. Which Finnish athlete won gold medals in the 5,000 and 10,000 metres at both the 1972 and 1976 Olympics?

17. What is the legal capital of Bolivia?

18. What is an earthstar?

19. Genseric was king of which Germanic tribe?

20. Which US author wrote *At the Mountains of Madness*?

ANSWERS: *1 Goethe, 2 Dark volcanic rock, 3 The Carthusians, 4 Malawi, 5 A deer, 6 William Joyce, 7 Sinn Féin, 8 Nikos Kazantzakis, 9 Belgium, 10 A fish, 11 Jacques Ibert, 12 A tree, 13 Dame Cicely Saunders, 14 Henry IV, 15 An iamb, 16 Lasse Viren, 17 Sucre, 18 A fungus, 19 The Vandals, 20 HP Lovecraft.*

General Knowledge

1. Which Irish author wrote *The Country Girls* and *Night*?

2. Malachite is an ore of which metal?

3. What sort of creature is a lumpsucker?

4. Which British composer wrote *Sinfonia Antarctica*?

5. Which Jewish religious movement was founded by the Ba'al Shem Tov?

6. With which sport is Hans Günter Winkler associated?

7. Which Swiss sculptor created the abstract construction *The Palace at 4 am*?

8. In which country is the river Xingu?

9. According to the Old Testament, who was the first King of Israel?

10. What is the highest mountain in Antarctica?

11. Which British historical novelist wrote *Lorna Doone*?

12. Which English Cavalier poet wrote *To Althea, from Prison*?

13. What is a pyrometer used to measure?

14. Which Egyptian god was the brother and husband of Isis?

15. What is the name for the equatorial belt within which the trade-wind zones converge?

16. What kind of creature is a cavy?

17. Who wrote *The Magus* and *The French Lieutenant's Woman*?

18. What is the capital of Qatar?

19. Which Christian sect was formally known as the Religious Society of Friends?

20. What was wax modeller Madame Tussaud's christian name?

ANSWERS: 1 Edna O'Brien, **2** Copper, **3** A fish, **4** Vaughan Williams, **5** Hasidism, **6** Showjumping, **7** Alberto Giacometti, **8** Brazil, **9** Saul, **10** Vinson Massif, **11** RD Blackmore, **12** Richard Lovelace, **13** High temperatures, **14** Osiris, **15** Doldrums, **16** A South American rodent, **17** John Fowles, **18** Doha, **19** Quakers, **20** Marie.

General Knowledge

1. What is the most populous island in Western Samoa?

2. Who wrote *The History of the Decline and Fall of the Roman Empire*?

3. In which city did the Easter Rising of 1916 take place?

4. Which branch of Christianity was founded by Mary Baker Eddy?

5. What kind of creature is a cayman?

6. Which John Updike novel won a Pulitzer Prize in 1982?

7. Which US novelist wrote *The Turn of the Screw* and *Roderick Hudson*?

8. What is the capital of Malawi?

9. In Greek legend, which son of Priam and Hecuba abducted Helen?

10. Polaris lies in which constellation?

11. Which Old Testament woman became the queen of the Persian King Ahasuerus?

12. Which French impressionist painted *Les Parapluies*?

13. The Haber-Bosch process is a method of producing which gas?

14. What is the smallest of the Greater Sunda Islands?

15. What nationality is the writer Amos Tutuola?

16. What sort of creature is a bulbul?

17. What kind of creature is a gurnard?

18. In which city is Holyrood House?

19. Which US folk singer wrote *This Land Is Your Land*?

20. John the Perfect and John the Fortunate were kings of which country?

ANSWERS: *1 Upolu, 2 Edward Gibbon, 3 Dublin, 4 Christian Science, 5 A reptile, 6 Rabbit is Rich, 7 Henry James, 8 Lilongwe, 9 Paris, 10 Ursa Minor, 11 Esther, 12 Renoir, 13 Ammonia, 14 Java, 15 Nigerian, 16 A bird, 17 A fish, 18 Edinburgh, 19 Woody Guthrie, 20 Portugal.*

Entertainment

1. Which actress played WDS Johnson in *The Bill*?
2. Which female vocalist had a *Dreamlover*?
3. Which *Cheers* spin-off won five Emmy awards in 1995?
4. Which *Young Frankenstein* star played opposite Richard Pryor in *Stir Crazy*?
5. Which comedy series starred Chris Barrie as manager of Whitbury Leisure centre?
6. Who had a hit single with *Mr Vain*?
7. Mr Don and Mr George were first seen in which comedy sketch show?
8. Who played the kinky catwoman in *Batman Returns*?
9. Which talent/game show is presented by Des O' Connor?
10. Which famous medical examiner was played by Jack Klugman?
11. Who played Jake La Motta in *Raging Bull*?
12. Which comedy series set in a youth club was by the creator of *Desmond's*?
13. Which retro rocker released an album called *Circus*?
14. Which comedians appeared as Derek and Clive?
15. Who released an EP called *Nuff Vibes*?
16. Which *Happy Days* star played the Father in *Father Dowling Investigates*?
17. Who had a No 1 in 1973 with *Tie a Yellow Ribbon Round the Old Oak Tree*?
18. Who received a vast sum for his brief role as *Superman's* father?

19. Which BBC2 series looked at the life and times of the telephone?
20. Who starred in and sang *Summer Holiday*?

General Knowledge

1. Which English author wrote *Le Morte d'Arthur*?

2. What kind of creature is a godwit?

3. Which Mediterranean country was awarded the George Cross for its resistance to German attack in WW2?

4. Who wrote the music to *Jerusalem*?

5. What is the capital of Guyana?

6. Who was the first Stuart King of England and Ireland?

7. On which island off the coast of Northumberland is there a monastery founded by St Aidan?

8. What sort of creature is a mangabey?

9. Which 17th-century Dutch astronomer and physicist formulated the wave theory of light?

10. Which castle was the scene of the investiture of Charles as Prince of Wales?

11. Which ancient city of Sumer is mentioned in Genesis as Abraham's homeland?

12. Tapioca is produced from the root of which plant?

13. Which metallic element is represented by the symbol Cd?

14. Which Italian poet addressed his *Canzoniere* to Laura?

15. Who wrote *King Solomon's Mines*?

16. Mount Narodnaya is the highest point of which mountain range?

17. What is the largest known living frog?

18. In which Hampshire village can the National Motor Museum be found?

19. With which musical instrument is Oscar Peterson associated?

20. How many players are there in an Australian Rules team?

ANSWERS: 1 *Sir Thomas Malory*, **2** *A bird*, **3** *Malta*, **4** *Sir Hubert Parry*, **5** *Georgetown*, **6** *James I*, **7** *Holy Island or Lindisfarne*, **8** *A monkey*, **9** *Huygens*, **10** *Caernarvon Castle*, **11** *Ur*, **12** *Cassava*, **13** *Cadmium*, **14** *Petrarch*, **15** *H Rider Haggard*, **16** *Ural Mountains*, **17** *The goliath frog*, **18** *Beaulieu*, **19** *Piano*, **20** *Eighteen*.

General Knowledge

1. Of which country was Adnan Menderes prime minister 1950-60?

2. How was Polish-born film producer Samuel Goldfish better known?

3. Which New Testament evangelist is the patron saint of doctors and artists?

4. What was the name of the first dog in space?

5. What does a petrologist study?

6. Encephalitis is inflammation of which organ?

7. Which legendary Spartan king was Agamemnon's brother and Helen's husband?

8. In 1987, who became the first batsman to score 10,000 runs in Test cricket?

9. In which city was the Peterloo Massacre of 1819?

10. What sort of creature is a turnstone?

11. Who was the first Tudor monarch?

12. Which Roman poet addressed 25 love poems to Lesbia?

13. What kind of creature is a gadwall?

14. Which viral infection is alternatively known as hydrophobia?

15. What is the state capital of Oklahoma?

16. Which German composer wrote the operas *Salome* and *Elektra*?

17. Which Spanish novelist wrote *The Three-Cornered Hat*?

18. How is chiromancy otherwise known?

19. In which city is the tomb of Mohammed?

20. Which Russian composer wrote *Rhapsody on a Theme of Paganini*?

ANSWERS: 1 *Turkey*, 2 *Samuel Goldwyn*, 3 *Saint Luke*, 4 *Laika*, 5 *Rocks*, 6 *The brain*, 7 *Menelaus*, 8 *Sunil Gavaskar*, 9 *Manchester*, 10 *A bird*, 11 *Henry VII*, 12 *Catullus*, 13 *A duck*, 14 *Rabies*, 15 *Oklahoma City*, 16 *Richard Strauss*, 17 *Pedro Antonio de Alarcon*, 18 *Palmistry*, 19 *Medina*, 20 *Sergei Rachmaninov*.

General Knowledge

1. What is the capital of Australia?

2. What were the first names of "Dizzy" Gillespie?

3. In which field of science would a particle accelerator be used?

4. What name is given to a place or region where tin is mined or worked?

5. What, in relation to mammals is a vibrissa?

6. Where is Stara Zagora?

7. What is the name of the winged goddess of victory in Greek mythology?

8. From what is the fibre coir obtained?

9. Who designed the Cenotaph in London's Whitehall?

10. Who was the composer of *Rule Britannia*?

11. What is a butcher's-broom?

12. Who composed the ballet *Coppelia*?

13. What kind of bird is a tragopan?

14. Which was the first British colony in Africa to gain independence?

15. What do the initials TAVR stand for?

16. What is the common name for sodium carbonate?

17. Which is the smallest state capital of the U.S.?

18. In which year was the Festival of Britain staged?

19. In which county in the Wrekin?

20. In which year did Kenny Dalglish join Liverpool as a player?

ANSWERS: *1 Canberra, 2 John Birks, 3 Nuclear physics, 4 Stannary, 5 A whisker, 6 Bulgaria, 7 Nike, 8 Coconut, 9 Sir Edward Lutyens, 10 Thomas Arne, 11 An evergreen shrub, 12 Leo Delibes, 13 Pheasant, 14 Gold Coast - now Ghana, 15 Territorial Army Volunteer Reserve, 16 Washing soda, 17 Pierre, South Dakota, 18 1951, 19 Shropshire, 20 1977.*

Entertainment

1. Which British sprinter appeared in the kids' comedy series *What You Looking At*?
2. Which all-girl soul group were *Right There*?
3. Who played the mad scientist father in *Honey, I Shrunk The Kids*?
4. In which classic comedy series did *Evening Shade's* Marilu Henner star with Danny De Vito?
5. Which deadpan comedian is married to Caroline Quentin?
6. Which ageless singer returned to the charts with a *Disco Inferno*?
7. Which 1956 Texan oil epic starred Rock Hudson, Elizabeth Taylor and James Dean?
8. Which animated hero battles against Skeletor?
9. Which TV presenter had a 60's No 1 with *Anyone Who Had A Heart*?
10. Which actress played Diane in *Cheers*?
11. Who played the shaven-headed leader of *The Magnificent Seven*?
12. Which *Bounder* co-starred with Penelope Keith in *To The Manor Born*?
13. Which group have been fronted by both Shane MacGowan and Joe Strummer?
14. Which *French Connection* star played an FBI agent in *Mississippi Burning*?
15. Who played the minister in *Yes Minister*?
16. Which goth group went *Under the Gun*?
17. In which year was *Coronation Street* first shown?
18. Who sang *Layla* and *Cocaine*?
19. Who played Arthur's mistress in *EastEnders*?
20. Which character did Macaulay Culkin play in *Home Alone*?

General Knowledge

1. Who wrote *Les Enfants terribles*?
2. What do the initials IDP stand for?
3. Who was the architect responsible for the president's palace and the cathedral in Brasilia?
4. What name is given to a probationer in a religious order?
5. Which plant has flower parts allegedly resembling the instruments of the crucifixion?
6. Who was the Norwegian whose name is synonymous with collaboration with an occupying enemy?
7. What was the maiden name of Wimbledon champion Evonne Cawley?
8. In which year was Britain's EEC membership endorsed by referendum?
9. What term of address is used in relation to an Anglican or Roman Catholic bishop?
10. What, in Germany, is forbidden?
11. Other than a plant, what is a veronica?
12. How many emirates comprise the United Arab Emirates?
13. Where are the Selkirk Mountains?
14. Who composed the opera *William Tell*?
15. How are Belgium, Luxembourg and the Netherlands collectively known?
16. Where is the Oaks run?
17. Who invented the first practicable motion picture camera?
18. John Alexander Macdonald was the first prime minister of which British dominion?
19. Of which kingdom is Fyn the second largest island?
20. What does the abbreviation PSBR stand for?

ANSWERS: *1 Jean Cocteau, 2 Integrated data processing, 3 Oscar Niemeyer, 4 Novice, 5 Passionflower, 6 Vidkun Quisling, 7 Goolagong, 8 1975, 9 Right reverend, 10 Verboten, 11 A bull-fighting pass, 12 Seven, 13 Canada, 14 Rossini, 15 The low countries, 16 Epsom, 17 William Friese-Greene, 18 Canada, 19 Denmark, 20 Public sector borrowing requirement.*

General Knowledge

1. Of which nationality is a member of the Red Guard?

2. Who was the god of sleep and dreams, of Greek mythology?

3. Who wrote *Little Boxes*?

4. Who is Mrs Tom Cruise?

5. What is an "MVO"?

6. Where would you spend a zloty?

7. What was the "W" of F.W. Woolworth, US founder of the chain of stores?

8. In which Italian region is Chianti produced?

9. What is produced on paper by a "dandy roll" or "dandy roller"?

10. Who are members of BALPA?

11. What name is given to the allowance voted by Parliament for the private expenses of the monarch?

12. Who won figure skating gold for Britain in the 1976 Olympic Games?

13. Which Fife city gives its name to Scotland's oldest university?

14. Who was the author of the verse drama *The Lady's Not for Burning*?

15. What is an "immortelle"?

16. What is the capital city of Liberia?

17. From the seed of which East African evergreen tree is the spice mace obtained?

18. What name is given to a skier's quilted trousers held up by shoulder straps?

19. For what was Churchill awarded a Nobel Prize in 1953?

20. Which board game takes its name from the Latin for *I play*?

ANSWERS: *1 Chinese, 2 Morpheus, 3 Malvina Reynolds, 4 Nicole Kidman, 5 Member of the Royal Victorian Order, 6 Poland, 7 Winfield, 8 Tuscany, 9 A watermark, 10 British airline pilots, 11 Privy purse, 12 John Curry, 13 St. Andrews, 14 Christopher Fry, 15 An everlasting flower, 16 Monrovia, 17 Nutmeg, 18 Salopettes, 19 Literature, 20 Ludo.*

General Knowledge

1. Of what kind of material are boules balls made?

2. Commonwealth Day, May 24th, is the anniversary of which monarch's birth?

3. Who played Lois Lane in the Christopher Reeve *Superman* films?

4. What do the initials WMO stand for?

5. Which anniversary is the 45th wedding anniversary?

6. In which of the arts was Nicolas Poussin expert?

7. Of which group is the island of Mindoro a member?

8. What is the name of Saddam Hussein's wife?

9. What is the real first name of "Fats" Domino?

10. Who wrote *Piers Plowman*?

11. In which year were women aged 21 and over given the vote in the UK?

12. What is a Kyloe?

13. What was developed by Sir Charles Parsons?

14. What does a Manx cat lack?

15. What is the speciality of Marcel Marceau?

16. Who directed the film *Rosemary's Baby*?

17. Which city was the setting for Anne Frank's diary?

18. What other name is given to Whit Sunday?

19. What is the capital of Lithuania?

20. Who was the Spanish composer of the ballet *The Three Cornered Hat*?

ANSWERS: 1 Metal, **2** Queen Victoria, **3** Margot Kidder, **4** World Meteorological Organisation, **5** Sapphire, **6** Painting, **7** Philippines, **8** Sajida, **9** Antoine, **10** William Langland, **11** 1928, **12** Scottish breed of beef cattle, **13** Steam turbine, **14** Tail, **15** Mime, **16** Roman Polanski, **17** Amsterdam, **18** Pentecost, **19** Vilnius, **20** Manuel de Falla.

Entertainment

1. Who played Demetrius in Mira Nair's *Mississippi Masala*?
2. Who partnered Annie Lennox in the Eurythmics?
3. Who played Dustin Hoffman's ex-wife in *Kramer vs Kramer*?
4. Which cockney comedian hosted *Big Break*?
5. Which supermodel was seen on the cover of *Vanity Fair* giving k. d. Lang a shave?
6. Which *Moonlighting* star was the object of female envy in *Death Becomes Her*?
7. Which 14-year-old American schoolgirl released an album entitled *Miss Thang*?
8. Which former Teardrop Explodes star released an album called *20 Mothers*?
9. Who wrote *The Tale of Samuel Whiskers*, which was animated for BBC1?
10. On which popular US series was *Brighton Belles* based?
11. What instrument does Charlie Watts play with the Rolling Stones?
12. Which computer programme has been presented by Dominik Diamond and Dexter Fletcher?
13. Who sang *The Best Things in Life Are Free* with Janet Jackson?
14. Who directed *Ferris Bueller's Day Off* and *The Breakfast Club*?
15. In which year was *Thunderbirds* first shown in the UK?
16. Who hosts *The Krypton Factor*?
17. Which Scandinavian superstars had a No1 with *Super Trouper*?
18. Which *Lethal Weapon* star appeared in *Lonesome Dove*?
19. Which characters finally got together in *The Upper Hand*?
20. Who was the lead singer of the Who?

ANSWERS: *1 Denzel Washington, 2 Dave Stewart, 3 Meryl Streep, 4 Jim Davidson, 5 Cindy Crawford, 6 Bruce Willis, 7 Monica, 8 Julian Cope, 9 Beatrix Potter, 10 The Golden Girls, 11 The drums, 12 Gamesmaster, 13 Luther Vandross, 14 John Hughes, 15 1966, 16 Gordon Burns, 17 Abba, 18 Danny Glover, 19 Caroline and Charlie, 20 Roger Daltrey.*

General Knowledge

1. Where is the river Demerara?

2. How many zeros follow the figure one to denote a sextillion?

3. How many acres are there in a hectare?

4. Under which sign are those born between October 23rd and November 21st?

5. What and where, is Bio-Bio?

6. What does rhinology deal with?

7. What word meaning "fellow traveller" was given to a series of Russian artificial satellites?

8. How many bytes are there to a kilobyte?

9. Which port in SE India was founded as Fort St. George?

10. Of which king was Jezebel the wife?

11. What anatomically, does 'inguinal' relate to?

12. What is the common name for the Chinese gooseberry?

13. Who was the king of the Belgians before king Baudouin?

14. Ile-de-France was once the name for which island?

15. What is the capital of the Transvaal province of South Africa?

16. Which was the best known verse of US poet and novelist Stephen Benet?

17. What is the nontechnical name for the calcaneus?

18. How many plane faces has a hexahedron?

19. Which Egyptian god was ruler of the underworld and judge of the dead?

20. From which country does retsina originate?

General Knowledge

1. In which Italian city is the Colosseum?

2. What is a moving staircase called?

3. Which is the heaviest and softest of the common metals?

4. Which four numbers precede an inner-London telephone number?

5. With whom did Ginger Rogers have a famous screen dancing partnership?

6. What is the name for the Roman punishment of death on a cross?

7. Which is the largest North American mountain system?

8. Smoking was banned on the London Undeground after a fire in which station?

9. In which sovereign state is Monte Carlo?

10. From which country was Sigmund Freud?

11. What kind of animal ate *Little Red Riding Hood*'s grandmother?

12. What is the tallest mammal?

13. Under which Soviet leader was "glasnost" introduced?

14. Which branch of medicine is concerned with care of the elderly sick?

15. In which ocean is Fiji?

16. For what are the letters CND an abbreviation?

17. How many leaves does a lucky clover have?

18. Who directed and starred in *Blazing Saddles*?

19. On which island is Brunei?

20. With which sport is Joe Montana associated?

ANSWERS: 1 Rome, 2 An escalator, 3 Lead, 4 0171, 5 Fred Astaire, 6 Crucifixion, 7 The Rocky Mountains, 8 King's Cross, 9 Monaco, 10 Austria, 11 A wolf, 12 The giraffe, 13 Mikhail Gorbachev, 14 Geriatrics, 15 The Pacific Ocean, 16 Campaign for Nuclear Disarmament, 17 4, 18 Mel Brookes, 19 Borneo, 20 American football.

General Knowledge

1.   In which religion are Brahma, Vishnu and Siva the chief gods?

2.   What colour does the skin turn when jaundiced?

3.   What is heated to produce caramel?

4.   On what type of surface is curling played?

5.   What is a water-filled ditch surrounding a castle called?

6.   Of which city was David Dinkins the first black mayor?

7.   In which county is Leeds?

8.   What type of fruit does a damson tree produce?

9.   What type of transport did mods favour?

10. For what type of literature is SF an abbreviation?

11. Which team does Kevin Keegan manage?

12. Who does Jack kill in *Jack and the Beanstalk*?

13. In which year will Hong Kong return to Chinese sovereignty?

14. What does eczema affect?

15. Between which two European countries was the Hundred Years' War?

16. For which environmental group is FoE an abbreviation?

17. In which condition is flesh frozen leading to tissue damage?

18. Which imperial measure is equivalent to 4.546 litres?

19. Which part of Pinocchio grew when he lied?

20. In which London cemetery is Karl Marx buried?

ANSWERS: *1 Hinduism, 2 Yellow, 3 Sugar, 4 Ice, 5 A moat, 6 New York City, 7 West Yorkshire, 8 Plums, 9 The scooter, 10 Science Fiction, 11 Newcastle, 12 The Giant, 13 1997, 14 The skin, 15 England and France, 16 Friends of the Earth, 17 Frostbite , 18 A gallon, 19 His nose, 20 Highgate Cemetery.*

Entertainment

1. Who had a 1962 No 1 hit with *The Young Ones*?
2. Who played the teenager-turned-adult in *Big*?
3. Which comedian played wily *Sergeant Bilko*?
4. Who played Adrian Cronauer in *Good Morning, Vietnam*?
5. Who was the lead singer of Bronski Beat and The Communards?
6. Which '60s model is married to actor Leigh Lawson?
7. Which country did the turtles time-travel to in *Teenage Mutant Ninja Turtles III*?
8. Who plays Curly Watts in *Coronation Street*?
9. Who sang No 1 hit *The Lady in Red*?
10. Which spooky family are Morticia, Gomez and Fester from?
11. Which *Little Big Man* star was the cross-dressing hero/heroine of *Tootsie*?
12. Which *Whose Line Is It Anyway?* star was question master on *The Music Game*?
13. Who had a Top Twenty Hit in 1981 with *There's a Guy Works Down the Chipshop Swears He's Elvis*?
14. Which medical drama series won eight Emmy awards in 1995?
15. Which zany British comedian had a 60's hit with *Tears*?
16. Who introduces the people's wildlife programme *Nature Detectives*?
17. Who played the big-nosed fireman in *Roxanne*?
18. Who played *Lovejoy's* love-interest Lady Jane Felsham?
19. Who had a No 1 in 1975 with the country classic *Stand By Your Man*?
20. Who was the female star of the *Terminator* films?

General Knowledge

1. Which fish makes an arduous up-river journey to spawn in the place it was spawned?

2. Which two countries cooperated to develop Concorde?

3. What was the stage name of Bud Abbott's comedy partner?

4. What colour represents jealousy?

5. Of which country was Salisbury capital?

6. Which star of *The Shining* was in *Terms of Endearment*?

7. Which 1969 film featured Dennis Hopper and Peter Fonda as freewheeling bikers?

8. Niagara Falls is on the border of which two countries?

9. What is used instead of a ball in badminton?

10. What is the highest-ranking naval officer?

11. Which vegetable is also called a zucchini?

12. Who wrote *A Passage to India*?

13. From what type of animal is mohair produced?

14. How many points does a Star of David have?

15. Through which process do plants use light to produce food?

16. From which animal is ivory primarily obtained?

17. What is a more common name for a whirlpool bath?

18. What type of electric charge is acquired through friction?

19. In which country was the Third Reich?

20. Which component of cigarette smoke causes bodily addiction?

ANSWERS: 1 *The salmon*, **2** *England and France*, **3** *Lou Costello*, **4** *Green*, **5** *Rhodesia*, **6** *Jack Nicholson*, **7** *Easy Rider*, **8** *The USA and Canada*, **9** *A shuttlecock*, **10** *Admiral of the Fleet*, **11** *A courgette*, **12** *E M Forster*, **13** *A goat*, **14** *6*, **15** *Photosynthesis*, **16** *The elephant*, **17** *A jacuzzi*, **18** *Static electricity*, **19** *Germany*, **20** *Nicotine*.

General Knowledge

1. What does the French word 'maison' mean in English?

2. Which animal is also called an ass?

3. Of which country is Kabul the capital?

4. Which silent movie hero starred in *The General* and *The Navigator*?

5. Which is the largest city in the USA?

6. Which body of administrative staff carries out the policies of the British government?

7. Which spear is used in athletic events?

8. In which county is Epping Forest?

9. Which political party does Bill Clinton represent?

10. How many playing cards are there in a deck?

11. Which *Rambo* star was the hero of *Cliffhanger*?

12. From what is solar energy derived?

13. In which forest was Robin Hood said to have lived?

14. Which infamous carnivorous freshwater fish comes from South America?

15. Who was Labour leader before John Smith?

16. Which knitting stitch is achieved by doing a plain stitch backwards?

17. Who wrote *Smiley's People*?

18. Which psychologist devised the theory of the Oedipus Complex?

19. In which French city is the Sorbonne?

20. What colour are the actor Paul Newman's eyes?

ANSWERS: 1 House, 2 A donkey, 3 Afghanistan, 4 Buster Keaton, 5 New York, 6 The Civil Service, 7 Javelin, 8 Essex, 9 The Democrats, 10 52, 11 Sylvester Stallone, 12 The Sun, 13 Sherwood Forest, 14 The Piranha, 15 Neil Kinnock, 16 Purl, 17 John Le Carré, 18 Sigmund Freud, 19 Paris, 20 Blue.

General Knowledge

1. In which city is Moss Side?

2. What type of criminal act is Dick Turpin most famous for?

3. Which beautiful Greek youth fell in love with his own reflection?

4. For which British regiment is SAS an abbreviation?

5. What is the name for a scene or picture which fools the eye?

6. Which *Back to the Future* star is in *Addams Family Values*?

7. What is *Robinson Crusoe*'s desert island companion called?

8. What type of food is a pecan?

9. How many 'deadly sins' are there in Christian theology?

10. Which force is not present in the state of weightlessness?

11. Who is the governor of Hong Kong?

12. Who wrote *Treasure Island*?

13. Which railway connects European Russia with Vladivostok on the Pacific?

14. In which country is the far-right party the AWB found?

15. At which weight did Henry Cooper box?

16. In which sport is the Ryder Cup contested?

17. What is removed in the process of dehydration?

18. Oil from which fish's liver is taken for vitamins A and D?

19. Whose column stands in the centre of Trafalgar Square?

20. In the German army, what was a cavalryman armed with a lance called?

ANSWERS: *1 Manchester, 2 Highway robbery, 3 Narcissus, 4 The Special Air Service, 5 An optical illusion, 6 Christopher Lloyd, 7 Man Friday, 8 A nut, 9 Seven, 10 Gravity, 11 Chris Patten, 12 Robert Louis Stevenson, 13 The Trans Siberian Railway, 14 South Africa, 15 Heavyweight, 16 Golf, 17 Water, 18 Cod, 19 Lord Nelson, 20 Uhlan.*

Entertainment

Your rating: ● 0-5   **Buy a TV**   ● 6-10   **Keep at it**
    ● 11-15   **Join a quiz team**   ● 16-20   **Enter Telly Addicts**

1. Which famous Liverpudlian presents *Blind Date*?
2. What were the surnames of *The Two Ronnies*?
3. Which Genesis star covered the Supremes hit *You Can't Hurry Love*?
4. Which *Biloxi Blues* star was in the Greenwich Village tale *The Night We Never Met*?
5. Which cult US TV programme featured Coach, Cliff and Woody?
6. Who entered the hit parade at No 1 in 1958 with *Jailhouse Rock*?
7. What are Dame Edna Everage's favourite flowers?
8. Who plays Charlie Fairhead in *Casualty*?
9. Which film about a mysterious law company starred Tom Cruise and Gene Hackman?
10. Who played unscrupulous reporter *Harry* ?
11. Who directed *Eraserhead*?
12. Which smooth crooner had a big 50's hit with *Magic Moments*?
13. Who played Mrs Boswell in *Bread*?
14. Which group had a No 1 with *Pass The Dutchie*?
15. Who starred as all eight murder victims in *Kind Hearts and Coronets*?
16. Who played *Worzel Gummidge*?
17. Who played the psychotic assassin in *In The Line of Fire*?
18. Which Beatles member had a big hit with *Woman*?
19. What is Gita's sister called in *EastEnders*?
20. Which *Record Breaker* starred in *Carry On Up the Khyber*?

General Knowledge

1. Between which two countries is Kashmir divided?

2. What did *The Ugly Duckling* turn into?

3. In which city is *Brookside* set?

4. Which is the only crime in Britain still punishable by death?

5. What is the monetary unit of Italy?

6. In which position does David Seaman play?

7. In the Bible, who baptised Jesus?

8. In which country is St. Moritz?

9. Which is the most prestigious court at Wimbledon?

10. Who was the skipper in the film *The African Queen*?

11. Through which two countries does the Rio Grande flow?

12. What is the art of arranging dance called?

13. At which London station do trains from Birmingham terminate?

14. Who was U.S. president during the Cuban missile crisis?

15. Which snooker ball is worth seven points?

16. Which floating object is used to mark channels for shipping?

17. Who did the Roundheads fight in the English Civil War?

18. In which religion is kosher food prescribed?

19. In which war was the Battle of the Bulge?

20. Which northern dish is made primarily from minced pork fat and pig's blood?

ANSWERS: *1 India and Pakistan, 2 A swan, 3 Liverpool, 4 Treason, 5 The Lira, 6 Goalkeeper, 7 John the Baptist, 8 Switzerland, 9 Centre court, 10 Humphrey Bogart, 11 USA and Mexico, 12 Choreography, 13 Euston, 14 President Kennedy, 15 Black, 16 A buoy, 17 The Cavaliers, 18 Judaism, 19 World War Two, 20 Black pudding.*

General Knowledge

1. Of which country was Nicolae Ceausescu leader until 1989?

2. How many hours time difference is there between London and New York?

3. To which political party did John Profumo belong?

4. In which Olympic Games did Mark Spitz win seven gold medals?

5. What is the highest British civilian award for bravery?

6. About which war has Oliver Stone made a trilogy of movies?

7. What type of ship is a dreadnought?

8. How many members does the US Supreme Court have?

9. What does a black hole absorb?

10. Which was the biggest box-office film of 1993?

11. From which bean is chocolate made?

12. Which saint is believed to guard the gates of heaven?

13. From which country is the sitar?

14. The Scilly Islands are part of which county?

15. In which decade did punk rock emerge?

16. What is the pub called in *EastEnders*?

17. What is the British theatrical equivalent of American vaudeville?

18. From which country was *Heidi* in the children's novel?

19. In which mountain range is K2?

20. Which bone is called the femur?

ANSWERS: 1 *Romania,* **2** *Five,* **3** *The Conservative Party,* **4** *The 1972 Olympics,* **5** *The George Cross,* **6** *The Vietnam War,* **7** *A battleship,* **8** *Nine,* **9** *Matter,* **10** *Jurassic Park,* **11** *The cocoa bean,* **12** *St Peter,* **13** *India,* **14** *Cornwall,* **15** *The 1970's,* **16** *The Queen Victoria,* **17** *Music hall,* **18** *Switzerland,* **19** *The Karakorams,* **20** *Thighbone.*

General Knowledge

1. Which cooking fat is prepared from pigs?

2. Which antiseptic is violet-black?

3. What type of creature is an Australian kookaburra?

4. In which American state is the Mojave Desert?

5. What was the former name of Ho Chi Minh City?

6. Which former England manager has been appointed coach of FC Porto?

7. What does an invertebrate not have?

8. Who starred as *Kojak*?

9. Which paper size is the standard for typewriters in the UK?

10. What is someone equally expert with each hand called?

11. Which motorway connects London and Wales?

12. Which Dickens character met trouble when asking for more gruel?

13. With which punk rock group was Sid Vicious primarily associated?

14. What are members of the junior scouting association called?

15. Off which continent are the Seychelles?

16. For which side did Robert E Lee fight in the American Civil War?

17. Which religious group would undertake a jihad?

18. For what is LCD an abbreviation in maths?

19. What is the inability to read and write called?

20. For which country did Diego Maradona play?

ANSWERS: 1 Lard, 2 Iodine, 3 A bird, 4 California, 5 Saigon, 6 Bobby Robson, 7 A backbone, 8 Telly Savalas, 9 A4, 10 Ambidextrous, 11 The M4, 12 Oliver Twist, 13 The Sex Pistols , 14 Cub Scouts, 15 Africa, 16 The Confederates, 17 Muslims, 18 Lowest common denominator, 19 Illiteracy, 20 Argentina.

Sports

1. Which boxer defeated Peter McNeeley in his first fight since leaving prison?
2. Which England team-mate described Will Carling as, "not more qualified than several others to be captain and with a rare arrogance"?
3. In which year was FIFA founded?
4. Which Watford-born footballer played for Chelsea and Sheffield United before returning to Wimbledon?
5. What nationality is golfer David Graham?
6. At what sport was Mysterious Billy Smith a champion?
7. In 1995, which cricket team lost their first Test series for 15 years?
8. Who won the 1994 Tennents Irish Cup in hockey?
9. In 1995, which team payed £4.5m for Chris Armstrong?
10. Which cricketer captained Australia in 93 Tests?

11. Who won the women's singles title at the 1995 US Open?
12. At what sport does Phil Whitlock compete?
13. From which club did Rangers sign Basile Boli?
14. Who won the 1987 rugby union world cup?
15. Which game does the Ukrainian Vladimir Malaniuk play?
16. Who was the 1994 women's USPGA champion?
17. To which team did Manchester United sell Paul Ince for £7.5m?
18. Who was the men's world figure skating champion in 1993?
19. Who was the first Welsh world snooker champion?
20. In which year was the Ryder Cup first held in Britain?

ANSWERS: 1 *Mike Tyson,* **2** *Brian Moore,* **3** *1904,* **4** *Vinny Jones,* **5** *Australian,* **6** *Boxing,* **7** *The West Indies,* **8** *Lisnagarvey,* **9** *Tottenham Hotspur,* **10** *Allan Border,* **11** *Steffi Graf,* **12** *Squash,* **13** *Marseille,* **14** *New Zealand,* **15** *Chess,* **16** *Laura Davies,* **17** *Inter Milan,* **18** *Kurt Browning,* **19** *Ray Reardon,* **20** *1929.*

General Knowledge

1. Who directed the film *Manhattan* ?

2. From which country is snooker player Ray Reardon?

3. Which two oceans does the Strait of Magellan join?

4. What type of person would have a "nom de plume"?

5. Which great military leader established the Mongol Empire?

6. In which year did the GCSE come into effect?

7. In which country did Pol Pot have a reign of terror?

8. In which World War was the spitfire used?

9. Which US president was a peanut farmer?

10. Chief Buthelezi is the head of which South African tribe?

11. What does FBI stand for?

12. Which country did Iraq invade to begin the Gulf War?

13. From which Premier League club was Graeme Souness fired?

14. What is the Church of England's ruling body called?

15. Of which country are the Faroe Islands a part?

16. Who played *The Fly* in the 1986 remake?

17. What is the roof of the mouth called?

18. Which Japanese motor company cut its ties with Rover?

19. In which element is spinach rich?

20. Who directed *E.T.*?

General Knowledge

1. What did Antoine Becquerel discover to win a Nobel Prize?

2. At which racecourse is the Derby run?

3. What was Cliff Richard's backing group called?

4. Where is a scorpion's venom located?

5. Which German composer wrote the *Eroica* symphony?

6. In which year were the Birmingham Six convicted?

7. In which century was *The Canterbury Tales* written?

8. What medal did Torvill and Dean win at the 1994 Winter Olympics?

9. Which number system uses combinations of the digits 1 and 0?

10. About which form of transport was the 1963 Beeching Report?

11. What was Picasso's first name?

12. In which US state is Death Valley?

13. In which religion is Rosh Hashanah celebrated?

14. What type of animal is a chow-chow?

15. On which date is Hallowe'en?

16. In which county is Halifax?

17. Of which American government agency was George Bush director 1976-81?

18. Which *Home Alone* star was in *My Girl*?

19. From what animal is cashmere derived?

20. Which country was ruled by Papa Doc?

ANSWERS: 1 *Radioactivity in Uranium*, **2** Epsom, **3** The Shadows, **4** The tail, **5** Beethoven, **6** 1975, **7** The Fourteenth Century, **8** Bronze, **9** The binary system, **10** The railways, **11** Pablo, **12** California, **13** Judaism, **14** A dog, **15** October 31, **16** West Yorkshire, **17** The CIA, **18** Macaulay Culkin, **19** A goat, **20** Haiti.

General Knowledge

1. The Book of Common Prayer is the service book of which church?

2. Which former East German city was devastated by Allied fire-bombing in 1945?

3. What is a Geiger counter used to measure?

4. In which county is Carlisle?

5. In which city institution would you find bears and bulls?

6. Which part of the body is affected by gingivitis?

7. Who starred in *Rebel Without A Cause* and *Giant*?

8. Who played Sally in *When Harry Met Sally...*?

9. In which European country was there a post-war Fourth Republic?

10. Jake La Motta and Sugar Ray Robinson fought at which weight?

11. Jakarta is the capital of which Asian country?

12. Who wrote *The Postman Always Rings Twice*?

13. A cygnet is the young of which bird?

14. What did alchemists believe a philosopher's stone could turn base metals into?

15. In which country is the Yangtze Kiang?

16. Which system of hills is known as 'the backbone of England'?

17. What is the highest rank in the British army?

18. For what is PAYE an abbreviation?

19. Who wrote *The Pilgrim's Progress*?

20. In which country was *A Dry White Season* set?

ANSWERS: 1 *The Church of England,* 2 *Dresden,* 3 *Radiation,* 4 *Cumbria,* 5 *The Stock Exchange,* 6 *The gums,* 7 *James Dean,* 8 *Meg Ryan,* 9 *France,* 10 *Middleweight,* 11 *Indonesia,* 12 *James M Cain,* 13 *A swan,* 14 *Gold,* 15 *China,* 16 *The Pennines,* 17 *Field Marshal,* 18 *Pay As You Earn,* 19 *John Bunyan,* 20 *South Africa.*

Entertainment

Your rating: ● 0-5   **Buy a TV**   ● 6-10   **Keep at it**
   ● 11-15   **Join a quiz team**   ● 16-20   **Enter Telly Addicts**

1. Which Spanish smoothie had a 1981 No 1 hit with *Begin the Beguine*?
2. Who was the spiky-haired presenter of the computer programmes *Bad Influence* and *Head to Head*?
3. Who played the brutal sheriff in *Unforgiven*?
4. Who held the No 1 spot for nine weeks with *Two Tribes*?
5. Which U.S. series is set in Cicely, Alaska?
6. Which *Betrayed* star is in steamy sex thriller *Sliver*?
7. Which former weather girl co-presents *Gladiators*?
8. Who played Sue Ellen in *Dallas*?
9. Which British group have had a record seventeen No 1 hits?
10. Who co-starred with Tom Hanks in *Sleepless in Seattle*?
11. Which star of *Terry and June* was in *Absolutely Fabulous*?
12. Which two rock idols covered *Dancing in the Street* in 1985?
13. Which prolific British film-maker directed *Much Ado About Nothing*?
14. Which 'middle-class' soap opera was axed by the BBC in 1995 after only 24 episodes?
15. Who sang *It's Not Unusual* in 1965?
16. Who starred as *The Assassin*?
17. Which writer created *Inspector Morse*?
18. Which singer had a big hit with *These Boots Are Made For Walkin'*?
19. Who played the agony aunt in *Agony* and *Agony Again*?
20. Who stars as psychologist Fitz in *Cracker*?

General Knowledge

1. What type of creature is a macaque?

2. In which European country is the Black Forest?

3. In which year was the Bhopal disaster in India?

4. In which US city was the St Valentine's Day Massacre?

5. Which country first issued a death decree against Salman Rushdie?

6. What type of professional would belong to RIBA?

7. In which year did Mathias Rust land a light aircraft in Red Square?

8. In which county is Cheddar, famous for its cheese production?

9. In which Californian city is Beverly Hills?

10. What is a small body that orbits a larger one called?

11. In which sport was 'Babe' Ruth an all-time great?

12. Digitalis increases the efficiency of which human organ?

13. In which branch of science is quantum theory used?

14. Which Russian author wrote *Crime and Punishment*?

15. What is the highest possible score with one throw in darts?

16. Dijon is famous for producing which condiment?

17. What is a cyclone called in the China Seas?

18. Who wrote *Death on the Nile*?

19. For which sporting body is IOC an abbreviation?

20. In which year did the Iran-Iraq war end?

ANSWERS: 1 A monkey, 2 Germany, 3 1984, 4 Chicago, 5 Iran, 6 An architect, 7 1987, 8 Somerset, 9 Los Angeles, 10 A satellite, 11 Baseball, 12 The heart, 13 Physics, 14 Dostoevsky, 15 60, 16 Mustard, 17 A typhoon, 18 Agatha Christie, 19 The International Olympic Committee, 20 1988.

General Knowledge

1. What is Mikhail Gorbachev's wife called?

2. From which city's stock-exchange is the Dow Jones average?

3. With which intellectual discipline are Marx, Weber and Durkheim associated?

4. Which composer wrote *Bolero*?

5. Which punctuation mark is used for vehement commands?

6. In which country is Lough Neagh?

7. What type of creature is an abalone?

8. Hodgkin's disease is a rare form of which condition?

9. Of which U.S. state is Atlanta capital?

10. In which armed forces has the Iron Cross been awarded since 1813?

11. Which minister lives at number 11 Downing Street?

12. In which US state is Cape Canaveral?

13. What is Tibet's Forbidden City?

14. What is the more common name for dyspepsia?

15. What is the collective name for large thick-skinned animals such as elephants and rhinoceroses?

16. The letter k is the symbol for which unit of weight?

17. In which motor sport do cars race short distances at up to 290 mph?

18. Which English novelist created Chief Inspector Wexford?

19. For which party was Stanley Baldwin prime minister?

20. Which monetary unit is worth one-hundredth of a French franc?

ANSWERS: 1 Raisa, 2 New York, 3 Sociology, 4 Maurice Ravel, 5 Exclamation mark, 6 Northern Ireland, 7 A marine mollusc, 8 Cancer, 9 Georgia, 10 German armed forces, 11 The Chancellor of the Exchequer, 12 Florida, 13 Lhasa, 14 Indigestion, 15 Pachyderms, 16 A kilogram, 17 Drag racing, 18 Ruth Rendell, 19 Conservative, 20 A centime.

General Knowledge

1. Through what does a butterfly suck up nectar?

2. Which Californian city is infamous for its smog?

3. With which instrument is Stradivarius primarily associated?

4. Who wrote and illustrated *The Tailor of Gloucester*?

5. Which landlocked country is bordered by Germany, Belgium and France?

6. In which country is Penang?

7. Who wrote *Schindler's Ark*?

8. Which star of *The Godfather* acted in *Guys and Dolls*?

9. Of which flightless bird are the emperor and jackass varieties?

10. Of which former country was Tito prime minister and president?

11. What nationality was Rembrandt?

12. What sank the *Titanic*?

13. Of which Motown trio were Diana Ross and Mary Wilson members?

14. In which Asian city is the famous Raffles Hotel?

15. How many sports comprise a pentathlon?

16. Which singer played the female lead in *Prince of Tides*?

17. What type of towns are Bath, Tunbridge Wells and Epsom?

18. Which snooker ball is worth six points?

19. Through which process are animal skins turned into leather?

20. In what voice range does Luciano Pavarotti sing?

ANSWERS: *1 A proboscis, 2 Los Angeles, 3 Aaron, 4 Beatrix Potter, 5 Luxembourg, 6 Malaysia, 7 Thomas Keneally, 8 Marlon Brando, 9 The penguin, 10 Yugoslavia, 11 Dutch, 12 An iceberg, 13 The Supremes, 14 Singapore, 15 Five, 16 Barbra Streisand, 17 Spa towns, 18 The pink, 19 Tanning, 20 Tenor.*

Entertainment

Your rating:
● 0-5 Buy a TV ● 6-10 Keep at it
● 11-15 Join a quiz team ● 16-20 Enter Telly Addicts

1. Who was the lead guitarist of Led Zeppelin?
2. Which rock-'n'-roller sang *My Ding-A Ling* and *Roll Over Beethoven*?
3. Who starred as Jerry Lee Lewis in *Great Balls of Fire*?
4. Which *Moonraker* star was *The Saint*?
5. Which icon of the '60s sang *Lay Lady Lay*?
6. Who presents knock-out general knowledge quiz *Fifteen to One*?
7. What is the police station called in *The Bill*?
8. Which actors played the wayward brothers in *The Blues Brothers*?
9. Which football manager had a Top 40 hit in 1979 with *Head Over Heels In Love*?
10. Who played *The Six Million Dollar Man*?
11. Who sang the original version of *First Time Ever I Saw Your Face*?
12. In which city was Armistead Maupin's Tales of the City set?
13. Who played the ambitious secretary in *Working Girl*?
14. What is the name of Mitch Buchannon's son in *Baywatch*?
15. With which group did Paul McCartney sing *Mull of Kintyre*?
16. Which actress plays Patricia Farnham in *Brookside*?
17. Who played the romeo husband in *I Love You to Death*?
18. Which star of *Orlando* became a living work of art in 1995 at the Serpentine Gallery?
19. Who directed the 1938 comedy/murder mystery *The Lady Vanishes*?
20. Which group sang *Hotel California*?

ANSWERS: 1 Jimmy Page, 2 Chuck Berry, 3 Dennis Quaid, 4 Roger Moore, 5 Bob Dylan, 6 William G Stewart, 7 Sun Hill, 8 John Belushi and Dan Aykroyd, 9 Kevin Keegan, 10 Lee Majors, 11 Roberta Flack, 12 San Francisco, 13 Melanie Griffith, 14 Hobie, 15 Wings, 16 Gabrielle Glaister, 17 Kevin Kline, 18 Tilda Swinton, 19 Alfred Hitchcock, 20 The Eagles.

General Knowledge

1. What is the collective name for Athos, Porthos and Aramis?

2. An ibex is a type of which creature?

3. From which country is opera singer Kiri Te Kanawa?

4. In which war was the My Lai massacre?

5. Who played the big-nosed fireman in *Roxanne*?

6. What is surgical removal of the uterus called?

7. In which year did the SAS storm the Iranian embassy?

8. What is a Muslim house of worship called?

9. Which instrument did Fats Domino play?

10. The statue of which mythological creature stands in front of the Egyptian pyramids at El Giza?

11. Aeroflot is the national airline of which country?

12. For what part of the body is umbilicus the technical term?

13. The eruption of which volcano buried Pompeii?

14. Which Steven Spielberg film has won seven Oscars?

15. What is the fairy called in *Peter Pan*?

16. In which county is Margate?

17. By which abbreviation is the explosive trinitrotoluene known?

18. Against which country did the UK wage the Opium Wars?

19. In which century did Samuel Pepys write his diary?

20. What is the name of the sled dog used in Arctic regions?

ANSWERS: *1 The Three Musketeers, 2 The goat, 3 New Zealand, 4 The Vietnam War, 5 Steve Martin, 6 Hysterectomy, 7 1980, 8 A mosque, 9 The piano, 10 The Sphinx, 11 Russia, 12 The navel, 13 Vesuvius, 14 Schindler's List, 15 Tinker Bell, 16 Kent, 17 TNT, 18 China, 19 The 17th century, 20 The husky.*

General Knowledge

1. What was the name of the donkey in *Winnie-the-Pooh*?

2. In which county is the Lake District?

3. Which English winger was known as "the Wizard of the Dribble"?

4. Which blind singer recorded *Superstition* and *Happy Birthday*?

5. For which Test cricket team do the Benjamin brothers play?

6. Which Manchester United player was sent off in successive games?

7. In which U.S. state is Venice Beach?

8. With which music are B.B. King and Muddy Waters associated?

9. On which London street did *Sherlock Holmes* live?

10. What is the English name for the Italian city Firenze?

11. For which invention is Samuel Colt famous?

12. Dacca is the capital of which Asian country?

13. Gobi and Kalahari are names of which natural feature?

14. In Greek mythology, of what was Aphrodite goddess?

15. With which international team did Ruud Gullit win the European Championship?

16. With which country are Boers associated?

17. Which eccentric fictional nanny was created by P L Travers?

18. By which method was Marie Antoinette executed?

19. Who wrote *The Old Curiosity Shop*?

20. Kerala, Goa and Bihar are states of which country?

ANSWERS: 1 Eeyore, 2 Cumbria, 3 Stanley Matthews, 4 Stevie Wonder, 5 The West Indies, 6 Eric Cantona, 7 California, 8 Blues, 9 Baker Street, 10 Florence, 11 The revolver, 12 Bangladesh, 13 Desert, 14 Love, 15 The Netherlands, 16 South Africa, 17 Mary Poppins, 18 The guillotine, 19 Charles Dickens, 20 India.

General Knowledge

1. Elephant and grey are varieties of which marine creature?

2. In which London borough is Mayfair?

3. A dialysis machine is used as a substitute for which organ?

4. Which detective writer wrote *The Maltese Falcon*?

5. What is measured on the Beaufort scale?

6. In which year was British India divided into Pakistan and India?

7. Which language is spoken in Israel?

8. The Volga is the longest river in which continent?

9. Which *Frantic* star played the futuristic cop in *Blade Runner*?

10. Which team won the 1994 Coca-Cola Cup in England?

11. The League of Nations was formed after which major war?

12. A mullah is a teacher in which religion?

13. Auschwitz was notorious as what in World War Two?

14. The Madeira islands form an autonomous region of what country?

15. Which famous martial artist starred in *Enter the Dragon*?

16. Who won the 1982 Football World Cup?

17. In which town is GCHQ, centre of electronic surveillance operations?

18. By what forename was Gabrielle Chanel known?

19. Cagliari is the capital of which Italian region?

20. Which singer made *Purple Rain*?

Entertainment

1. Which rap stars sang *Boom! Shake The Room*?
2. Who directed and starred in *Braveheart*?
3. Who presents *Telly Addicts*?
4. Which soap features Doctor Legg?
5. Which *Gladiator* is heptathlete Judy Simpson?
6. Which Beach Boy released an album called *I Just Wasn't Made For These Times*?
7. Who played the male half of *Bonnie and Clyde* in the classic outlaw film?
8. Which post-war comedy drama starred Griff Rhys Jones and Martin Clunes?
9. Who presented the youth-culture series *D Energy*?
10. Who played the black Philadelphia detective in *In The Heat of the Night*?
11. From which city did Frankie Goes To Hollywood come from?
12. Which Coen brothers' film starred Nicolas Cage and Holly Hunter as a couple who steal a baby?
13. Who, after some *Dreams,* was *Going Nowhere*?
14. Which rock star played a drugged-out rock star in *Performance*?
15. What is *Roseanne's* sister called?
16. Which high-voiced trio sang *Night Fever* and *Stayin' Alive*?
17. Which veteran comedy actor played *Dennis's* grumpy neighbour?

18. Tony Slattery broke the head off a £1,000 antique figurine during the relaunch of which TV quiz show?
19. Who sang *Goldfinger*, the theme from the James Bond film?
20. Who played Ike Turner in *What's Love Got To Do With It*?

General Knowledge

1. The headquarters of the International Olympic Committee are in which Swiss city?

2. Who was king of England 1272-1307?

3. How was jazz musician Ferdinand Joseph La Menthe Morton better known?

4. What is the capital of the state of Alabama?

5. Which 19th century French nun was known as the Little Flower of Jesus?

6. Which dramatist wrote *School for Scandal* and *The Rivals*?

7. Which metal is represented by the symbol Os?

8. What is a theodolite used to measure?

9. Which Russian theatre company was co-founded by Konstantin Stanislavsky?

10. What is the capital of the Bahamas?

11. Which Turkish town was the birthplace of St Paul?

12. Who was the first Bourbon king of Spain?

13. Nation of Islam leader Louis Farrakhan inspired a 'million man march' in which city?

14. On which Hebridean island is Fingal's Cave?

15. Jan Smuts was prime minister of which country 1919-24 and 1939-48?

16. Who wrote *She Stoops to Conquer* and *The Vicar of Wakefield*?

17. The Pilgrimage of Grace was a revolt against which English king?

18. What sort of creature was a tarpan?

19. Who directed *The Grapes of Wrath* and *Stagecoach*?

20. Which poem polled the most votes in the BBC's 1995 National Poetry Day competition?

General Knowledge

1. Which *Blade Runner* star played a mercenary pilot in *Star Wars*?

2. Who wrote and recorded *Walk on the Wild Side*?

3. In the Bible, for how many years did the Israelites wander in the wilderness?

4. In which country is the Royal and Ancient golf club?

5. How many letters does the Greek alphabet have?

6. In which country is legend-rich Transylvania?

7. Of which country is Wellington capital?

8. For what is VIP an abbreviation?

9. What are raced in the Isle of Man TT?

10. Victoria, damson and greengage are varieties of which fruit?

11. In which Greater London borough is Wembley Stadium?

12. In *Jack and the Beanstalk*, what does Jack exchange for magic beans?

13. For what is china clay another name?

14. What is the capital of Mali?

15. Of which radio comedy team were Peter Sellers and Spike Milligan members?

16. Which British politician founded the British Union of Fascists?

17. From which country was the composer Haydn?

18. David Byrne was lead singer of which new-wave rock group from 1975?

19. What is the technical name for the collarbone?

20. Which country music singer starred in *Nine to Five*?

ANSWERS: 1 Harrison Ford, 2 Lou Reed, 3 Forty, 4 Scotland, 5 24, 6 Romania, 7 New Zealand, 8 Very important person, 9 Motorcycles, 10 The plum, 11 Brent, 12 A cow, 13 Kaolin, 14 Bamako, 15 The Goons, 16 Oswald Mosley, 17 Austria, 18 Talking Heads, 19 Clavicle, 20 Dolly Parton.

General Knowledge

1.   For which UN agency is WHO an abbreviation?

2.   Sark is one of which islands?

3.   In which county is Sellafield nuclear power plant?

4.   Which country launched the Voyager space probes?

5.   On which planet was *Superman* born?

6.   Which duo had a huge hit with *Bye Bye Love*?

7.   The ill-fated Maginot Line was supposed to defend which country?

8.   What is poetry without metrical form called?

9.   Who wrote *The Water-Babies*?

10. What is the highest mountain in Wales?

11. Which American president introduced the New Deal in 1933?

12. In which country did mah-jongg originate?

13. What colour was the whale in *Moby Dick*?

14. Which horse won the 1994 Grand National?

15. Who wrote *The Railway Children*?

16. Sumo wrestling is from which Asian country?

17. In which county is the port and resort Felixstowe?

18. Who played the zany scientist in *Honey I Shrunk the Kids*?

19. Agents of which American agency were nicknamed the G-men?

20. Jesse Jackson contested the 1984 and 1988 presidential nominations for which party?

ANSWERS: *1 The World Health Organisation, 2 The Channel Islands, 3 Cumbria, 4 The USA, 5 Krypton, 6 The Everly Brothers, 7 France, 8 Free verse, 9 Charles Kingsley, 10 Snowdon, 11 Franklin D Roosevelt, 12 China, 13 White, 14 Minnehoma, 15 Edith Nesbit, 16 Japan, 17 Suffolk, 18 Rick Moranis, 19 The FBI, 20 The Democratic Party.*

Entertainment

1. Which jazz band had a Top Ten hit in 1961 with *Take Five*?
2. Which *Crossroads* character was played by actor Paul Henry?
3. Which comic great starred in *The Gold Rush* and *The Great Dictator*?
4. Which former Wimbledon and Aston Villa footballer has presented *Gladiators*?
5. What was Chaka Demus and Pliers's follow-up to *Tease Me*?
6. Who wrote the book on which the 1959 adventure movie *Journey to the Centre of the Earth* was based?
7. Who played the charismatic preacher in *Mr Wroe's Virgins*?
8. Who sang *Crocodile Rock* and *Daniel*?
9. Who played James Bond in *Goldfinger*?
10. Which *Malcolm X* star was in *Much Ado About Nothing*?
11. Who has co-presented *Live and Kicking* and *Talking Telephone Numbers*?
12. Which 1995 Joel Hershman comedy film starred Sean Young and Diane Ladd?
13. Who had a hit with *Alphabet Street*?
14. Which British actress starred in *The Stepford Wives*?
15. Which British band released an album called *The Great Escape*?
16. Who played the tough private detective in *Chinatown*?
17. Which slogan did Wolfie shout at the end of every *Citizen Smith* episode?
18. Which Beatles member had a big 70's hit with *My Sweet Lord*?
19. Who directed *Raiders of the Lost Ark*?
20. Which comedian played timeshare salesman Simon Treat in *One for the Road*?

ANSWERS: 1 Dave Brubeck Quartet, 2 Benny, 3 Charlie Chaplin, 4 John Fashanu, 5 She Don't Let Nobody, 6 Jules Verne, 7 Jonathan Pryce, 8 Elton John, 9 Sean Connery, 10 Denzel Washington, 11 Emma Forbes, 12 Hold Me, Thrill Me, Kiss Me, 13 Prince, 14 Nanette Newman, 15 Blur, 16 Jack Nicholson, 17 "Power to the people", 18 George Harrison, 19 Steven Spielberg, 20 Alan Davies.

General Knowledge

1. What kind of creature is a chiffchaff?

2. Cider is made from which fruit?

3. Juan Peron was dictator of which country?

4. Stanley is capital of which Atlantic islands?

5. With which animal would you associate the constellation Ursa Major?

6. In which US state is Key West?

7. Which dance movement comprises a complete turn of the body on one leg with the other raised?

8. The Weimaraner is a breed of which animal?

9. In which sport was Pat Smythe European champion four times?

10. Of which game was Bobby Fischer world champion?

11. In which county is the Peak District National Park?

12. Who played the female lead in *Cabaret*?

13. Which Jamaican-Canadian sprinter was disqualified for steroid abuse at the 1988 Olympics?

14. What is a theorbo?

15. In Roman mythology, who was the god of war?

16. Who played Peter Pan in *Hook*?

17. Which architect laid out Regent's Park?

18. Who played the devil in *The Witches of Eastwick*?

19. Which football team plays at Molineux?

20. Who wrote *Orlando*?

ANSWERS: *1 A bird, 2 The apple, 3 Argentina, 4 The Falkland Islands, 5 A bear, 6 Florida, 7 A pirouette, 8 Dog, 9 Showjumping, 10 Chess, 11 Derbyshire, 12 Liza Minnelli, 13 Ben Johnson, 14 A string instrument, 15 Mars, 16 Robin Williams, 17 John Nash, 18 Jack Nicholson, 19 Wolverhampton Wanderers, 20 Virginia Woolf.*

General Knowledge

1. In which US state is the Valley of Ten Thousand Smokes?

2. Who wrote *The Sun Also Rises*?

3. Theravada is a school of which religion?

4. What is the capital of Niger?

5. In England, which organisation controls heraldry?

6. Which Australian island was once known as Van Diemen's Land?

7. Which 1920s cinema idol starred in *The Sheik* and *Blood and Sand*?

8. Which former UK prime minister died in October 1995?

9. Which royal dynasty of France succeeded the Capetians in 1328?

10. What is the second largest state of the USA?

11. Which Italian poet wrote *Rinaldo* and *Aminta*?

12. For which academic qualification does PhD stand?

13. The beating of which black motorist sparked off the 1992 LA riots?

14. What type of creature is Beethoven in *Beethoven's Second*?

15. Which commonly used Latin phrase means "the other way around"?

16. Who wrote children's fantasy *Charlie and the Chocolate Factory*?

17. Which group had hits with *Caravan of Love* and *Happy Hour*?

18. Which unit of astronomical distance is equivalent to approximately 5.87 billion miles?

19. Who wrote *To Kill a Mockingbird*?

20. In which year did Edmund Hillary first reach the summit of Mount Everest?

ANSWERS: *1* Alaska, *2* Ernest Hemingway, *3* Buddhism, *4* Niamey, *5* The College of Arms, *6* Tasmania, *7* Rudolf Valentino, *8* Sir Alec Douglas-Home, *9* Valois, *10* Texas, *11* Torquato Tasso, *12* Doctor of Philosophy, *13* Rodney King, *14* A dog, *15* Vice versa, *16* Roald Dahl, *17* The Housemartins, *18* A light year, *19* Harper Lee, *20* 1953.

General Knowledge

1. In which county is Aldershot?

2. Who was British prime minister 1970-74?

3. Which Russian playwright wrote *The Cherry Orchard*?

4. From which religion are the gods Vishnu, Siva and Brahma?

5. Which group had hits with *My Girl* and *Baggy Trousers*?

6. How many feet above the ground is a basketball hoop?

7. Which U.S. civil rights leader made the famous "I have a dream" speech?

8. Which classic TV comedy concerned Norman Stanley Fletcher?

9. Which mythological character died when he flew too close to the sun?

10. In which country would you find a kibbutz?

11. Which film is about the 'fifth Beatle' Stuart Sutcliffe?

12. By what name is Constantinople now known?

13. An ibex is a wild type of which creature?

14. Conjunctivitis affects which part of the body?

15. Oscar-winning film *The Last Emperor* was set in which country?

16. Which book of the Old Testament includes the flight of the Israelites from Egypt?

17. Which part of London is famous for a (now inoperative) power station and a dogs' home?

18. Basque and Catalan are spoken in which country?

19. MSc is an abbreviation for which educational qualification?

20. In which county is Hastings?

ANSWERS: *1 Hampshire, 2 Edward Heath, 3 Anton Chekhov, 4 Hinduism, 5 Madness, 6 Ten feet, 7 Martin Luther King, 8 Porridge, 9 Icarus, 10 Israel, 11 Backbeat, 12 Istanbul, 13 Goat, 14 The eye, 15 China, 16 Exodus, 17 Battersea, 18 Spain, 19 Master of Science, 20 East Sussex.*

Entertainment

1. Which popular TV programme introduced Mr Blobby to the world?

2. Which comedian took us on a *World Tour of Scotland* on TV?

3. Which punk band released an album entitled *Soapy Water & Mr Marmalade*?

4. Which actress played Humphrey Bogart's lost love in *Casablanca*?

5. Who was nominated for a Best Actor Oscar for his performance in *Four Weddings and a Funeral*?

6. Which late British comedian had a No 1 with *Ernie (The Fastest Milkman in the West)*?

7. What is the *Teenage Mutant Ninja Turtles'* favourite food?

8. Which interviewer can be seen *Face to Face*?

9. Which Motown favourite had a hit with *Chain Reaction*?

10. Who played Rene in *'Allo 'Allo!*?

11. Who had a No 1 with *Bohemian Rhapsody*?

12. Which comedy series set in a solicitor's office stars Imelda Staunton and Patrick Barlow?

13. Which Midlands band sang the rather oddly-titled *RSVP/Familus Horribilus*?

14. What was *Boon's* first name?

15. Who played Steve Biko in *Cry Freedom*?

16. Which *Brookside* character is played by Vince Earl?

17. Who sang the original version of *I'm Every Woman* in 1978?

18. Which camp comedian starred in *Terry and Julian*?

19. Who wrote the book on which the 1975 thriller *Farewell My Lovely* was based?

20. Who crossed the world in *Pole to Pole*?

ANSWERS: 1 *Noel's House Party,* **2** *Billy Connolly,* **3** *Sham 69,* **4** *Ingrid Bergman,* **5** *Hugh Grant,* **6** *Benny Hill,* **7** *Pizza,* **8** *Jeremy Isaacs,* **9** *Diana Ross,* **10** *Gorden Kaye,* **11** *Queen,* **12** *Is It Legal?,* **13** *Pop Will Eat Itself,* **14** *Ken,* **15** *Denzel Washington,* **16** *Ron Dixon,* **17** *Chaka Khan,* **18** *Julian Clary,* **19** *Raymond Chandler,* **20** *Michael Palin.*

General Knowledge

1. What was the nationality of Edvard Munch, painter of *The Scream*?

2. What is the only mammal which can truly fly?

3. Which war was fought between Russia and England, France, Turkey and Sardinia?

4. Which Greek mythological hero performed 12 arduous labours?

5. With which instrument is Ray Charles associated?

6. *The Marriage of Figaro* was composed by which Austrian composer?

7. DPP is an abbreviation for which legal position?

8. Space shuttle landing site Edwards Air Force Base is in which American state?

9. Which aquatic rodent constructs dams and lives in a lodge?

10. Which American scientist invented the phonograph and electric filament lamp?

11. Which glasses have lenses with two different focuses?

12. What is the capital of the Czech Republic?

13. Which star of *The World According to Garp* was in *Toys*?

14. Which legendary Greek epic poet wrote the *Iliad* and the *Odyssey*?

15. Which American playwright wrote *Death of a Salesman*?

16. What nationality was racing driver Ayrton Senna?

17. Which islands are home to giant tortoises and Darwin's finches?

18. Which composer wrote the US folk opera *Porgy and Bess*?

19. Which Republican politician led the anti-Communist "witch-hunts" in the 1950s?

20. Which of the knights in Arthurian legend found the Holy Grail?

ANSWERS: *1 Norwegian, 2 The bat, 3 The Crimean War, 4 Heracles or Hercules, 5 The piano, 6 Mozart, 7 The Director of Public Prosecutions, 8 California, 9 The beaver, 10 Thomas Edison, 11 Bifocals, 12 Prague, 13 Robin Williams, 14 Homer, 15 Arthur Miller, 16 Brazilian, 17 The Galapagos Islands, 18 George Gershwin, 19 Joe McCarthy, 20 Sir Galahad.*

General Knowledge

1. Chiang Kai-shek was president of which country after leaving China?

2. What is the study and tracing of family histories called?

3. The Jarrow Crusade in 1936 was a march from Jarrow to which city?

4. Which Irish playwright wrote *The Plough and the Stars*?

5. What was the largest known meat-eating dinosaur?

6. Which New Zealander won the Booker Prize for *The Bone People*?

7. Which composer is associated with the Aldeburgh festival?

8. Which classic 1973 film starred Paul Newman and Robert Redford as con artists?

9. In which year were the Olympic Games held in Moscow?

10. In which South American country did the Inca civilisation originate?

11. In which year was the Space Shuttle first launched?

12. Osiris was a god in which country's mythology?

13. Who composed the opera *Carmen*?

14. Brazil was colonised by which European country from 1500?

15. Which *Starsky and Hutch* star had a No. 1 with *Don't Give Up on Us*?

16. What is usually the first hole on the inward half of a round of golf?

17. Which Soviet leader introduced the policy of glasnost?

18. What is the highest rank in the British Army?

19. Which debonair British actor played Phileas Fogg in the 1956 film *Around the World in Eighty Days*?

20. Times Square is in which American city?

ANSWERS: *1 Taiwan, 2 Genealogy, 3 London, 4 Sean O'Casey, 5 Tyrannosaurus rex, 6 Keri Hulme, 7 Benjamin Britten, 8 The Sting, 9 1980, 10 Peru, 11 1981, 12 Egypt, 13 Georges Bizet, 14 Portugal, 15 David Soul, 16 The tenth, 17 Mikhail Gorbachev, 18 Field Marshal, 19 David Niven, 20 New York City.*

General Knowledge

1. Sunni and Shi'ite are the two main sects of which religion?

2. Bouillabaisse is a rich stew originating in which country?

3. Truro is the administrative headquarters of which county?

4. Which imperial measure of length is equal to 1760 yards?

5. Which country singer had hits with *Lucille* and *Coward of the County*?

6. The SALT and START talks were between which two countries?

7. Turmeric is a seasoning and dye of which colour?

8. Which American tennis player won the Wimbledon men's singles title in 1974 and 1982?

9. How many cents are there in a nickel?

10. A pascal is a unit measuring what?

11. Patagonia is a geographic area of which continent?

12. What was the name of the vehicles in which both Donald and Malcolm Campbell set speed records?

13. Peterhouse and Clare are colleges of which famous university?

14. With what type of music were The Wailers associated?

15. Who is the patron saint of Wales?

16. Which Tolkien novel introduces Bilbo Baggins?

17. The name of which American state contains four s's and four i's?

18. Kurt Waldheim was elected president of which country in 1986?

19. Which British football team won the 1994 European Cup Winners' Cup?

20. Which of the Kennedy clan was U.S. Attorney General 1961-64?

ANSWERS: *1 Islam, 2 France, 3 Cornwall, 4 A mile, 5 Kenny Rogers, 6 The USA and the USSR, 7 Yellow, 8 Jimmy Connors, 9 Five, 10 Pressure, 11 South America, 12 Bluebird, 13 Cambridge University, 14 Reggae, 15 St David, 16 The Hobbit, 17 Mississippi, 18 Austria, 19 Arsenal, 20 Robert Kennedy.*

Entertainment

1. Which veteran British comedian played Claude Jeremiah Greengrass in *Heartbeat?*

2. Which jazz singer was also known as 'Lady Day'?

3. Which controversial film about East and West starred Sean Connery and Wesley Snipes?

4. Who was *The Man From Auntie*?

5. Which *Fidder on the Roof* star was in *Seaquest DSV*?

6. Who is the lead singer of INXS?

7. Who starred as Bruce in *Dragon: The Bruce Lee Story*?

8. Who presented the *Life On Earth* series?

9. Who had a hit with *Wuthering Heights* in 1978?

10. Which *Drugstore Cowboy* became *Mr Wonderful*?

11. Who plays Bob Louis in *The Detectives*?

12. Which film featured Elsa, the lioness?

13. Who played Aidan in *EastEnders*?

14. Who sang *Both Sides of the Story*?

15. Who was Tweety-Pie's mortal cartoon enemy?

16. Which comedian had a Top Twenty hit in 1965 with *A Hard Day's Night*?

17. In which Spanish city was *All in the Game* set?

18. Which *Reservoir Dog* starred in *The Piano*?

19. Which *Doctor Who* also starred in *The Hitch Hiker's Guide to the Galaxy*?

20. Who had a No 1 hit in 1976 with *Save Your Kisses For Me*?

ANSWERS: *1 Bill Maynard, 2 Billie Holiday, 3 Rising Sun, 4 Ben Elton, 5 Topol, 6 Michael Hutchence, 7 Jason Scott Lee, 8 David Attenborough, 9 Kate Bush, 10 Matt Dillon, 11 Jasper Carrot, 12 Born Free, 13 Sean Maguire, 14 Phil Collins, 15 Sylvester, 16 Peter Sellers, 17 Barcelona, 18 Harvey Keitel, 19 Peter Davison, 20 Brotherhood of Man.*

General Knowledge

1. Islamabad was designated capital of which country in 1967?

2. In which year did Neil Kinnock resign as Labour Party leader?

3. Who directed and starred in *Much Ado About Nothing*?

4. Michael Manley was prime minister of which country 1972-80 and 1989-92?

5. Iceland is located in which ocean?

6. Which comedian starred as *The Jerk*?

7. Kidderminster is in which county?

8. What is a word that means the same as another word called?

9. In the Bible, whom did Jesus raise from the dead?

10. Damascus is the capital of which Middle Eastern country?

11. Which American comedian starred in *Boomerang*?

12. Who wrote *The Catcher in the Rye*?

13. Which device automatically maintains aircraft on a preset course?

14. Whipsnade Zoo is in which English county?

15. Which *Chinatown* star played *Hoffa*?

16. Who did Jacques Chirac succeed as French president?

17. Who succeeded Nigel Lawson as Chancellor?

18. From which musical is the song *Some Enchanted Evening*?

19. What is the name of a triangular block of glass used to 'bend' a ray of light?

20. A supernova is the explosive death of what?

ANSWERS: 1 Pakistan, 2 1992, 3 Kenneth Branagh, 4 Jamaica, 5 Atlantic , 6 Steve Martin, 7 Hereford and Worcester, 8 A synonym, 9 Lazarus, 10 Syria, 11 Eddie Murphy, 12 JD Salinger, 13 An autopilot, 14 Bedfordshire, 15 Jack Nicholson, 16 Francois Mitterrand, 17 John Major, 18 South Pacific, 19 A prism, 20 A star.

General Knowledge

1. Weston-super-Mare is in which county?

2. Which chess piece can move one square only in any direction?

3. Anwar Sadat was president of which country from 1970 to 1981?

4. For which creatures is ursine the related adjective?

5. Agoraphobia is the fear of what?

6. The Jacobites were supporters of which royal house?

7. Lech ski resort is in which country?

8. Which mathematical term describes the likelihood that an event will occur?

9. Over which female cartoon character do Popeye and Bluto fight?

10. The Seychelles are off the coast of which continent?

11. What type of creatures were *Lady and The Tramp*?

12. Who wrote *The War of the Worlds*?

13. Bobbin and needlepoint are types of which material?

14. Who wrote *Lord of the Flies*?

15. What is the common name for a smoked herring?

16. Who played the insane sister in the 1962 film *What Ever Happened to Baby Jane*?

17. Which pop singer starred in *Desperately Seeking Susan*?

18. The Dail Eireann is part of which country's legislature?

19. In basketball, what is the maximum number of points one shot can score?

20. Who wrote *Heart of Darkness*?

ANSWERS: 1 Avon, **2** The king, **3** Egypt, **4** Bears, **5** Open public spaces, **6** The House of Stuart, **7** Austria, **8** Probability, **9** Olive Oyl, **10** Africa, **11** Dogs, **12** H G Wells, **13** Lace, **14** William Golding, **15** A kipper, **16** Bette Davis, **17** Madonna, **18** The Republic of Ireland, **19** 3, **20** Joseph Conrad.

General Knowledge

1. In Greek mythology, who was the god of dreams?

2. What is social organisation in which women head the family called?

3. Who succeeded Saul as King of Israel?

4. What does the Beaufort Scale measure?

5. Which frozen body deposits moraine?

6. Which invasion took place at Omaha and Juno beaches, among others?

7. IMF is an abbreviation for which financial agency?

8. In which continent have Berbers lived since prehistoric times?

9. What is the Russian currency unit called?

10. The dogfish is a species of which marine creature?

11. What type of vessel is the *Ark Royal*?

12. Which Chinese medical system involves sticking needles into the body?

13. What is the Mexican capital called?

14. Which group recorded the album *Brothers in Arms*?

15. A loon is what type of creature?

16. *A Doll's House* is by which playwright?

17. Which river does the Queen Elizabeth II Bridge cross?

18. Which gold coin was worth 21 shillings?

19. What is the capital of Denmark?

20. The Adriatic is an arm of which sea?

ANSWERS: *1 Morpheus, 2 Matriarchy, 3 David, 4 Wind force, 5 A glacier, 6 D-Day, 7 The International Monetary Fund, 8 Africa, 9 The rouble, 10 The shark, 11 An aircraft carrier, 12 Acupuncture, 13 Mexico City, 14 Dire Straits, 15 A bird, 16 Henrik Ibsen, 17 The Thames, 18 The guinea, 19 Copenhagen, 20 The Mediterranean.*

Sports

1. From which sport was Mir Zaman Gul banned for headbutting?
2. Which manager went from Aston Villa to Coventry in 1995?
3. At what sport does Jan Svorada compete?
4. Which horse won the 1994 Irish Derby?
5. Which golfer won both the Masters and the British Open in 1990?
6. Which US tennis player said , "There is something comforting about having something on your head"?
7. In which field event has athlete Scott Huffman competed?
8. Which golfers entered the three-way play-off in the 1994 US Open?
9. In which sport would you find calf roping and steer wrestling?
10. What nationality was swimmer Lorraine Crapp?
11. In which country was England rugby union full-back Mike Catt born?
12. What nationality is triple jumper Agnieszka Stanczyk?
13. Who ended Mike Tyson's reign as heavyweight champion in Tokyo in 1990?
14. Which Spanish golf course will host the 1997 Ryder Cup?
15. Who did Newcastle chairman Sir John Hall acclaim as "the Kevin Keegan of Rugby Union"?
16. Which Arsenal player received a four-game ban after exceeding 41 points in the '94-'95 season?
17. From which cricket county did David Gower retire in 1993?
18. In 1995, which Yorkshire boxer stopped Steve Robinson in the eighth round?
19. Who won the mens 5,000 and 10,000 metres at the 1956 Olympics?
20. What was the nickname of tennis player Rene Lacoste?

ANSWERS: 1 Squash, 2 Ron Atkinson, 3 Cycling, 4 Balanchine, 5 Nick Faldo, 6 Andre Agassi, 7 Pole vault, 8 Colin Montgomerie, Ernie Els & Loren Roberts, 9 Rodeo, 10 Australian, 11 South Africa, 12 Polish, 13 Buster Douglas, 14 Valderrama, 15 Rob Andrew, 16 Ian Wright, 17 Hampshire, 18 Naseem Hamed, 19 Vladimir Kuts, 20 The Crocodile.

General Knowledge

1. Which port is the administrative headquarters of West Glamorgan?

2. Who wrote *The Picture of Dorian Gray*?

3. Bettino Craxi was prime minister of which country?

4. Haemoglobin carries which gas?

5. In which American state is Detroit?

6. Which batsman broke another world record with 501 not out against Durham?

7. What is the mistral?

8. For which American legal official is DA an abbreviation?

9. Which teams contested the first match of the 1994 World Cup?

10. Freezing point is at what temperature in Fahrenheit?

11. In Greek mythology, which creature lured sailors on to rocks by singing?

12. What is the governing body of English horse racing called?

13. What is the capital of Costa Rica?

14. In which county is Jodrell Bank?

15. Which planet is encircled by bright rings?

16. Sodom and Gomorrah were destroyed by what in the Old Testament?

17. Who starred as the *Marathon Man*?

18. What is the first name of Chancellor Kohl?

19. In the Christian calendar, which day follows Shrove Tuesday?

20. Which actor starred as *Mad Max*?

General Knowledge

1. Which old coin was informally known as a tanner?

2. In which country does the bullet train operate?

3. Which *Moonlighting* star played *Hudson Hawk*?

4. In which county is the market town Taunton?

5. A teal is a freshwater variety of which bird?

6. What is probate the official validation of?

7. In Greek mythology, which monster lived in the labyrinth and was killed by Theseus?

8. Which firework gets its name from a martyred saint?

9. Yosemite National Park is in which American state?

10. Which government post did John Major hold before becoming prime minister?

11. Which actor took his family to hell and back in *National Lampoon's Vacation*?

12. The SAS is an abbreviation for which British regiment?

13. What does sickle-cell disease affect?

14. In which continent is the Orinoco river?

15. Magyars are the largest ethnic group in which country?

16. Who played the horse-mad 11-year-old in Oscar-winning *National Velvet*?

17. In which London park is Kenwood House?

18. A speakeasy was an illegal type of what?

19. Which is the largest Mediterranean island?

20. In the old rhyme, what would two magpies signify?

ANSWERS: 1 *A sixpence,* **2** *Japan,* **3** *Bruce Willis,* **4** *Somerset,* **5** *Duck,* **6** *A will,* **7** *The Minotaur,* **8** *Catherine Wheel,* **9** *California,* **10** *Chancellor of the Exchequer,* **11** *Chevy Chase,* **12** *The Special Air Services,* **13** *The blood,* **14** *South America,* **15** *Hungary,* **16** *Elizabeth Taylor,* **17** *Hampstead Heath,* **18** *Bar,* **19** *Sicily,* **20** *Joy.*

General Knowledge

1. Which country is also known as Nippon?

2. Which gas forms about 78% of the atmosphere's lowest layer?

3. What type of drug is penicillin?

4. Which singer co-starred with James Garner in *Move over, Darling*?

5. The Atlas mountains are in which continent?

6. Which force do pilots experience when their craft accelerates rapidly?

7. Which chalk hills run across Sussex to Beachy Head?

8. Zen is a form of which religion?

9. What is the practice of seeking water with a forked twig called?

10. Riyadh is capital of which Arabian country?

11. Zeebrugge, scene of the 1987 ferry disaster, is in which country?

12. Which unit of heat is equal to 4.1868 joules?

13. In which metropolitan county is Gateshead?

14. Who wrote *The Forsyte Saga*?

15. Dermatitis is inflammation of what?

16. "Kiss me, Hardy" are said to be whose last words?

17. What is a starlike punctuation mark called?

18. What does CD-ROM stand for?

19. Which England striker joined Spurs from Nottingham Forest?

20. Who wrote the novel *Lady Susan*?

ANSWERS: *1 Japan, 2 Nitrogen, 3 An antibiotic, 4 Doris Day, 5 Africa, 6 G-force, 7 The South Downs, 8 Buddhism, 9 Dowsing or divining, 10 Saudi Arabia, 11 Belgium, 12 A calorie, 13 Tyne and Wear, 14 John Galsworthy, 15 The skin, 16 Lord Nelson, 17 An asterisk, 18 Compact Disc Read Only Memory, 19 Teddy Sheringham, 20 Jane Austen.*

Entertainment

1. Who plays Mike Barratt in *Casualty*?
2. About which famous London institution was the TV programme *The Ark*?
3. What type of vehicle was *Chitty Chitty Bang Bang*?
4. Which band had a hit with *Living on the Ceiling*?
5. Which husband-and-wife team sang *Nutbush City Limits*?
6. Who wrote the mini-series *Riders*?
7. What type of dog was *Lassie*?
8. Which snooker player referees in *Big Break*?
9. What type of alien was Spock in *Star Trek*?
10. Who directed *The Godfather*?
11. In which country was *M*A*S*H* set?
12. Which Osmond had No 1's with *Puppy Love* and *The Twelfth of Never*?
13. Which author wrote *Brideshead Revisited*, on which the TV series was based?
14. To which grunge group did Kurt Cobain belong?
15. What type of job did *Rosie* have?
16. Which Canadian singer had a hit with *Please Forgive Me*?
17. Who played the sadistic literary fan in the film *Misery*?
18. Which Smiths star released an album called *Southpaw Grammar*?
19. Who starred as the broken-down lawyer in *The Verdict*?
20. Which *Baker Street* star released an album called *Over My Head*?

ANSWERS: 1 Clive Mantle, **2** London Zoo, **3** A car, **4** Blancmange, **5** Ike and Tina Turner, **6** Jilly Cooper, **7** a collie, **8** John Virgo, **9** A Vulcan, **10** Francis Ford Coppola, **11** Korea, **12** Donny Osmond, **13** Evelyn Waugh, **14** Nirvana, **15** Policeman, **16** Bryan Adams, **17** Kathy Bates, **18** Morrissey, **19** Paul Newman, **20** Gerry Rafferty.

General Knowledge

1. If someone is vulpine, what do they resemble?

2. By what name is infectious mononucleosis better known?

3. Labrador is an area of which country?

4. Earl Grey and Keemun are types of what?

5. Which international agreement of 1864 regulates the treatment of prisoners of war?

6. How many British kings have been called George?

7. In which American city is Greenwich Village?

8. Which English cricket ground is the headquarters of the MCC?

9. What is the Luftwaffe?

10. Which golfer won the 1994 US Open?

11. In which county is Godalming?

12. Who starred with Olivia Newton-John in *Grease*?

13. GNP is an abbreviation for which measurement of wealth?

14. Offset litho is a common method of what?

15. What is a bunch of herbs tied together and used to flavour soups called?

16. Which American state is nicknamed the Grand Canyon state?

17. By what acronym is the US space agency known?

18. Which branch of surgery is concerned with the spine and joints?

19. Which Monty Python member directed *Brazil* and *The Fisher King*?

20. Who wrote classic detective novel *The Thin Man*?

ANSWERS: *1 A fox, 2 Glandular fever, 3 Canada, 4 Tea, 5 The Geneva Convention, 6 Six, 7 New York, 8 Lord's, 9 The German airforce, 10 Ernie Els, 11 Surrey, 12 John Travolta, 13 Gross National Product, 14 Printing, 15 A bouquet garni, 16 Arizona, 17 NASA, 18 Orthopaedics, 19 Terry Gilliam, 20 Dashiell Hammett.*

General Knowledge

1. What is the largest lake in England?

2. Chemical warfare research facility Porton Down is in which county?

3. Gros point and petit point are types of stitches used in what?

4. Which *Dracula* star went on *Bill and Ted's Excellent Adventure*?

5. In the Bible, the walls of which city fell due to Joshua's trumpets?

6. What is the domination of a market by a single company called?

7. Hurley and shinty are similar to which Olympic sport?

8. Which musician recorded the hugely successful album *Tubular Bells*?

9. Baroque, high tech and Gothic are all styles of what?

10. What was the sequel to *Star Wars* called?

11. *Midnight Express* was set in which country?

12. Guam is an unincorporated territory of which country?

13. What painful payment did Shylock demand from Antonio in *The Merchant of Venice*?

14. Jerusalem is a type of which vegetable?

15. What is North America's chief mountain system?

16. Who co-starred with Debra Winger in *An Officer and a Gentleman*?

17. Mesmerism was a term for which therapeutic process?

18. Which one-wheeled vehicle is driven by pedals?

19. Which *Pretty Woman* star played a troubled member of the *Steel Magnolias*?

20. Which red-brown coloured ape is found solely in Borneo and Sumatra?

General Knowledge

1. Which imaginary creature was a horse with a long horn growing from its forehead?

2. K is an abbreviation for which temperature scale?

3. In the Old Testament, who made the Golden Calf?

4. Which legal title is given to the wife of a knight?

5. Emphysema affects which part of the body?

6. Baton Rouge is the capital of which American state?

7. Who played *Arthur*?

8. How many times a day is a Muslim required to pray?

9. In which country is Lake Winnipeg?

10. The kabbala is a philosophical tradition of which people?

11. What is the last Greek letter?

12. Which English composer wrote *Dido and Aeneas*?

13. Kublai Khan was the Mongol emperor of which country from 1259?

14. Who directed classic thriller *Psycho*?

15. Rickets is the result of a lack of which vitamin?

16. In which county is Windsor Castle?

17. The Falashas are a black Jewish people in which African country?

18. What is the infectious agent that causes AIDS called?

19. Tallahassee is the capital of which American state?

20. Which actress starred in 1991 weepy *Dying Young*?

ANSWERS: *1 A unicorn, 2 Kelvin, 3 Aaron, 4 Dame , 5 The lungs, 6 Louisiana, 7 Dudley Moore, 8 Five, 9 Canada, 10 The Jews, 11 Omega, 12 Henry Purcell, 13 China, 14 Alfred Hitchcock, 15 Vitamin D, 16 Berkshire, 17 Ethiopia, 18 HIV, 19 Florida, 20 Julia Roberts.*

Entertainment

1. Which singer starred in *The Bodyguard*?

2. What is the name of the pub in *Coronation Street*?

3. Who directed and starred in *Annie Hall*?

4. Who played Pod in *The Borrowers*?

5. Who had a Top Ten hit in 1964 with *My Guy*?

6. Which successful film-maker devised *Wild Palms*?

7. What does EMI stand for?

8. Who wrote *Civvies*?

9. What was the name of the main family in *Dallas*?

10. Which female vocalist sang about her *Hero*?

11. Which travel show was presented by Jill Dando?

12. What is the name of the murderous boy in the numerous *Friday the Thirteenth* films?

13. Which *Whose Line is it Anyway?* performer starred in the cricketing comedy *Outside Edge*?

14. Which industrialist was the *Troubleshooter*?

15. Who sang the hit James Bond theme tune *Nobody Does it Better*?

16. Which film starred Susan Sarandon as a mother of seven young men?

17. Who plays comic caricature *Rab C Nesbitt*?

18. How many *Rocky* films have been made so far?

19. Which comedian presents game show *You Bet Your Life*?

20. Which manic brothers starred in *A Night at the Opera*?

General Knowledge

1. In which sport was Jahangir Khan world champion numerous times?

2. Which American novelist wrote *Tender is the Night*?

3. In which part of the body is the thyroid gland?

4. Which chess piece can only move diagonally?

5. In which county is Welwyn Garden City?

6. Luxor is on the bank of which African river?

7. By what name is kerosene known in the UK?

8. On which London thoroughfare is Madame Tussaud's?

9. In which French city is the Centre Pompidou?

10. How many notes are in an octave?

11. Who played the renegade submarine commander in *The Hunt for Red October*?

12. In which county is the Isle of Sheppey?

13. Which architect designed the Lloyd's building?

14. Martinique is an overseas region of which country?

15. What sort of material is associated with Honiton in Devon?

16. What is a draughts piece which can move in any direction called?

17. Which author wrote *Journey to the Centre of the Earth*?

18. Which team knocked the holders Germany out of the 1994 World Cup?

19. Which term describes the chief members of the parliamentary opposition?

20. Which tax did the Community Charge replace?

General Knowledge

1. Who won the 1994 British Grand Prix?

2. What is a potter's oven called?

3. In which year did men first walk on the moon?

4. In which country is Ostend?

5. Tijuana is on the border between which two countries?

6. Who played *Carrie* in the 1976 suspense film?

7. Elland Road is the home ground of which football team?

8. Which element is also called quicksilver?

9. On what type of object would you find an ISBN?

10. Orthodontics is a branch of which medical discipline?

11. Greg LeMond became the first rider from which country to win the Tour de France in 1986?

12. In the Christian calendar, what is the Sunday before Easter called?

13. Which prehistoric period preceded the Iron Age?

14. In which country is the river Liffey?

15. Katmandu is the capital of which Asian country?

16. Which composer wrote *Nessun Dorma*?

17. Which of the Kennedy clan was involved in the Chappaquiddick scandal?

18. For what does the abbreviation ANC stand?

19. At what age has an Italian woman become the oldest to give birth

20. Which actor played the private eye in John Huston's classic *The Maltese Falcon*?

ANSWERS: *1 Damon Hill, 2 A kiln, 3 1969, 4 Belgium, 5 The USA and Mexico, 6 Sissy Spacek, 7 Leeds United, 8 Mercury, 9 A book, 10 Dentistry, 11 The USA, 12 Palm Sunday, 13 The Bronze Age, 14 The Republic of Ireland, 15 Nepal, 16 Giacomo Puccini, 17 Edward Kennedy, 18 African National Congress, 19 62, 20 Humphrey Bogart.*

General Knowledge

1. Who directed *1941* and *Jaws*?

2. In which West Indian dance do people attempt to pass under a low horizontal pole?

3. Which range of hills runs from Bristol to Chipping Camden?

4. In which county is St Ives?

5. RADA is an abbreviation for which theatrical school?

6. Which actress starred in spy comedy *Jumpin' Jack Flash*?

7. Which biblical figure was found among the bulrushes as a baby?

8. Which horse race, held at Doncaster, is the last Classic of the season?

9. What is the Lone Star State of America?

10. Which golfer won the 1994 Open championship?

11. Which British commander won the Battle of Waterloo?

12. Which composer wrote *La Traviata* and *Aida*?

13. In which county is King's Lynn?

14. Which Russian won the Nobel Peace Prize in 1991?

15. Which landlocked principality is situated between Austria and Switzerland?

16. The Grand Lodge is the governing body of which organisation?

17. Which instrument did George Formby play in his films?

18. The *Calypso* was the ship of which famous French underwater explorer?

19. What is *Tintin*'s dog called?

20. What type of creature is a silverfish?

ANSWERS: 1 Steven Spielberg, 2 Limbo, 3 The Cotswolds, 4 Cornwall, 5 Royal Academy of Dramatic Art, 6 Whoopi Goldberg, 7 Moses, 8 St Leger, 9 Texas, 10 Nick Price, 11 Duke of Wellington, 12 Giuseppe Verdi, 13 Norfolk, 14 Mikhail Gorbachev, 15 Liechtenstein, 16 The Freemasons, 17 The ukulele, 18 Jacques Cousteau, 19 Snowy, 20 An insect.

Entertainment

1. Who is Adrian Edmondson's *Absolutely Fabulous* wife?
2. Who sang the theme from *Shaft*?
3. Which Brookside star was voted most popular actress at the 1995 National TV Awards?
4. What type of animals were the stars of *Lady and the Tramp*?
5. *Speed* star Sandra Bullock played a toll booth attendant in which film?
6. Who hosts *Catchphrase*?
7. Which funnyman starred as *Chef*?
8. Which *Room With A View* actor starred in the critically-panned *Boxing Helena*?
9. Which *Lovejoy* character is played by Dudley Sutton?
10. Who were the *Sultans of Swing* in the 70s?
11. Which Hollywood actor presents the TV series *Future Quest*?
12. In which US city is cop drama *Homicide: Life on the Streets* set?
13. Who wrote and directed *Westworld*?
14. Who had a Top Ten Hit in 1979 with *Green Onions*?
15. Which *K-9* star played Harry Wyckoff in *Wild Palms*?
16. In which decade was *The House of Eliott* set?
17. Which British rock star played *Tommy* in the 1975 film?
18. Which group sang *When You're In Love With A Beautiful Woman*?
19. In *The X Files*, which character is played by David Duchovny?
20. Who played *The Buddha of Suburbia* in the TV adaptation of Hanif Kureishi's novel?

ANSWERS: 1 *Jennifer Saunders*, 2 *Isaac Hayes*, 3 *Anna Friel*, 4 *Dogs*, 5 *While You Were Sleeping*, 6 *Roy Walker*, 7 *Lenny Henry*, 8 *Julian Sands*, 9 *Tinker*, 10 *Dire Straits*, 11 *Jeff Goldblum*, 12 *Baltimore*, 13 *Michael Crichton*, 14 *Booker T. and the M.G.'s*, 15 *James Belushi*, 16 *The 1920s*, 17 *Roger Daltrey*, 18 *Doctor Hook*, 19 *Fox Mulder*, 20 *Roshan Seth*.

General Knowledge

1. Who plays Fred in the movie *The Flintstones*?

2. Which cyclist won the 1995 Tour de France?

3. What is a monkey puzzle?

4. Who wrote *The Camomile Lawn*?

5. Which England cricketer was fined for "an unusual action" against South Africa?

6. Which city is the capital of Brazil?

7. Which band had a Number One with *Walking on the Moon*?

8. Which British athlete broke the world decathlon record four times?

9. Which Greek author wrote fables involving animals?

10. In which year was Germany reunified?

11. In which ocean are the Azores?

12. Which bestselling writer wrote *The Cinder Path*?

13. Who sang *I Just Called To Say I Love You*?

14. What is the collective name for kangaroos, wombats and opossums?

15. Which title, used by German emperors, is derived from the Latin Caesar?

16. Which TV puppet series was about International Rescue?

17. In which county is Bath?

18. Moose is the North American name for which mammal?

19. What type of food is bratwurst?

20. Which royal residence is in the Grampian region?

ANSWERS: *1 John Goodman, 2 Miguel Indurain, 3 A tree, 4 Mary Wesley, 5 Mike Atherton, 6 Brasilia, 7 The Police, 8 Daley Thompson, 9 Aesop, 10 1990, 11 Atlantic Ocean, 12 Catherine Cookson, 13 Stevie Wonder, 14 Marsupials, 15 Kaiser, 16 Thunderbirds, 18 Elk, 19 A (pork) sausage, 20 Balmoral.*

General Knowledge

1. Which comedian played *The Man With Two Brains*?

2. Who originated the penny post?

3. What do we call an anaesthetic which only affects part of the body?

4. Gamal Abdel Nasser was president of which country?

5. Armistice Day commemorates the ending of which war?

6. Which Canadian rocker sang *Run to You*?

7. Which country has Helvetia on its stamps?

8. Which artistic form can be picaresque?

9. Which sport begins with a face-off?

10. In which county is Slough?

11. Romany is the language of which travelling people?

12. Which band sang the original of *Stairway to Heaven*?

13. Which king defeated the French in the Battle of Agincourt?

14. How many points is a try worth in Rugby Union?

15. Hyperglycaemia involves an excess of what in the blood?

16. Who wrote successful farce *Noises Off*?

17. In which Middle-Eastern city is the Dome of the Rock?

18. Which American actress starred as *The French Lieutenant's Woman*?

19. Of which country was General Jaruzelski president?

20. Which writer created fictional teenager Adrian Mole?

ANSWERS: *1 Steve Martin, 2 Sir Rowland Hill, 3 Local, 4 Egypt, 5 World War One, 6 Bryan Adams, 7 Switzerland, 8 Literature, 9 Ice hockey, 10 Berkshire, 11 Gypsies, 12 Led Zeppelin, 13 Henry V, 14 Five, 15 Sugar, 16 Michael Frayn, 17 Jerusalem, 18 Meryl Streep, 19 Poland, 20 Sue Townsend.*

General Knowledge

1.   What is another name for the white ball in snooker?

2.   Which American TV series featured the Fonz?

3.   Who is the traditional author of the first Gospel?

4.   Which part of the body does lumbago affect?

5.   What is the value of the Roman numeral D?

6.   In which country is the volcano Krakatoa?

7.   Which American comedian starred in *The Cat and the Canary*?

8.   To which city is someone who is being ignored sent?

9.   In which American state is winter resort Palm Beach?

10. Who wrote *Roll Over Beethoven*?

11. What is the home ground of the England Rugby Union team?

12. Who starred in 1989 baseball movie *Field of Dreams*?

13. What is the smallest unit of an organism able to function independently called?

14. Flemish is one of the two official languages of which country?

15. Which act of Parliament binds government employees to secrecy?

16. Which flower is also called a fleur-de-lis?

17. In the Bible, with which people did God agree a covenant?

18. On which London street is the Cenotaph war memorial?

19. What nationality is tennis player Gabriela Sabatini?

20. How is the crane fly more commonly known?

ANSWERS: 1 *The cue ball*, 2 *Happy Days*, 3 *St Matthew*, 4 *The back*, 5 *500*, 6 *Indonesia*, 7 *Bob Hope*, 8 *Coventry*, 9 *Florida*, 10 *Chuck Berry*, 11 *Twickenham*, 12 *Kevin Costner*, 13 *A cell*, 14 *Belgium*, 15 *Official Secrets Act*, 16 *An iris*, 17 *The Israelites*, 18 *Whitehall*, 19 *Argentinian*, 20 *The Daddy-long-legs*.

Entertainment

1. In which U.S. state is *The Golden Girls* set?
2. Who played crooked ex-cop Keaton in *The Usual Suspects*?
3. Who sang *Una Paloma Blanca* in 1975?
4. For which film did Humphrey Bogart win an Oscar?
5. Which Aussie soap is set in Summer Bay?
6. Which '70s progressive rock band has released a live double album called *B'BOOM*?
7. Who sang about *Little Fluffy Clouds*?
8. Which late actor played the sleepy hustler in *My Own Private Idaho*?
9. Which *Rocky Horror Show* writer presented *The Crystal Maze*?
10. Who left Take That in 1995?
11. Which TV chef presented *Taste of the Sea*?
12. Who directed *Rain Man*?
13. Which former US Marine and reggae star had a hit with *Boombastic*?
14. What were the first names of the *Hart to Hart* couple?
15. Which US female vocalist had a hit with *Again*?
16. Who wrote the book on which *One Flew Over The Cuckoo's Nest* was based?
17. Who plays Dave Tucker in *Soldier, Soldier*?
18. Who directed the 1989 film *Do The Right Thing*?
19. Which British group sang *Hit Me With Your Rhythm Stick*?
20. Who played the cantankerous old lady in *Driving Miss Daisy*?

ANSWERS: 1 *Florida*, 2 *Gabriel Byrne*, 3 *Jonathan King*, 4 *The African Queen*, 5 *Home and Away*, 6 *King Crimson*, 7 *Orb*, 8 *River Phoenix*, 9 *Richard O'Brien*, 10 *Robbie Williams*, 11 *Rick Stein*, 12 *Barry Levinson*, 13 *Shaggy*, 14 *Jonathan and Jennifer*, 15 *Janet Jackson*, 16 *Ken Kesey*, 17 *Robson Green*, 18 *Spike Lee*, 19 *Ian Dury and the Blockheads*, 20 *Jessica Tandy*.

General Knowledge

1. Which word is the name for a computer-programming language and a unit of pressure?

2. For which party was Clement Attlee prime minister?

3. Which part of the body does periodontal disease affect?

4. What gender would a patriarch be?

5. Who did Michael Jackson marry?

6. How many game birds make up a brace?

7. Of which country was Golda Meir prime minister 1969-74?

8. Which orchestral percussion instrument produces the lowest sound?

9. In which polar region did Laurence Oates die?

10. Which Australian screen idol played a runner in *Gallipoli*?

11. How many English kings have been called Henry?

12. Anthracite and lignite are types of which fossil fuel?

13. What is the science and technology of metals called?

14. Which two Houses make up the British parliament?

15. Ayatollah Khomeini was ruler of which country from 1979?

16. Orcadians come from which Scottish islands?

17. What type of object does a dust jacket protect?

18. In which National Park is Scafell Pike?

19. In which American state would you find Oahu?

20. Which unit of measurement can be preceded by nautical and statute?

ANSWERS: *1 Pascal, 2 Labour Party, 3 Gums and surrounding tissue, 4 Male, 5 Lisa Marie Presley, 6 Two, 7 Israel, 8 Bass drum, 9 The Antarctic, 10 Mel Gibson, 11 Eight, 12 Coal, 13 Metallurgy, 14 (Houses of) Commons and Lords, 15 Iran, 16 Orkney Islands, 17 A book, 18 Lake District, 19 Hawaii, 20 Mile.*

General Knowledge

1. Which classic 1974 adventure movie starred Paul Newman in a blazing building?

2. In physics, which term represents the quantity of matter in a body?

3. For which group of states does the abbreviation UAE stand?

4. Where did the Mafia originate?

5. In which country did Buddhism originate?

6. Which revolution was effected by the Bolsheviks?

7. What is the capital of Cape Verde?

8. What type of creature is a caracal?

9. In which sport is Wayne Gretzky a legend?

10. Which author created detective-priest Father Brown?

11. Who won the men's javelin title at the 1994 European Championships?

12. Which romantic novelist wrote *Moments of Love*?

13. The name of which insect can be preceded by praying?

14. The American presidents Theodore and Franklin D shared which surname?

15. A mangelwurzel is a variety of which plant?

16. Who wrote *First Among Equals*?

17. Laissez-faire is a theory from which academic discipline?

18. Which glamorous actress starred in *The Seven Year Itch*?

19. Which brothers played in the 1966 World Cup-winning team?

20. What is a male goat, hare or rabbit called?

ANSWERS: 1 *Towering Inferno*, 2 Mass, 3 United Arab Emirates, 4 Sicily, 5 India, 6 Russian Revolution, 7 Praia, 8 A (big) cat, 9 Ice-hockey, 10 G K Chesterton, 11 Steve Backley, 12 Barbara Cartland, 13 Mantis, 14 Roosevelt, 15 The beet, 16 Jeffrey Archer, 17 Economics, 18 Marilyn Monroe, 19 Bobby and Jack Charlton, 20 A buck.

General Knowledge

1. In which American state is Philadelphia?

2. Which vegetable is also called an eggplant?

3. Which star of *The Big Chill* played a newscaster in *Broadcast News*?

4. Who played the psychopath in the 1991 remake of *Cape Fear*?

5. Which mythological winged horse sprang from the blood of Medusa?

6. Willy Brandt was federal chancellor of which country 1969-74?

7. Kelp is a variety of which plant?

8. In which American state is Newark?

9. What type of creature is a ruff?

10. Which TV playwright wrote *Lipstick On Your Collar*?

11. What type of question does not require an answer?

12. For what is UFO an abbreviation?

13. What name is given to the period 1811-20 in British history?

14. Which American national holiday was first celebrated by the Pilgrim Fathers?

15. The monarch and large blue are types of which insect?

16. Which Hollywood great starred as *Bullitt*?

17. Which group sang *Stayin' Alive* and *Night Fever*?

18. Who was prime minister before Margaret Thatcher?

19. For which food additive is MSG an abbreviation?

20. Which American author wrote *The Bostonians*?

ANSWERS: 1 *Pennsylvania,* **2** *Aubergine,* **3** *William Hurt,* **4** *Robert De Niro,* **5** *Pegasus,* **6** *West Germany,* **7** *Seaweed,* **8** *New Jersey,* **9** *A bird,* **10** *Dennis Potter,* **11** *A rhetorical question,* **12** *Unidentified Flying Object,* **13** *The Regency,* **14** *Thanksgiving (Day),* **15** *Butterfly,* **16** *Steve McQueen,* **17** *Bee Gees,* **18** *James Callaghan,* **19** *Monosodium glutamate,* **20** *Henry James.*

Entertainment

1. Who is Laura Dern's actress mother?
2. Which soap queen starred in *Mama's Back*?
3. Which "Godfather of Funk" released an album entitled *The Music Of Red Shoe Diaries*?
4. Which martial artist was a *Hard Target*?
5. Which TV comic is nicknamed 'Motormouth'?
6. Which crooner had a No 1 in 1954 with *Three Coins In The Fountain*?
7. In which city is *Byker Grove* set?
8. Which *Oscar* star was also in *Demolition Man*?
9. Which late comedian played *Nona*?
10. Which Irish rock band had a hit with *Stay*?
11. With which cop series is the line "Book him Dano" associated?
12. Which camp group had a hit in 1978 with *YMCA*?
13. Who is the British director of *Naked*?
14. Which Labour MP made a cameo appearance in *A Woman's Guide to Adultery*?
15. With which group did Debbie Harry sing *Union City Blues*?
16. Which actor starred as *Magnum*?
17. Who wrote *Orlando,* on which the film was based?
18. With whom did Barbara Streisand sing the 1978 No 1 hit *You Don't Bring Me Flowers*?
19. What sort of creature is Willy in *Free Willy*?
20. Who was the captive heroine of the original *King Kong*?

General Knowledge

1. Which loose garment was worn by citizens of ancient Rome?

2. For which time system is GMT an abbreviation?

3. Which part of the body does asbestosis primarily affect?

4. What type of numerals are the signs 1,2,3,4, etc?

5. Which Swiss dish consists of food dipped in melted cheese?

6. Corazon Aquino was president of which country 1986-92?

7. What type of creature is a yellowhammer?

8. Which religion involves castes?

9. Which fat, bespectacled schoolboy was created by Frank Richards?

10. Which valuable metal is stored at Fort Knox?

11. What does the French word chanson mean?

12. Who starred as the rebellious teacher in *Dead Poets Society*?

13. How many British kings have been called George?

14. John Monks is General Secretary of which organisation?

15. An electrocardiogram records changes in which organ?

16. Which is the largest of the anthropoid apes?

17. In which county is Dartmoor?

18. Of which sport were John Lowe and Jocky Wilson world champions?

19. On what sort of paper did the ancient Egyptians write?

20. British Columbia is a province of which country?

ANSWERS: 1 Toga, 2 Greenwich Mean Time, 3 The lungs, 4 Arabic numerals, 5 Fondue, 6 The Philippines, 7 A bird, 8 Golf, 9 Billy Bunter, 10 Gold, 11 Song, 12 Robin Williams, 13 Six, 14 The TUC, 15 The heart, 16 The Gorilla, 17 Devon, 18 Darts, 19 Papyrus, 20 Canada.

General Knowledge

1. Which two digits are used in binary code?

2. What type of creature is a Portuguese man-of-war?

3. In which ocean is Madagascar?

4. Which fairy tale features a witch in a gingerbread cottage?

5. Which French expression, literally 'white paper', means complete freedom of action?

6. Which range of hills extends northwards from the Thames valley?

7. Which year is represented by Roman numerals MXMXCII?

8. A muezzin calls people of which religion to prayer?

9. What is the annual end-of-season match called in American Football?

10. In which county is Rye?

11. Which former first lady did Aristotle Onassis marry?

12. Which medical specialty is concerned with management of pregnancy and childbirth?

13. What is a therm used to measure?

14. How many degrees are there in a full circle?

15. Which crime writer created private eye Philip Marlowe?

16. Which ancient region was the 'Promised Land' of the Israelites?

17. Which African people are renowned for their small stature?

18. Of which team is Bryan Robson manager?

19. Who sang *Evergreen* and *Woman In Love*?

20. What is the study of weather systems called?

ANSWERS: 1 One and zero, **2** A jellyfish, **3** Indian Ocean, **4** Hansel and Gretel, **5** Carte blanche, **6** Chilterns, **7** 1992, **8** Islam, **9** Super Bowl, **10** East Sussex, **11** Jacqueline Kennedy, **12** Obstetrics, **13** Heat, **14** 360, **15** Raymond Chandler, **16** Canaan, **17** Pygmies, **18** Middlesbrough, **19** Barbra Streisand, **20** Meteorology.

General Knowledge

Your rating: ● 0-5   Join a library   ● 6-10   Keep at it
              ● 11-15 Join a quiz team   ● 16-20 Enter Mastermind

1. Swing and bebop are types of which music?

2. What does a driver depress to change gear in a manual car?

3. In which African city was the 1994 UN population summit?

4. In which American city is the World Trade Center?

5. What is the collective name for Lakes Superior, Michigan, Huron, Erie and Ontario?

6. Who won this year's U.S. Open tennis title?

7. In which county is Epsom?

8. From which type of creature is eiderdown taken?

9. Which Wet Wet Wet single was Number One for 15 weeks?

10. Who wrote *The Mill on the Floss*?

11. Which mythical sea creature has a man's torso and a fish's tail?

12. Which comedian had a famous Half Hour on radio and television?

13. Che Guevara helped effect revolution in which country?

14. Who had an *Endless Love* with Mariah Carey?

15. With which scientist do you associate the equation $E = MC$ squared?

16. Of which country is King Fahd monarch?

17. What type of weapons were the V1 and V2?

18. How many players are in a volleyball team?

19. The condor and turkey buzzard are types of which bird?

20. What was Ho Chi Minh City called before the Vietnam War?

ANSWERS: *1 Jazz, 2 The clutch, 3 Cairo, 4 New York City, 5 Great Lakes, 6 Andre Agassi, 7 Surrey, 8 A duck, 9 Love is All Around, 10 George Eliot, 11 Merman, 12 Tony Hancock, 13 Cuba, 14 Luther Vandross, 15 Albert Einstein, 16 Saudi Arabia, 17 Flying bombs, 18 Six, 19 Vulture, 20 Saigon.*

Entertainment

1. With which country superstar did George Jones release an album called *One*?

2. Who played Annie in *Sitting Pretty*?

3. Who sang *Brown Girl In The Ring* in 1978?

4. Who are The Three Tenors?

5. On which TV programme did Zig and Zag begin creating havoc?

6. Who played the mystical martial artist in *Kung Fu*?

7. Big Audio Dynamite frontman Mick Jones was a founder member of which successful punk band?

8. Which Icelandic singer had a hit with *Big Time Sensuality*?

9. Who plays Ian in *EastEnders*?

10. Who had a Top Ten Hit in 1977 with *White Christmas*?

11. About which jazz musician was *Bird*?

12. On which day is *Top of the Pops*?

13. Which teen heart-throbs sang *What's My Name*?

14. On which island was *Bergerac* set?

15. Which Peter Segal film starred Rob Lowe and Bo Derek?

16. What was *Doctor Who*'s time travelling vehicle called?

17. Which folk singer released an album called *Ring Them Bells*?

18. Which British group had a Top Ten Hit in 1969 with *Pinball Wizard*?

19. Who starred as *Dave*?

20. Who directed the original silent classic *Metropolis*?

- 281 -

General Knowledge

1. What was Cliff Richard's backing group?

2. Of which country is Tehran capital?

3. Which government department deals with immigration and the police?

4. What do Americans call the pavement?

5. Which former Conservative prime minister was nicknamed Supermac?

6. Single and double-entry are methods of what?

7. Which top London store is owned by the Fayed brothers?

8. Which *Frantic* star is in *Clear and Present Danger*?

9. What do leatherjackets turn into?

10. In which gambling game does a dice score of seven or eleven win the bet?

11. Which football team plays at Maine Road?

12. Which king was overthrown by the French Revolution?

13. Of which continent is Cape Horn the most southerly point?

14. La Manche is the French name for which stretch of water?

15. What is a number only divisible by one and itself called?

16. In which county is Milton Keynes?

17. The island Stromboli belongs to which country?

18. Brian Walden was an MP for which party 1964-77?

19. What is the study of God or gods called?

20. On whose poem is the hymn *Jerusalem* based?

General Knowledge

1. What type of creature is a rorqual?

2. Which former Wimbledon men's doubles winner died in 1994 aged 40?

3. In which county is Bournemouth?

4. Who plays *Murphy Brown* in the award-winning comedy drama?

5. Which former U.S. president helped persuade the Haitian military leaders to stand down?

6. Which indigenous people inhabit Greenland and the Arctic?

7. In which country was Martina Navratilova born?

8. The faces of how many American presidents are carved into Mount Rushmore?

9. What type of weather phenomenon is a sirocco?

10. How many siblings does the Queen have?

11. Which word describes the ability to speak two languages?

12. Who lost his WBC title to Oliver McCall, and later regained it?

13. From which country is the haiku verse form?

14. What is the tallest mammal in the world?

15. What is the correct term for word-blindness?

16. Who wrote *The Holcroft Covenant*?

17. What type of television series was originally sponsored by washing-powder manufacturers?

18. The name of which type of creature can be preceded by white, basking or whale?

19. How many strikes does a batter receive in baseball before being out?

20. Which *Alfie* star was in classic crime movie *The Italian Job*?

ANSWERS: *1 Whale, 2 Vitas Gerulaitis, 3 Dorset, 4 Candice Bergen, 5 Jimmy Carter, 6 Eskimos (Inuit), 7 Czechoslovakia, 8 Four, 9 Wind, 10 One (Princess Margaret), 11 Bilingual, 12 Lennox Lewis, 13 Japan, 14 Giraffe, 15 Dyslexia, 16 Robert Ludlum, 17 Soap opera, 18 Shark, 19 Three, 20 Michael Caine.*

General Knowledge

1. In which county is the market town Nuneaton?

2. Which mineral was used to produce a spark in guns?

3. From which garden were Adam and Eve expelled by God?

4. From which direction does the sun rise?

5. Which British author created *Dr Jekyll and Mr Hyde*?

6. In which American city is a famous Mardi Gras festival held annually?

7. D is the international car registration for which country?

8. What type of creature is a mudskipper?

9. Which eminent English actor played *Arthur*'s butler?

10. Of which country was Pol Pot leader?

11. In which American state did the *Mayflower* land?

12. What nationality was author and politician Machiavelli?

13. In which county is Portsmouth?

14. Which of the Monty Python team played *The Missionary*?

15. Who scored his 100th goal for Arsenal in 1994?

16. Which English admiral won the Battle of Trafalgar?

17. Which international relief agency was founded by the Geneva Convention?

18. Who directed *Jaws*?

19. In which religion was suttee practised?

20. To which organ does the adjective renal refer?

ANSWERS: 1 *Warwickshire*, 2 *Flint*, 3 *Eden*, 4 *East*, 5 *Robert Louis Stevenson*, 6 *New Orleans*, 7 *Germany*, 8 *A fish*, 9 *Sir John Gielgud*, 10 *Cambodia (Kampuchea)*, 11 *Massachusetts*, 12 *Italian*, 13 *Hampshire*, 14 *Michael Palin*, 15 *Ian Wright*, 16 *Lord Nelson*, 17 *The Red Cross*, 18 *Steven Spielberg*, 19 *Hinduism*, 20 *The kidneys*.

Sports

1. Who won two individual Olympic golds at the modern pentathlon?
2. About which football manager did MP Kate Hoey make allegations under Parliamentary privilege?
3. Who is the 1995 Tour de France champion?
4. What nationality is the athlete Vebjoern Rodahl?
5. Who won the 1994 Winter Olympic ice hockey gold?
6. From which sport was Zhong Weiyue banned for two years?
7. Which Premiership team signed Savo Milosevic for £3.5m in 1995?
8. Who defeated Steffi Graf in the 1994 French Open?
9. For which country does Jonty Rhodes play cricket?
10. How many points is a try worth in Rugby Union?
11. Who scored the first goal in the 1994 World Cup finals?
12. Whose long standing long-jump record did Mike Powell break in 1991?
13. Which football team plays at Boundary Park?
14. Which woman ran a British record half marathon time of 68min 42sec in 1992?
15. Who scored the winning goal for England in Terry Venables's first match?
16. Who was runner up in the 1992 Wimbledon men's final?
17. What sport does Hakeem Olajuwon play?
18. Which manager went from Bolton Wanderers to Arsenal in 1995?
19. Which boxing promoter was fined £5,000 in 1995 for insulting Chris Eubank?
20. In which year did Hanif Mohammad score his famous innings of 499?

General Knowledge

1. Which family group sang *ABC*?

2. Which Greek letter also means a tiny amount?

3. Who sang the classic song *Blueberry Hill*?

4. Who wrote *The Eagle Has Landed*?

5. In which county is Shrewsbury?

6. In which country is the Negev desert?

7. Shem, Ham and Japheth were sons of which biblical character?

8. Who wrote *A Room With a View*?

9. Who won the 1994 Booker Prize?

10. In which sport are touchdowns scored?

11. Managua is the capital of which Central American country?

12. Who played *The Bodyguard*?

13. The oesophagus connects the mouth with which part of the body?

14. What is the second highest mountain in the world?

15. For which white supremacist society is KKK an abbreviation?

16. Which planet is named after the Roman god of the sea?

17. In which year was the National Curriculum introduced?

18. Which is the smallest American state?

19. Which football club are nicknamed the Magpies?

20. Where in Britain are the Black Mountains?

ANSWERS: *1 The Jackson Five, 2 Iota, 3 Fats Domino, 4 Jack Higgins, 5 Shropshire, 6 Israel, 7 Noah, 8 E M Forster, 9 James Kelman, 10 American football, 11 Nicaragua, 12 Kevin Costner, 13 Stomach, 14 K2, 15 Ku Klux Klan, 16 Neptune, 17 1989, 18 Rhode Island, 19 Newcastle United, 20 Wales.*

General Knowledge

1. In which sport is the Pilkington Cup contested?

2. How many time zones are there in the world?

3. In which horror film did Freddy Krueger first appear?

4. What is another name for the cougar or mountain lion?

5. Which heavy metal is commonly used as a radiation shield?

6. In which London park is the Serpentine?

7. What is the official name for a sleeping policeman?

8. Which Scottish economist wrote *The Wealth of Nations*?

9. In which year was Terry Waite freed from captivity in Beirut?

10. What are the lowest members of the Indian caste system called?

11. For which party was John F. Kennedy president?

12. To which class of vertebrates do frogs, toads and salamanders belong?

13. Consumption was a former name for which disease?

14. Which mountain system runs from the Arctic to the Caspian Sea?

15. In which decade did Prohibition start?

16. What are two circles that share the same centre called?

17. Which peninsula includes Cambodia, Laos and Vietnam?

18. With which instrument did James Galway find fame?

19. Which farming machine both reaps and threshes the crop?

20. 8-ball and straight are forms of which game?

General Knowledge

1. For which expression is COD an abbreviation?

2. In which continent is the Kalahari Desert?

3. Which point is diametrically opposite to the zenith?

4. Which is the principal wine producing state of the USA?

5. In which month is the Henley Royal Regatta held?

6. Who wrote *The Day of the Jackal*?

7. What type of creature is a coot?

8. In which county is sea port Harwich?

9. Of which country was Imre Nagy prime minister?

10. What type of precious stone is the hard crystalline form of carbon?

11. What is the astronomical term for a shooting star?

12. How is the fairground ride the big wheel also known?

13. Which science-fiction writer wrote *Something Wicked This Way Comes*?

14. What is the American term for an underground railway?

15. Which mischievous schoolboy was created by Richmal Crompton?

16. Which long-running Radio 4 series is set in Ambridge?

17. Of which country is the Garda Siochana the police force?

18. Which of Henry VIII's wives survived him?

19. What type of car was Herbie in the popular films?

20. Who beat Michael Moorer in 1994 to become WBA and IB champion?

ANSWERS: 1 *Cash on delivery,* 2 *Africa,* 3 *The nadir,* 4 *California,* 5 *July,* 6 *Frederick Forsyth,* 7 *A bird,* 8 *Essex,* 9 *Hungary,* 10 *A diamond,* 11 *A meteor,* 12 *Ferris wheel,* 13 *Ray Bradbury,* 14 *The subway,* 15 *(Just) William,* 16 *The Archers,* 17 *The Republic of Ireland,* 18 *Catherine Parr,* 19 *A Volkswagen Beetle,* 20 *George Foreman.*

Entertainment

1. Who had a No. 1 hit with *Space Oddity*?

2. Which Michael Winterbottom film starred Saskia Reeves and Amanda Plummer?

3. Which US talk show host spent more than £75,000 on her sick cocker spaniel, Solomon?

4. Which Irish answer to Take That released an album called *Said And Done*?

5. Who played the title role in the 1974 film of *The Great Gatsby*?

6. Which duo teamed up again to sing *True Love*?

7. Which *Young Ones* star played Gordon in *If You See God, Tell Him*?

8. In which northern city was *When The Boat Comes In* set?

9. Who co-starred with James Belushi in *Red Heat*?

10. With whom did Dick Clement write *The Likely Lads*?

11. *It's Great When You're Straight ... Yeh* was the debut album from which band?

12. Who played Lucy Honeychurch in *A Room With A View*?

13. What is the home of King Alpha and Queen Bet?

14. Which puppet series is set in Marineville?

15. Which newsreader claimed that she welcomed "being the first woman to read the news with grey hair"?

16. Which British actor played the villainous Simon in *Die Hard With A Vengeance*?

17. With which British singer did guitarist Bill Frisell release an album called *Deep Dead Blue*?

18. Who starred in *The Deer Hunter* and *Angel Heart*?

19. Who had a hit with *Runaway Train*?

20. Which composer was *Amadeus* about?

General Knowledge

1. Which English artist is famous for his matchstick figures?

2. How is the language Siamese now known?

3. Which Tory MP left his wife for Lady Penelope Cobham?

4. To which royal house did Queen Victoria belong?

5. What type of creatures are the eland and gnu?

6. Which singer had a huge hit with *Let's Twist Again*?

7. Who played *Popeye* in the 1980 comedy?

8. What is the scientific study of language called?

9. What is the French name for a castle or country house?

10. Of which country was Toshiki Kaifu prime minister?

11. Who played James Bond in *Moonraker*?

12. Java is the most important island of which country?

13. What nationality is the inventor of the Rubik cube?

14. In what part of the body is the jugular vein?

15. Which company runs the National Lottery?

16. Of which European country is the guilder the monetary unit?

17. What type of cow's milk has the lowest fat content?

18. With which hand does an orthodox boxer lead?

19. Which continent is around the South Pole?

20. Which mechanical device indicates the exact tempo of music?

ANSWERS: 1 L S Lowry, 2 Thai, 3 David Mellor, 4 House of Hanover, 5 Antelope, 6 Chubby Checker, 7 Robin Williams, 8 Linguistics, 9 Chateau, 10 Japan, 11 Roger Moore, 12 Indonesia, 13 Hungarian, 14 The neck, 15 Camelot, 16 The Netherlands, 17 Skimmed milk, 18 The left hand, 19 Antarctica, 20 A metronome.

General Knowledge

1. What type of professional must belong to one of the Inns of Court?

2. In which part of the body is a goitre formed?

3. Of which country is Alberta a province?

4. Which imperial unit is equivalent to 0.453592 kg?

5. Who was the 1994 and 1995 world driver's champion?

6. Which day precedes All Saints' Day?

7. Which English Puritans sailed on the Mayflower?

8. Which act of spiritual contemplation is practised by a Buddhist?

9. Which small sovereign state is located within southern France?

10. Who wrote *Vanity Fair*?

11. Which West Indian country is especially associated with voodoo?

12. How many rings are on the Olympic flag?

13. Who wrote *The Hobbit*?

14. What sweet substance is used in making mead?

15. What is the collective name for the sun and the bodies in its gravitational field?

16. What type of meat is a porterhouse?

17. For which creature is river horse an informal name?

18. What is the horse's fastest gait?

19. What is the daily record of events on board a ship called?

20. Of which country is Bucharest capital?

ANSWERS: 1 A barrister, **2** The neck, **3** Canada, **4** A pound, **5** Michael Schumacher, **6** Hallowe'en, **7** The Pilgrim Fathers, **8** Meditation, **9** Monaco, **10** William Makepeace Thackeray, **11** Haiti, **12** Five, **13** JRR Tolkien, **14** Honey, **15** The solar system, **16** Beef, **17** The hippopotamus, **18** Gallop, **19** A log, **20** Romania.

General Knowledge

1. Who beat James Toney in Las Vegas to become the IBF super-middleweight champion in 1994?

2. Of which North American Indian tribe was Sitting Bull chief?

3. Of which country is Bujumbura capital?

4. For what type of animal is bruin a literary name?

5. In which country is the Dordogne?

6. Which superhero is played by Alec Baldwin in a film?

7. The name of which creature can be preceded by killer or blue?

8. Which disorder produces an overwhelming desire to steal?

9. What type of person would wear a chasuble?

10. In which war was the Battle of Bunker Hill?

11. In which county is Sheerness?

12. To which type of alcoholic drink does the adjective brut refer?

13. Which Welsh island is separated from the mainland by the Menai Strait?

14. What type of creature is a bulbul?

15. Who painted *Dedham Vale*?

16. Which actor co-starred with Arnold Schwarzenegger in *Twins* and *Junior*?

17. What is the biblical personification of wealth and greed called?

18. What is the capital of Barbados?

19. In which county is Sutton Hoo?

20 What is Margaret Thatcher's middle name?

ANSWERS: 1 Roy Jones, **2** The Sioux, **3** Burundi, **4** A bear, **5** France, **6** The Shadow, **7** The whale, **8** Kleptomania, **9** A priest, **10** The War of American Independence, **11** Kent, **12** Champagne, **13** Anglesey, **14** A bird, **15** John Constable, **16** Danny De Vito, **17** Mammon, **18** Bridgetown, **19** Suffolk, **20** Hilda.

Entertainment

1. Which German band had a No 1 in 1981 with *Computer Love/The Model*?

2. Who directed the 1968 movie version of *Romeo and Juliet*?

3. Who sang *Careless Whisper*?

4. Which comedian played the hustler who became an executive in *Trading Places*?

5. Which *EastEnders* character is played by Bill Treacher?

6. Who played the handsome hero in the fairy-tale fantasy *Legend*?

7. About what type of business was *Moonlighting*?

8. Who had a '93 hit with *Boss Drum*?

9. Which English cricketer had his moustache shaved off and auctioned for charity on the *Big Breakfast*?

10. Which British film studios produced *The Ladykillers* and *Kind Hearts and Coronets*?

11. Which BBC comedy series was about a friendly Jewish ghost?

12. Which British reggae group had a No 1 in 1983 with *Red Red Wine*?

13. About which organisation was *All Quiet on the Preston Front*?

14. Who directed *The War of the Roses*?

15. Who played *Shoestring*?

16. Who played Inspector Clouseau in *The Pink Panther*?

17. Which British actor presented the crime series *In Suspicious Circumstances*?

18. Who played Mariner in *Waterworld*?

19. Which group sang *Holding Back the Years*?

20. On which show can we hear "the voice of the balls"- Alan Dedicoat?

General Knowledge

1.   With which art movement were Dali and Magritte associated?

2.   How is J M Barrie's play *The Boy Who Wouldn't Grow Up* better known?

3.   Which U.S. president made the Emancipation Proclamation?

4.   Who wrote *The Guns of Navarone*?

5.   Which English comedian sang *Cleaning Windows*?

6.   Of which US state is Boston capital?

7.   In which London park was the 1851 Great Exhibition held?

8.   What type of ship is powered by oars?

9.   In which American state is Pearl Harbor?

10. Which team shocked Celtic by winning the 1994 Scottish Coca-Cola Cup?

11. Which mountain range separates the Highlands from the Lowlands of Scotland?

12. What does DC stand for in Washington DC?

13. By what name is the aurora borealis commonly known?

14. Who wrote *The War of the Worlds*?

15. Which famous American outlaw was shot by Sheriff Pat Garrett?

16. Patagonia is divided between Chile and which other country?

17. What is Scotland's third largest city?

18. Which element has the symbol C?

19. Which judge conducted the bloody assizes?

20. Of which planet is Titan the largest satellite?

ANSWERS: *1 Surrealism, 2 Peter Pan, 3 Abraham Lincoln, 4 Alistair Maclean, 5 George Formby, 6 Massachusetts, 7 Hyde Park, 8 A galley, 9 Hawaii, 10 Raith Rovers, 11 The Grampian Mountains, 12 District of Columbia, 13 The Northern Lights, 14 H G Wells, 15 Billy the Kid, 16 Argentina, 17 Aberdeen, 18 Carbon, 19 Judge Jeffreys, 20 Saturn.*

General Knowledge

1. What is a triangle with three equal sides called?

2. What is the highest mountain in England?

3. Who created Tom Sawyer?

4. In which county is Stansted Airport?

5. Who wrote the orchestral suite *The Planets*?

6. What was the profession of John Singer Sargent?

7. What is the popular name for BSE?

8. Who was chancellor when Britain joined the ERM?

9. In which US state is San Antonio?

10. Who wrote *Pygmalion* and *St Joan*?

11. On which day does the Jewish sabbath begin?

12. Which playwright is married to Antonia Fraser?

13. On which island was the Duke of Edinburgh born?

14. Which angel revealed the birth of Jesus to the Virgin Mary?

15. Who wrote *Joseph Andrews* and *Tom Jones*?

16. During which war did the term 'fifth column' originate?

17. At which ground is the Scottish F.A. Cup final usually played?

18. In which country is the city of Graz?

19. Of which Eastern European country is St Nicholas patron saint?

20. Which migratory songbird is *Erithacus rubecula*?

ANSWERS: *1 Equilateral, 2 Scafell Pike, 3S Mark Twain, 4 Essex, 5 Gustav Holst, 6 Painter, 7 Mad cow disease, 8 John Major, 9 Texas, 10 George Bernard Shaw, 11 Friday, 12 Harold Pinter, 13 Corfu, 14 Gabriel, 15 Henry Fielding, 16 Spanish Civil War, 17 Hampden Park, 18 Austria, 19 Russia, 20 Robin.*

General Knowledge

1. From which collection of stories do Aladdin and Ali Baba come?

2. Which fruit grows on the tree *Ficus carica*?

3. What is the musical based on *Pygmalion* called?

4. Which biblical character lived in the belly of a whale?

5. In which northern city is Headingley?

6. Who was the last Labour Chancellor of the Exchequer?

7. Who starred as *The Graduate*?

8. In what religion is the eating of halal meat necessary?

9. In which disease is blood clotting impaired?

10. Who wrote *East of Eden*?

11. What is the ethical theory that pleasure should be the main goal in life called?

12. Who played the social climbing shop-assistant in *Half a Sixpence*?

13. For which country did Sir Richard Hadlee play cricket?

14. In which former British colony is Kowloon?

15. What was Beethoven's first name?

16. Who wrote *Stark*?

17. Which country does Hellenic refer to?

18. What is the collective name for the flute, clarinet and recorder?

19. After which Norse god is Thursday named?

20. In which London park is the Serpentine?

ANSWERS: *1 Arabian Nights, 2 Fig, 3 My Fair Lady, 4 Jonah, 5 Leeds, 6 Denis Healey, 7 Dustin Hoffman, 8 Islam, 9 Haemophilia, 10 John Steinbeck, 11 Hedonism, 12 Tommy Steele, 13 New Zealand, 14 Hong Kong, 15 Ludwig, 16 Ben Elton, 17 Greece, 18 Woodwind instruments, 19 Thor, 20 Hyde Park.*

Entertainment

Your rating:
● 0-5   Buy a TV   ● 6-10   Keep at it
● 11-15   Join a quiz team   ● 16-20   Enter Telly Addicts

1. Who recorded the album *Sgt. Pepper's Lonely Hearts Club Band*?
2. In which country was the lavish epic *Farewell My Concubine* set?
3. *Take It Like A Man* is the autobiography of which '80s pop megastar?
4. Which hit single was a conjunction between Bryan Adams, Rod Stewart and Sting?
5. Who played his first "baddie" in Clint Eastwood's *A Perfect World*?
6. Which *Blackadder* star hosts archaeology show *Time Team*?
7. Who played the hero in *True Grit*?
8. Which singer was backed by The Dakotas?
9. Which soap celebrated its 2000th episode in 1995 with an extended show?
10. Which *Scarface* star played the gangster-turned-good in *Carlito's Way*?
11. Which heavy rocker played Eddie in *The Rocky Horror Picture Show*?
12. Which group believed *Things Can Only Get Better*?

13. Which *Working Girl* also starred in *Dave*?
14. In which city was *Bread* set?
15. Who made the funk classic *Sex Machine*?
16. Who was the *Hard Target* in John Woo's no-holds-barred action film?
17. Which veteran English actor played Simon Hall in *Headhunters*?
18. Who were *Dis-infected*?
19. Who hosts *That's Showbusiness*?
20. What was the first James Bond film?

General Knowledge

1. In which county is Swindon?

2. Who wrote *The Cherry Orchard*?

3. Of which group was Jim Morrison the lead singer?

4. Who directed *Bridge on the River Kwai* and *Lawrence of Arabia*?

5. Which husband and wife discovered radium on Boxing Day in 1898?

6. Which composer wrote *The Messiah*?

7. Which German brothers published a collection of fairy tales?

8. By what name is penal reform campaigner Frank Pakenham better known?

9. In which country is *Hamlet* set?

10. Who wrote *The Snowman* and *Father Christmas*?

11. In which county is Basingstoke?

12. Which insect can jump 130 times its own height?

13. Who created James Bond?

14. With which Roman statesman is the phrase "Veni vidi vici" associated?

15. What is India's largest city?

16. Which British king was beheaded in 1649?

17. Whom did Paris abduct, causing the Trojan War?

18. How many fluid ounces are there in a pint?

19. Who is tenth in line to the throne?

20. Who wrote the musical *Oliver*?

General Knowledge

1. In psychoanalysis, which part of the unconscious mind is governed by irrational instinctive forces?

2. Which British sculptor is famous for his Peter Pan in Kensington Gardens?

3. What sort of creature is a nutcracker?

4. In Greek mythology, what form did Zeus take when he carried Europa to Crete?

5. What was Tanganyika renamed in 1964 after union with Zanzibar?

6. Which British poet wrote *Pauline* and *My Last Duchess*?

7. What is the capital of Tuvalu?

8. How is hyperopia better known?

9. In which year did the Queen marry?

10. Who is second to the Lord Chancellor in the judicial hierarchy?

11. How is the plant *Zingiber officinale* better known?

12. Which 19th century artist painted *The Last of England*?

13. In which river is the islet of Philae?

14. In which country are the Ellora Caves?

15. Who was the first Valois king of France?

16. Who was crowned emperor of the West by Pope Leo III in 800 AD?

17. Antananarivo is the capital of which country?

18. Who was the first Australian to score over 7,000 Test runs?

19. What is the brightest star in the constellation Gemini?

20. Which rare-earth metal is represented by the symbol La?

ANSWERS: 1 The id, 2 Sir George Frampton, 3 A bird, 4 A bull, 5 Tanzania, 6 Robert Browning, 7 Funafuti, 8 Long-sightedness, 9 1947, 10 Lord Chief Justice, 11 Ginger, 12 Ford Madox Brown, 13 Nile, 14 India, 15 Philip VI, 16 Charlemagne, 17 Madagascar, 18 Greg Chappell, 19 Pollux, 20 Lanthanum.

General Knowledge

- 0-5   Join a library
- 11-15   Join a quiz team
- 6-10   Keep at it
- 16-20   Enter Mastermind

1. What was the nickname of Charles Edward Stuart, the Young Pretender?

2. What is the medical name for the human equivalent of mad cow disease?

3. Which member of the Royal Family has been a *Smash Hits* pin-up?

4. In which US mountain range is Pikes Peak?

5. Which French artist painted the New Orleans Cotton Office?

6. What are the Prince of Wales's three middle names?

7. What is a wentletrap?

8. Who created Horatio Hornblower?

9. What is the capital of Malta?

10. Gingivitis describes the inflammation of which body part?

11. Which Hungarian-born film maker produced *The Scarlet Pimpernel* and *Anna Karenina*?

12. Which Sikh ruler was known as the Lion of the Punjab?

13. Which index is the principal indicator of share price movements in the USA?

14. In which city is the Parthenon?

15. What is the longest side of a right-angled triangle called?

16. Who wrote *The Wind in the Willows*?

17. What is the highest mountain in Britain?

18. How is comic film director Melvin Kaminsky better known?

19. What was Gabrielle Chanel's nickname?

20. What is the Scottish name for New Year's Eve?

ANSWERS: *1 Bonnie Prince Charlie, 2 Creutzfeldt-Jakob Disease, 3 Prince William, 4 Rocky Mountains, 5 Degas, 6 Philip Arthur George, 7 A mollusc, 8 CS Forester, 9 Valletta, 10 The gums, 11 Sir Alexander Korda, 12 Ranjit Singh, 13 The Dow-Jones index, 14 Athens, 15 The hypotenuse, 16 Kenneth Grahame, 17 Ben Nevis, 18 Mel Brooks, 19 Coco, 20 Hogmanay.*

Entertainment

1. Which *Cheers* regular was one of the *Cousins*?
2. What was the English butler called in *Magnum*?
3. What is the family's name in *The Cosby Show*?
4. Which prolific production/direction team gave us *Maurice* and *Howard's End*?
5. Who was a *Cornflake Girl*?
6. Who played Fletcher Christian in the 1962 film *Mutiny On The Bounty*?
7. In *Waterworld*, who played Deacon, the villainous leader of the Smokers?
8. Which 400m hurdler co-presents *Body Heat*?
9. Which 53-year-old founding member of the Grateful Dead died in 1995?
10. Which US TV series stars Melissa Joan Hart as a schoolgirl?
11. Who had a hit in 1978 with *Ole Ola (Muhler Brasileira)* featuring the Scottish World Cup Football Squad?
12. On which Shakespeare play was the musical *West Side Story* based?
13. Clifford the Rastafarian is a member of which puppet gang?
14. Who played the lonely bachelor who lived in *The Apartment*?
15. Who won the Best Actor Oscar in 1971 for his role as Popeye Doyle in *The French Connection*?
16. Which Wigan band released an album called *A Northern Soul*?
17. Who directed the 1991 film *The Doors*?
18. Which crooner released an album of duets with Bono and Aretha Franklin, among others?
19. Which sitcom, featured Judi Dench and Geoffrey Palmer?
20. Who is the lead singer of Simple Minds?

General Knowledge

1. With which poet is *Auld Lang Syne* associated?

2. Who is younger, Bobby or Jack Charlton?

3. Which Turkish city was once called Constantinople?

4. What was Cinderella's lost slipper made of?

5. Which soap opera was launched in 1960?

6. What is the state capital of West Virginia?

7. Which English classic horse race was named after the 12th Earl of Derby's stately home?

8. What do the initials I.Q. stand for?

9. Which substance is used as pencil "lead"?

10. Which Central American country was called British Honduras before independence in 1981?

11. When British women finally got the vote in 1918, how old did they have to be to enjoy this new right?

12. Which Beatle was the youngest?

13. Which city was England's capital before London?

14. The failure of which gland in the body causes diabetes?

15. Who was the English inventor of the jet engine in 1930?

16. What is the sixth colour of the rainbow, counting from red?

17. Who was the manager of the victorious England team in the World Cup of 1966?

18. Who is the only British solo female singer to have had 3 No.1 UK single hits?

19. Who was Henry VIII's second wife but the first to lose her head?

20. Which Shakespearian play features the feud between the Montagues and the Capulets?

General Knowledge

1. What is the predominant colour of the U.N. flag?

2. Which was the first Cambridge college, founded in 1284?

3. What is Britain's largest county?

4. What is the average human gestation period in weeks, to the nearest whole number?

5. Which alcoholic drink, native to Russia and Poland, was first made from potatoes, but now mainly from cereal grain?

6. How is diluted acetic acid better known in culinary terms?

7. Which gas makes up almost 80% of the air we breathe?

8. What is the capital of Chile?

9. Which famous Hollywood film star was born in Bristol in 1904?

10. Which house plant, popular at Christmas time, has largish green leaves topped by a crown of mainly red leaves?

11. What does the "A" stand for in "AIDS"?

12. In which town in Lincolnshire was Margaret Thatcher born?

13. Which is the largest of the Great Lakes of N. America?

14. The shortest verse of the Bible consists of only two words. What are they?

15. Where was the first modern Olympic Games held in 1896?

16. Where is the HQ of the Open University?

17. Which duct connects the middle ear to the back of the throat?

18. Under normal conditions, how much does a gallon of water weigh?

19. What is both a city in Morocco and a red felt hat worn by Muslims?

20. Which Oscar-winning American actress has also been US ambassador to Ghana and Czechoslovakia?

ANSWERS: *1 Blue, 2 Peterhouse, 3 North Yorkshire, 4 40, 5 Vodka, 6 Vinegar, 7 Nitrogen, 8 Santiago, 9 Cary Grant, 10 Poinsettia, 11 Acquired (Immune Deficiency Syndrome), 12 Grantham, 13 Lake Superior, 14 Jesus wept (John, 11, 35), 15 Athens, 16 Million Keynes, 17 The Eustachian Tube, 18 Ten pounds, 19 Fez, 20 Shirley Temple.*

General Knowledge

1. Who was the British 800m gold medallist at the 1980 Olympic Games in Moscow?

2. Who was the Wimbledon men's singles champion of 1988 and 1990?

3. Why do some people hope it will not rain on 15th July?

4. Which capital city is also the name of the mythological Trojan prince who slew Achilles?

5. What do Australians call their native wild dog?

6. Which instrument, mainly used for jazz, can have various sizes, known as Soprano, Alto, Tenor and Baritone?

7. Who has been president of the N.U.M. since 1981?

8. According to the book of Daniel, at whose feast did the guests see the Writing on the Wall?

9. In the world of computers, what does V.D.U. stand for?

10. Which vegetable is also called zucchini?

11. Which channel, crossed by the Arctic Circle, used to be of great strategic importance during the Cold War?

12. Which former capital of Scotland stands on the River Tay?

13. Who was the first lady MP to actually take up her seat in Parliament?

14. What is the most southerly province of Portugal?

15. Which famous King of Israel, renowned for his wisdom, was the son of David and Bathsheba?

16. Which Royal House was called Saxe-Coburg-Gotha until 1917?

17. Which is the longest continuous bone in the human body?

18. Which former England cricket captain played for Somerset from 1973-1986?

19. Which building, purpose-built for the Great Exhibition of 1851, burned down in 1936?

20. What is the capital of Jersey?

ANSWERS: 1 Steve Ovett, 2 Stefan Edberg, 3 Because it is St. Swithin's Day, 4 Paris, 5 The dingo, 6 The saxophone, 7 Arthur Scargill, 8 Belshazzar, 9 Visual Display Unit, 10 The courgette, 11 The Bering Strait, 12 Perth, 13 Nancy Astor, 14 The Algarve, 15 Solomon, 16 The House of Windsor, 17 The femur, 18 Ian Botham, 19 Crystal Palace, 20 St. Helier.

Entertainment

1. Which chart-topping '80s band was fronted by Kevin Rowland?
2. Who are the two regular team captains of *Have I Got News For You*?
3. How are Hula and Malik, who had a No 1 with *Boom Boom Boom*, better known?
4. Who played Alfie in *A Man Of No Importance*?
5. With which band did Bill Haley record *Rock Around the Clock*?
6. Who starred in *Saturday Night Fever* and *Pulp Fiction*?
7. Which American singer recorded the original of *Just the Way You Are* in 1979?
8. Who had a Top Ten hit in 1984 with *Nelson Mandela*?
9. From which musical did the song *I Don't Know How To Love Him* come?
10. Which rockers had a hit with *Pincushion*?
11. Who directed *The Age of Innocence*?
12. Which TV presenter did tycoon Donald Trump describe as "sleazy, unattractive, obnoxious and boring"?
13. Who wrote the play *A Patriot For Me*?
14. Who had a No 2 hit in 1983 with *China Girl*?
15. Which sci-fi series features Ensign Ro, Keiko and Guinan?
16. Who starred in *Giant* and *East of Eden*?
17. On which street is *Neighbours* set?
18. How is off-beat film director and actor Allen Stewart Konigsberg better known?
19. Who played Miss Jones in *Rising Damp*?
20. Which *Howard's End* star played the butler in *Remains of the Day*?

General Knowledge

1. Who was the author of *Don Quixote*?

2. Who is the present Duke of Cornwall?

3. What is the state capital of Tennessee?

4. What is the medical name for the windpipe?

5. What is the illness in which the sufferer eats a lot and then induces vomiting?

6. How many players are there on each side in Australian Rules Football?

7. Which official body in the UK sets and maintains the standards for over 100 recognised breeds of dogs?

8. Which prime minister took the U.K. into the E.C. in 1973?

9. Which of the gifts given to baby Jesus by the Three Kings is an aromatic, yellow-red gum resin?

10. Formed in 1933 under Goering, how were the Geheime Staatspolizei better known?

11. Which creature's name means "terrible lizard" in Greek?

12. What was the small, unsuccessful electric car, introduced in 1985 at under £400, called?

13. Who was the Formula 1 World Champion in 1985, 1986 and 1989?

14. Who was the British artist best known for his paintings of horses?

15. What is the art of fine handwriting called?

16. What is the term given to the liver complaint which is often associated with alcoholism?

17. Which family has ruled the tiny principality of Monaco since 1297?

18. What is a town in France, the name of the Dutch royal family and a citrus fruit?

19. Which Egyptian president was assassinated in 1981?

20. How did David Dinkins make history in New York in 1989?

ANSWERS: *1 Miguel de Cervantes, 2 Prince Charles, 3 Nashville, 4 The trachea, 5 Bulimia Nervosa, 6 18, 7 The Kennel Club, 8 Edward Heath, 9 Myrrh, 10 The Gestapo, 11 Dinosaur, 12 The Sinclair C5, 13 Alain Prost, 14 George Stubbs, 15 Calligraphy, 16 Cirrhosis, 17 The Grimaldi family, 18 Orange, 19 Anwar Sadat (of Egypt), 20 He became the first black mayor.*

General Knowledge

1. Which religious movement was founded in Pittsburgh by Charles Taze Russell?

2. Who wrote *The Moonstone*?

3. Which West-End play has had an unparalleled long run since its opening in 1952?

4. What is the more familiar name for the wild plant *Altropa Belladonna*?

5. What is the green pigment present in organisms capable of photosynthesis called?

6. Who was captain of the England Cricket team 1986-88 and captained an unofficial tour of South Africa in 1990?

7. Which famous character did Leslie Charteris create in 1930?

8. Which U.S. film actor was born William Claude Dukenfield?

9. How many American presidents have been assassinated in office?

10. Which is the fourth planet from the sun?

11. Who won an Oscar for his portrayal of a retired blind colonel in *Scent of a Woman* in 1992?

12. What is the nickname of the infamous British pirate, Edward Teach, who was killed in 1718?

13. How is Deuterium oxide better known?

14. Which nationality drink the most wine per head of the population?

15. Which device, pioneered by American inventor Carl Magee, appeared in London streets in 1958?

16. Who has had the most hits in the U.K. Singles charts since charts were first published in Britain in 1952?

17. On what date did Germany sign the Armistice in 1918 to end WWI?

18. Which instrument is used to record earth tremors and earthquakes?

19. What nationality was the composer Franz Liszt?

20. In which part of the body would you find the cochlea?

ANSWERS: 1 *The Jehovah's Witnesses*, 2 *Wilkie Collins*, 3 *The Mousetrap* (Agatha Christie), 4 *Deadly nightshade*, 5 *Chlorophyll*, 6 *Mike Gatting*, 7 *Simon Templar* (The Saint), 8 *W.C. Fields*, 9 4 (Lincoln, Garfield, McKinley and Kennedy), 10 *Mars*, 11 *Al Pacino*, 12 *Blackbeard*, 13 *Heavy water*, 14 *The French*, 15 *The parking meter*, 16 *Elvis Presley*, 17 *November 11th*, 18 *The Seismograph*, 19 *Hungarian*, 20 *The ear*.

General Knowledge

1. Which chemical compound is used in baking powder, fizzy drinks and medicinal antacids?

2. Which Welsh county, formed in 1974, has its administrative centre in Llandrindod Wells?

3. Who wrote the popular novels *A Town Like Alice* and *On the Beach*?

4. On which lake in N.W. England were world water speed records established by Malcolm and Donald Campbell?

5. Which American president brought about the historic signing of the peace treaty between Israel and Egypt in 1979?

6. In fencing, what is the marked-out area on which the competition is fought called?

7. In which year did Queen Victoria celebrate her Golden Jubilee?

8. Which South African surgeon performed the first human heart transplant?

9. In which English city would you find the Walker Art Gallery?

10. How was American comedian Julius Marx better known?

11. What is the name of the clipper built at Dumbarton in 1869 and now preserved as a museum in Greenwich?

12. What is the medical term for tooth decay?

13. Which fruit is also known as the Chinese gooseberry?

14. Who painted the Last Supper in a church in Milan?

15. What is the longest river in France?

16. Who wrote *Winnie-the-Pooh* and the *House at Pooh Corner*?

17. What does VTOL stand for in aviation?

18. Which instrument measures time using a shadow cast by the sun?

19. Which Southern European country borders only one other?

20. Which famous actor was born Maurice Micklewhite?

ANSWERS: 1 Sodium bicarbonate, 2 Powys, 3 Nevil Shute, 4 Coniston Water, 5 Jimmy Carter, 6 The piste, 7 1887, 8 Christiaan Barnard, 9 Liverpool, 10 Groucho (Marx), 11 The Cutty Sark, 12 Caries, 13 Kiwi fruit, 14 Leonardo da Vinci, 15 The Loire, 16 A.A. Milne, 17 Vertical Take-off and Landing, 18 The sundial, 19 Portugal, 20 Michael Caine.

Entertainment

Your rating:
● 0-5   Buy a TV
● 11-15   Join a quiz team
● 6-10   Keep at it
● 16-20   Enter Telly Addicts

1. Jazzy B is the driving force behind which dance outfit?

2. Who played Steed in *The Avengers*?

3. In which U.S. city was the Motown record company founded?

4. Which *Kojak* star was one of *The Dirty Dozen*?

5. Which controversial group were determined to *Give It Away*?

6. Which *Big* star was *Sleepless In Seattle*?

7. Which *Talking Telephone Numbers* presenter played *Joseph* in a West End production?

8. Stretch, Fatso and Stinkie are uncles of which friendly ghost?

9. Who starred as the would-be-mother in *Bambino Mio*?

10. Whose 1987 debut album was called *Introducing The Hard Line According To ...*?

11. What was the spaceship called in *Star Trek*?

12. Which Radio One DJ hosted *Home Truths*?

13. Which band made a successful *Return To Innocence*?

14. Which Woody Allen movie featured Alan Alda and Anjelica Huston?

15. Which honorary Grateful Dead pianist released an album called *Hot House*?

16. *Rhoda* was a spin-off from which US sitcom?

17. Who won the Best Actress Oscar in 1988 for her role in *The Accused*?

18. Who starred as cynical baseball player Crash David in *Bull Durham*?

19. What is Mavis Wilton's husband called in *Coronation Street*?

20. Which children's programme introduced us to Zippy and Bungle?

ANSWERS: 1 Soul II Soul, 2 Patrick MacNee, 3 Detroit, 4 Telly Savalas, 5 Red Hot Chilli Peppers, 6 Tom Hanks, 7 Philip Schofield, 8 Casper, 9 Julie Walters, 10 Terence Trent D'Arby, 11 The Starship Enterprise, 12 Steve Wright, 13 Enigma, 14 Manhattan Murder Mystery, 15 Bruce Hornsby, 16 The Mary Tyler Moore Show, 17 Jodie Foster, 18 Kevin Costner, 19 Derek, 20 Rainbow.

General Knowledge

1. How is the children's illness pertussis more commonly known?

2. On which mountain did Moses receive the Ten Commandments?

3. What was the first antibiotic drug, discovered in 1928?

4. Which creature's young is called a leveret?

5. Who composed the music used for *Land of Hope and Glory*?

6. What is the familiar Italian term for the brownish-red baked clay used in pottery, etc.?

7. First held in 1776, which is the oldest English classic horse race?

8. How was the element mercury formerly known?

9. Which singer/songwriter starred in *The Man Who Fell to Earth* in 1976?

10. Which American city is the HQ of the Coca Cola Company?

11. Who is the British director of *Gandhi* and *Cry Freedom*?

12. Which famous Indian mausoleum was built on the river Jumna near Agra?

13. How is the American singer/songwriter Robert Allen Zimmerman better known?

14. Of which country is Lima the capital?

15. Of which group of islands in the Indian Ocean is Malé the capital?

16. On the 5th of November of which year was the unsuccessful Gunpowder Plot involving Guy Fawkes?

17. On which island in the South Atlantic did Napoleon end his days?

18. Which famous man of comedy and satire died, aged 57, in 1995?

19. Whose wife disobeyed instructions not to look back at Sodom burning and was turned into a pillar of salt?

20. Who wrote *The Darling Buds of May*?

ANSWERS: *1 Whooping cough, 2 Mt. Sinai, 3 Penicillin, 4 Hare, 5 Edward Elgar, 6 Terracotta, 7 The St. Leger, 8 Quicksilver, 9 David Bowie, 10 Atlanta, 11 Richard Attenborough, 12 The Taj Mahal, 13 Bob Dylan, 14 Peru, 15 The Maldives, 16 1605, 17 St. Helena, 18 Peter Cook, 19 Lot, 20 H.E. Bates.*

General Knowledge

1. Who became the youngest ever world heavyweight boxing champion in 1986?

2. Which war was sparked off by the assassination of Archduke Francis Ferdinand in Sarajevo?

3. How many centimetres in diameter is a standard CD?

4. Which famous Manchester orchestra was set up in 1857?

5. For men, what increased from 48 in 1906 to 72 in 1989?

6. From which political party did the Liberal Party develop?

7. Which hot wind blows from the North African desert across the Mediterranean to southern Europe?

8. Who followed Ian Botham to become the second Test cricketer to score 3000 runs and take 300 wickets?

9. Who was Chancellor of the Exchequer from 1983 to 1989?

10. Which disease was introduced into the U.K. in the 1950s to control numbers of rabbits and hares?

11. Whose book *Centuries*, published in the 1550s, gave many predictions?

12. Which fortified wine is produced in and around Jerez de la Frontera in southern Spain?

13. What kind of bird is a kittiwake?

14. Which Henry was the first of the Tudor monarchs?

15. Which Hollywood actress made her screen debut in *To Have and Have Not* with Humphrey Bogart in 1944?

16. Who was the first prime minister of Israel from 1948?

17. Which people, besides the Walloons, make up most of the population of Belgium?

18. Which city is the capital of Western Australia?

19. In which Berkshire village was the Royal Military Academy for officer training founded in 1799?

20. Who was leader of the Liberal Party from 1976-1988?

ANSWERS: *1 Mike Tyson, 2 World War 1, 3 12 cm, 4 The Hallé, 5 Life Expectancy, 6 The Whigs, 7 The Sirocco, 8 Kapil Dev, 9 Nigel Lawson, 10 Myxomatosis, 11 Nostradamus, 12 Sherry, 13 A gull, 14 Henry VII, 15 Lauren Bacall, 16 David Ben-Gurion, 17 The Flemish, 18 Perth, 19 Sandhurst, 20 Sir David Steel.*

General Knowledge

1. Which skyscraper, built in the early 30s was the tallest in the world until the early 70s?

2. In the medical world, what is Louise Brown's claim to fame?

3. Which form of Japanese wrestling was first included in the Olympic Games in 1964?

4. In which London cemetery can the graves of Karl Marx, George Eliot and Herbert Spencer be found?

5. Who was the Formula 1 motor racing champion of 1976?

6. Which British novelist wrote *Lord of the Flies* in 1954?

7. Which scale is used to measure the magnitude of earthquakes?

8. Who took Edelweiss to the top of the singles chart in 1967?

9. Which sports championships were first held in Chamonix in 1924?

10. What is monotheism?

11. How is the skin blemish "naevus" more commonly known?

12. Who wrote the humorous novel *Three Men in a Boat*?

13. Who was known as the Maid of Orleans?

14. Who became the first woman to receive the Order of Merit in 1907?

15. Which host of *The Generation Game* died in January 1995?

16. Which British motor-racing champion was killed in an air crash in 1975?

17. Who was the Roman equivalent of the principal Greek god Zeus?

18. Which former British liner, now a hotel, can be found in Longbeach, California?

19. Which Louis was known as the Sun King?

20. Which man won five consecutive Wimbledon Singles Championships?

ANSWERS: *1 The Empire State Building, 2 She was the first test-tube baby, 3 Judo, 4 Highgate, 5 James Hunt, 6 Sir William Golding, 7 The Richter scale, 8 Vince Hill, 9 The Winter Olympics, 10 Belief in only one God, 11 A mole, 12 Jerome K. Jerome, 13 St. Joan of Arc, 14 Florence Nightingale, 15 Larry Grayson, 16 Graham Hill, 17 Jupiter, 18 The Queen Mary, 19 The fourteenth, 20 Bjorn Borg.*

Sports

1. Who was 1993's top earning British sportsman?
2. Which American won the 1995 Open at St Andrews?
3. In which city was Gary Lineker born?
4. Which country's basketball team was nicknamed 'The Dream Team' at the Barcelona Olympics?
5. Which woman won the 1966 Commonwealth Games long jump?
6. Who was the youngest footballer to play for Wales?
7. Who won the 1994 Benson and Hedges Masters snooker title?
8. Which tennis legend died in February 1995 at the age of 85?
9. For which country did rugby player Sid Going play?
10. In what year was athlete Zola Budd born?
11. Which Romanian player decided 'it was a big mistake' to have joined Tottenham Hotspur?
12. Which sport does New Zealander Blair Pocock play?
13. What name has snooker champion Chuchart Triratanapradit adopted?
14. In which sport could you win a Brownlow Medal?
15. In which city was footballer Denis Law born?
16. Which Australian wicketkeeper had his nose broken, allegedly by English fans?
17. Who won the 1994 Le Mans 24-hour race?
18. Which club signed veteran Republic of Ireland international David O'Leary from Arsenal?
19. When did Martina Navratilova win her first Wimbledon singles title?
20. At which sport does Richard Corsie compete?

General Knowledge

1. Which Spanish surrealist painter died in 1989?

2. Which city's new cathedral was opened in 1962?

3. How were Currer, Ellis and Acton Bell better known?

4. Which future British king did Mary of Teck marry in 1893?

5. Which French underwater film-maker was co-inventor of the aqualung in 1943?

6. How is Indian prince Gautama Siddhartha better known?

7. What was the capital of Brazil from 1763-1960?

8. What are the ankles of a horse called?

9. How was William Bonney better known?

10. Which wars were fought by the British from 1880-81 and 1899-1902?

11. In which south-coast resort did George V convalesce after illness in 1929?

12. The yellow-green female flowers of which climbing herb are used in brewing?

13. Which is the second largest island in the Mediterranean?

14. The liberation of which Nazi death camp was on 27th January 1945?

15. Who became president of the European Commission at the end of January 1995?

16. Which fruit is a cross between a raspberry and a blackberry?

17. What was the title of the ancient Egyptian rulers?

18. Which great Australian operatic soprano retired in 1990?

19. Which language did Jesus Christ speak?

20. Which British novelist created the detective Father Brown?

ANSWERS: 1 Salvador Dali, 2 Coventry, 3 The Brontë sisters, 4 George V, 5 Jacques Cousteau, 6 Buddha, 7 Rio de Janeiro, 8 The fetlocks, 9 Billy the Kid, 10 The Boer Wars, 11 Bognor Regis, 12 The hop, 13 Sardinia, 14 Auschwitz, 15 Jacques Santer, 16 The loganberry, 17 Being in open spaces, 18 Dame Joan Sutherland, 19 Aramaic, 20 G. K. Chesterton.

General Knowledge

1. Which famous composer had 20 children, 3 of whom also became well-known composers?

2. Which Bavarian town has put on a passion play every ten years since 1633?

3. What is the medical specialty concerned with illness in children called?

4. Who wrote the music for the ballet *Romeo and Juliet* ?

5. What is the largest natural monolith in the world?

6. Whose third husband was US playwright Arthur Miller?

7. What is the official language of Brazil?

8. Who has succeeded Timothy Dalton as the new James Bond?

9. Which large bird belongs to the genus *Cygnus*?

10. Who became Chancellor of the Exchequer when John Major became P.M. in 1990?

11. Which famous wine is named after the range of hills in N central Italy between Florence and Siena?

12. What does the tax-free investment "PEP" stand for?

13. Which Apollo first landed on the moon in July 1969?

14. Which zodiac sign lies between Capricorn and Pisces?

15. Where can the only wild monkeys in Europe be found?

16. Which city became the capital of modern Turkey in 1923?

17. How many pieces are there on a full chess board?

18. What is the highest mountain in Africa?

19. What is the term given to a large cloud of interstellar gas and dust?

20. Which film starred Tom Hulce as Mozart?

ANSWERS: *1 Johann Sebastian Bach, 2 Oberammergau, 3 Paediatrics, 4 Prokofiev, 5 Ayers Rock in Australia, 6 Marilyn Monroe, 7 Portuguese, 8 Pierce Brosnan, 9 The swan, 10 Norman Lamont, 11 Chianti, 12 Personal Equity Plan , 13 Apollo 11, 14 Aquarius, 15 Gibraltar (Barbary Apes), 16 Ankara, 17 32, 18 Kilimanjaro, 19 A nebula, 20 Amadeus.*

General Knowledge

1. What is the outermost layer of the earth called?
2. Who wrote the famous trilogy *The Lord of the Rings*?
3. Which of the three armed services was founded in the 9th century by Alfred the Great?
4. What is an instrument for measuring atmospheric pressure called?
5. Whom did Mrs Anna Anderson claim to be from 1920 until her death in 1984?
6. Which Old Testament prophet was born at Ur in Chaldaea in c. 2000 BC?
7. In which field was British physicist William Henry Fox Talbot a pioneer?
8. Which flap of cartilage at the root of the tongue prevents food, etc., from entering the windpipe?
9. Who was the Greek god of wine?
10. Whom did Mark David Chapman shoot and kill on 8th December, 1980?
11. Which American state separates the Atlantic Ocean and the Gulf of Mexico?
12. Which river has Vienna, Bratislava, Budapest and Belgrade along its course?
13. Which famous composer had an affair with French novelist George Sand?
14. Which is the northernmost American state?
15. Which war lasted from 1936-1939?
16. Which building is to be found at 1600 Pennsylvania Avenue, Washington DC?
17. On which island are citizens elected to the House of Keys?
18. Who is the Czechoslovakian-born British writer of the play *The Real Thing*?
19. Which clubfooted poet died while training troops at Missolonghi in Greece?
20. Which Gorgon was so ugly that all who saw her face were turned to stone?

ANSWERS: 1 The crust, 2 J.R.R. Tolkien, 3 The Royal Navy, 4 A barometer, 5 Princess Anastasia of Russia, 6 Abraham, 7 Photography, 8 The epiglottis, 9 Dionysus, 10 John Lennon, 11 Florida, 12 The Danube, 13 Frédéric Chopin, 14 Alaska, 15 The Spanish Civil War, 16 The White House, 17 The Isle of Man, 18 Tom Stoppard, 19 Lord Byron, 20 Medusa.